NATIONAL CERTIFICATE WORKSHOP TECHNOLOGY

NATIONAL CERTIFICATE
WORKSHOP
TECHNOLOGY

T. NUTTALL
A.M.I.Mech.E., A.M.I.P.E.

THE ENGLISH UNIVERSITIES PRESS LIMITED
102 NEWGATE STREET
LONDON E.C.1

First edition 1950
Second edition 1955
Second impression 1956
Third impression 1958
Fourth impression 1960
Fifth impression 1963
Sixth impression 1964

Printed in Great Britain for the English Universities Press, Limited,
by Richard Clay and Company Ltd., Bungay, Suffolk

GENERAL EDITOR'S FOREWORD

THE last twenty years have seen far-reaching changes in technical education, changes whose objectives have been to meet the ever increasing demands of technology. A new pattern of technical education is now emerging as a result of a series of Government committees and white papers. Initially, attention was directed perhaps more intensely to the education of technologists resulting in the expansion of the universities, a greater emphasis on the teaching of science in schools and the establishment of the Colleges of Advanced Technology.

The training of technologists has hitherto fallen into two broad categories: university courses and National Certificate courses arranged on a part-time day release basis for apprentices in industry. These part-time courses have become the route through which the majority of professional engineers have received their training. It is, however, unlikely that this state of affairs will continue in the future. The professional Institutions have rightly raised their entrance requirements to a level which the part-time day release student will find extremely difficult to achieve: at the same time the greatly increased facilities for full-time and sandwich courses will provide a much more satisfactory educational system for those wishing to attain professional status.

Latterly, more attention has been given to the better training of technicians, craftsmen and operatives. The Government white paper " Better Opportunities in Technical Education " seeks to establish a new pattern for technical college courses at these levels. The very high failure rate in Ordinary and Higher National Certificate courses which has caused such concern in recent years is, it is hoped, to be avoided by the introduction of the new General Course. This is designed as a diagnostic course to determine whether a student is best suited to continue with an Ordinary National Certificate course, a craft or operative course, or a technician course. The City and Guilds of London Institute are making radical changes in their existing courses, and designing new technician courses to fulfil these objectives.

The Technical College Series of books covers the National Certificate, General Course in Engineering and the very wide field of technician courses. Many of the books in the series are now standard works, having stood the test of time over a long period of years. Such books are reviewed from time to time and new editions published to keep them up to date, both in respect of new technological developments and changing examination requirements. New works are constantly being added to the list as new courses are arranged and new techniques developed. The publishers are fully aware of the part that well-written up-to-date text-books can play in supplementing teaching, and it is their intention that the Technical College Series shall continue to make a substantial contribution to the development of technical education.

E. G. STERLAND.

PREFACE

THE study of Workshop Technology follows a different path from that of most other subjects in the National Certificate course. With a few exceptions, it does not lend itself to a mathematical exposition. The scientific ground from which it springs is mainly physical and chemical, but the ground has been so well trodden that it is not easy to see the scientific source behind the empirical technique. Even the experienced teacher is liable to lose his direction in a maze of processes and to forget that his duty is to reveal and explain the scientific principles which govern correct workshop practice.

The engineering industry is the workshop for making the tools of our civilization. It is not surprising to find that its industrial technique follows the scientific pattern of thought. It must be admitted that in most workshops the technique lags very far behind modern thought; this is due largely to unscientific leadership and excessive reliance on tradition by all ranks of workers.

The aim of Workshop Technology is to close the gap between scientific thought and industrial practice and this book is an attempt to provide a foundation in the method of Workshop Technology. The ground covered is that of the Ordinary National Certificate Course. By further study of books and methods, the student may build a sound knowledge of the principles of engineering production. A bibliography has been appended; it is far from exhaustive, but it is intended to provide a general selection. The student who has access to a good technical library should find it useful.

It is hoped that the teacher who uses the book in class may be freed to some extent from the bane of all descriptive subjects—the dictation of notes. He will have a little more time for explanation and the relating of practice to principle. Some of the time saved could be spent most profitably in a suitable workshop. Such a workshop will contain modern machine tools specially arranged for demonstration purposes, and will be equipped with scientific instruments of observation which are maintained in good condition. The patient teacher can do good even in the type of workshop which still lingers on at so many colleges.

There are two sections of questions. The large section A should be suitable for the average student at the standard of the Ordinary National Certificate; section B questions demand a more advanced study of the subject.

It is suggested that the odd-numbered questions in section A should be used first. In another group or another session the even-numbered questions may be used, thus avoiding repetition.   Section B questions are suitable for advanced students or for those classes which continue to meet after the examination has been held; in this latter case they will serve as a preparation for a Higher National Certificate Course.

A number of illustrations in the book have been provided by manufacturers.   The help given by some of these firms has been considerable, going far beyond the provision of illustrations.   Their interest and advice are greatly appreciated.

A number of friends have made suggestions, and the author offers his thanks.   In this respect, the practical help and advice of Mr. R. Cleary, G.I.Mech.E., must be singled out; his assistance has been invaluable.

CONTENTS

CHAPTER I

ENGINEERING MATERIALS—ELEMENTARY PROPERTIES

THE choice of material to be used in a component is governed by three principal considerations :—

(1) The material must be suitable for the working conditions to which the component will be subjected in service.

(2) The material must be amenable to the processes required to make the component.

(3) The cost of the material must not be excessive in relation to the selling price of the article.

Most engineering materials are metallic, and the important subdivisions are :—

(1) **Ferrous** materials, which consist chiefly of iron with comparatively small additions of other materials.

(2) **Non-Ferrous** materials, which contain little or no iron.

Iron is the commonest and cheapest metal in engineering ; other common metals are copper, aluminium, zinc, magnesium, tin, lead, nickel, chromium, manganese and tungsten. Of these, aluminium is the most abundant in the earth's crust, but it is dearer than iron, owing to the method of refining the ore.

Pure metals are little used in engineering practice ; some common metals (e.g., iron) are difficult to produce in anything like the pure state ; furthermore, pure metals rarely possess all the desirable properties. Consequently, **alloys** are the common materials of practice.

Generally, an alloy has a base—this is a single metal which forms more than 50% of the total mass—and one or more **alloying** elements which may be present in large or extremely small amounts. Obviously, the cost of the base material will have a big effect on the cost of the alloy, therefore cheap base materials are used whenever possible. Steel is an excellent example of this. Iron is the base of steel, and is quite cheap, but expensive alloying elements, such as molybdenum and vanadium, may be present in quite small quantities. These small additions can have decisive influence on certain desirable properties.

Properties of Metals and Alloys

Certain properties of metals are of great importance to engineers, and various methods are employed to investigate these properties.

Tenacity

The resistance to rupture when subjected to tensile forces. The measure of tenacity is **tensile strength**, usually stated as the minimum stress in tons or lb. per square inch cross-sectional area which will break the material. Two similar properties are **compressive strength** and **shear strength**. These are related to compressive forces and shear forces respectively. The values of these strengths usually fall when the metal is heated.

Elasticity

The property of regaining original shape after deformation. When a material is subjected to a force, a change of shape can be detected; if the force is tensile, the material is elongated. With some metals, removal of the force will cause the metal to return to its original shape. However, if the value of the force is increased, the metal may be permanently deformed. Fig. 1 shows the approximate load-extension diagram for mild steel. With loads up to point E the material is elastic, and this point is termed the **elastic limit**. The elastic limit is lowered by heating.

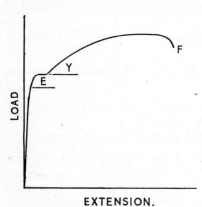

EXTENSION.

FIG. 1.—LOAD-EXTENSION DIAGRAM.

Modulus of Elasticity

If mild steel is loaded beyond the elastic limit, ductile extension takes place; but provided this does not occur, the mild-steel part will regain its original shape when the load is removed. This is the usual status of engineering components, and the elastic deformation in service must be allowed for in design. The modulus of elasticity is a standard used with great frequency in design work. It may be defined crudely as the stress which would double the length of a piece of the material if elastic extension could go on to such an extent.

Thus the Modulus of Elasticity for mild steel is 13,000 tons per square inch. Obviously, a much smaller stress would break the metal, but the assumption has practical utility.

Since 13,000 tons per square inch will make a 1-in. length of steel extend in length to 2 in., it follows that a stress of 1 ton will produce an extension of $\frac{1}{13000}$ in., and problems such as the following may be solved.

A steel bolt 10 in. long is stressed to 4 tons per square inch. What will be the increase in length? $E = 13,000$ tons.

$$\text{Increase} = 10 \times 4 \times \tfrac{1}{13000} = 0 \cdot 00307 \text{ in.}$$

It is interesting to note that the modulus of elasticity of almost all steels is 13,000 tons. This means that whilst some steels have a much higher elastic limit than others, all steels stretch the same amount for the same stress, providing the elastic limit is not exceeded.

Ductility

A ductile material is one which can be drawn out permanently by a tensile force. Referring to Fig. 1, it may be noted that at point Y (the yield point) an increase in extension occurs, and further loading causes considerable extension. This is termed **ductile extension**; the material permanently increases in length and at the same time decreases in

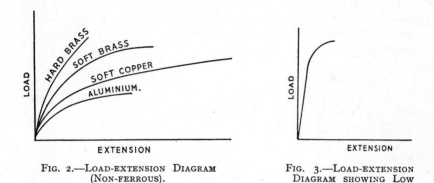

FIG. 2.—LOAD-EXTENSION DIAGRAM (NON-FERROUS).

FIG. 3.—LOAD-EXTENSION DIAGRAM SHOWING LOW DUCTILITY.

diameter; eventually, rapid thinning occurs at one point and the metal breaks.

The yield point shown on Fig. 1 is typical of mild steel. Many non-ferrous metals have considerable ductility, but no definite yield point. Fig. 2 shows certain of these metals. Fig. 3 is the diagram of a material of low ductility. With many materials ductility increases rapidly with heat.

Malleability

The ability to be hammered or rolled out without cracking. Very few metals have good cold malleability, but most are malleable when heated to a suitable temperature.

Plasticity

The property of flowing to a new shape under pressure and retaining this new shape. An appreciable time may elapse before plastic flow is completed. Increase of pressure and increase of temperature improve plastic flow.

Toughness

Resistance to fracture by blows, i.e., considerable energy is required to crack or break the material. Tough materials usually have high tenacity combined with good or fair ductility. Toughness decreases with heating.

Hardness

Resistance to indentation or scratching. The hardness of a material is usually stated relative to the hardness of other materials. Scales of hardness usually give high numbers to hard materials and low numbers to soft materials. Hardness is decreased by heating.

Brittleness

Opposite of toughness; a brittle material breaks easily under a sharp blow, although it may resist a steady load quite well. Brittle materials are neither ductile nor malleable, but they often have considerable hardness.

CHAPTER II

COMMERCIAL TESTING OF MATERIALS

THE testing of materials is done to determine their suitability for a given duty and also to test their suitability for the working processes which must be used to shape them. In buying materials, the engineer specifies certain tests and the desired performance figures under these tests. Much useful work has been done by the British Standards Institute in setting up certain test standards for all the common engineering materials. By conforming to these standards, the maker knows that his product is of good quality; and the buyer, in asking for the standard test, has a guarantee of suitability.

Many materials are sold under trade names; the maker usually states the test figures that can be obtained, and also gives a list of suitable applications.

The Tensile Test

A typical standard test-piece is shown in Fig. 4. The test-piece is circular, and has a cross-sectional area of 0·25 sq. in. The stress in tons

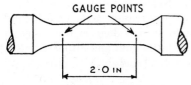

FIG. 4.—STANDARD TEST-PIECE.

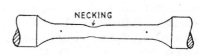

FIG. 5.—TEST-PIECE BEFORE BREAKAGE.

per square inch will thus be four times the load applied by the machine. Two centre-punch marks are placed 2·0 in. apart, and are used to determine the extension produced by the load. This extension is measured by an instrument called an extensometer.

In the case of ductile materials, the appearance of the specimen just before breakage is shown in Fig. 5. The reduction near the centre is termed " necking " or local extension. Since this reduction is not equal throughout the 2-in. length, a longer specimen would not extend proportionately. For example : suppose the original 2·0-in. length became

2·5 in. at fracture, then the " percentage elongation " would be $\frac{0\cdot5}{2\cdot0} = 25\%$.

If, however, the specimen were 10 in. long and still the same diameter, " necking " would occur to the same extent as the 2-in. specimen, and the percentage elongation would be much less. To ensure comparable results, all British Standard specimens have the same proportion $\dfrac{\text{length}}{\text{cross-sectional area}}$, and the formula used is $L = 4\sqrt{A}$, where L is the length of the specimen and A is the cross-sectional area.

The information obtained from a commercial tensile test is :—

    1. Ultimate tensile strength.
    2. Elastic limit.
    3. Yield point (this applies chiefly to steel).
    4. Percentage elongation.
    5. Percentage reduction in area (this is taken at the point of maximum necking).

The elastic limit is of great interest to the designer, since he is usually concerned with **stable structures**, i.e., those structures which do not permanently change their shape in service. The production engineer is more interested in the other four properties, since he is concerned with the shaping of the material, and the elastic limit must always be exceeded if shaping is to be done. If the metal is to be torn apart, as in machining, chipping, filing, etc., then the ultimate tensile stress must be exceeded. Generally, the higher the ultimate strength, the more power will be required to rupture the material.

If the metal is to be shaped without fracture, as in forging, rolling or drawing, then stresses greater than the elastic limit, but lower than the ultimate tensile strength, must be used. Referring to Fig. 1, the portion of the curve between Y and F is the ductile extension range for cold mild steel, and cold rolling or drawing of mild steel is done in this range of stresses. If the steel is heated, both the elastic limit and ultimate tensile strength are reduced, and consequently rolling and drawing stresses will be less.

The elongation and reduction in area indicate the cold ductility of the material; the ultimate tensile strength, together with the percentage elongation, are a guide to toughness.

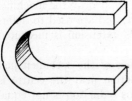

FIG. 6.—BEND TEST
SPECIMEN.

Bend Tests

A simple method of assessing the ductility and freedom from brittleness of a metal is to bend a flat bar through a certain angle. If the bar cracks, it is deemed to have failed. A specification might state that " the bar is to be bent through 180°, the inner radius of the bend to be one and a half times the thickness of the bar ". The bent specimen would therefore be as shown in Fig. 6.

With certain very ductile materials the **continuous bend test** is applied.

A strip is alternately bent and straightened through a prescribed angle, usually 90° or 180°. The number of bends required to cause fracture is taken as a measure of ductility.

Hardness Tests

There are a number of hardness tests; the **Brinell test** may be taken as typical. A hardened steel ball is forced into the surface of the metal under a standard load. The load is maintained for 15 seconds, to allow plastic flow to finish, and the specimen is then removed. The diameter of the impression made is measured with a microscope containing a **graticule** or measuring scale. The diameter is then compared with a table from which the hardness number is read off; the smaller the impression, the higher the number.

Other hardness tests are the Vickers Diamond Pyramid and the Rockwell. In the former a diamond of pyramid shape is substituted for the ball of the Brinell test. The Brinell and Vickers numbers are identical for soft and medium materials, but with hard materials the Vickers numbers are higher, and are considered more reliable. The Rockwell machine forces a specially shaped indentor, termed a " brale ", into the material and automatically records the depth of the impression; the hardness number is then read on a dial on the machine. The Rockwell test is very quick, and is suitable for mass inspection of parts.

It should be noted that these tests only indicate the **surface hardness** of the material.

Impact Tests

The principle of the Izod or " notched-bar impact " test is illustrated in Fig. 7.

The specimen is of square section, and is firmly gripped by the vice-jaws *A* and *B*. It has a small notch, which is set level with the top of the vice.

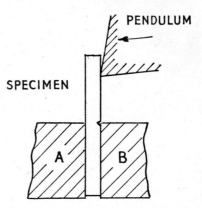

FIG. 7.—NOTCHED-BAR IMPACT TEST.

A pendulum of known weight and length is allowed to swing freely from a fixed height so as to hit and break the specimen. After breakage of the specimen the pendulum swings on, but naturally with less momentum, and the greater the energy required to break the material, the less momentum will be left in the pendulum. The Izod machine registers the initial energy and the energy after breakage, and thus the energy required to break the specimen can be calculated. This energy is stated in ft. lb.

The impact test is a measure of shock resistance or toughness. The notch imitates conditions often found in practice, and also ensures that the point of fracture shall be the same for all specimens.

Machineability

The tests described, particularly the tensile and hardness tests, are very useful in assessing the relative ease with which materials may be machined. Experience is still required, however, if the best results are to be obtained, as there are many variable factors in the machining of metals. Variations in structure, invisible to the naked eye, can have a pronounced effect. Small quantities of lead make little difference to the test properties of gunmetal, but considerable difference to the machineability.

A number of research workers have considered the problems of machineability, and it appears likely that a testing instrument actually mounted on the machine tool will be the standard used eventually.

CHAPTER III

THE WORKING OF METAL

THE working of metal may be divided into two types of process : **hot working** and **cold working**. Hot working is done at a temperature which enables the metal to be shaped easily—i.e., the tensile strength, hardness and toughness are reduced and the ductility, malleability and plasticity increased. The most suitable hot-working temperature for each material has been found by experience ; since the temperature cannot be held unchanged, hot-working **temperature ranges** have been settled for different materials.

In the cold-working processes the material is kept approximately at room temperature. The friction of cold working generates heat, but this is incidental, and usually confined to the surface of the material. One important process which may be regarded as cold working is machining ; this will be considered separately in later chapters.

The two principal hot-working processes are **forging** and **rolling**.

Forging

For small work forging is carried out with hand hammers, but for larger work hammers and forging presses operated by steam, air, water or electricity are used. The hammer deforms the surface of the work ; the heavier the blow, the deeper this " working " will proceed. But there are limits to the size of section which can be worked throughout by hammering. For large forgings the **hydraulic press**, which squeezes the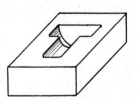

FIG. 8.—DIE AND COMPONENT.

hot metal, is invariably used. The plastic deformation is followed by the continuous heavy pressure exerted, thus working the metal right through to the centre.

Many small parts are **drop forged**. A " slug " or " blank " of hot metal is forced to shape by two dies ; the upper die is fixed to the head of a **drop hammer**—a type of mechanical hammer. The upper and lower dies meet, and if the blank was of the correct volume the die space will be filled exactly. Fig. 8 shows one of a typical pair of dies and the article produced.

Fig. 9 is a cross-section through a pair of dies. It is essential that the die space should be filled if a part with the correct shape is to be produced : therefore the blank is left a little large, and the excess metal is forced into the gutter of the die. The "flash" which is thus produced on the component is trimmed off later, but signs of it often remain visible unless the drop forging is machined at these points.

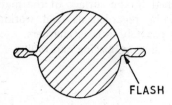

IMPRESSION   GUTTER

FLASH

FIG. 9.—DIE GUTTER AND "FLASH".

Drop forgings can be made to quite accurate dimensions and with a good surface, so that machining may not be necessary. The limitations of the process are : the number of parts required must be large, as the dies are expensive, and there are many shapes which cannot be produced, as they could not be removed from the dies. Where large numbers of parts are required, drop forging is a very quick and economical method; it is useful for certain tool steels which are not easy to machine. Typical drop forgings are engineer's spanners, hammer heads, black bolts, petrol-engine connecting rods and rocking levers.

A process known as **hot pressing** uses a press in place of the mechanical hammer, but is otherwise very similar to drop forging. Certain types of brass are very suitable for the manufacture of hot pressings.

Forging alters the internal structure of the metal. The reshaping produces a definite "fibre", and the forging should always be done in such a way as to take advantage of this fibre. Fig. 10 contrasts two components, one made from bar in a lathe and the other produced by forging. If subjected to a force in the direction of the arrow F, the forged part will be the stronger of the two.

It has already been mentioned that there is a correct temperature range

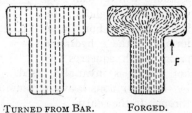

TURNED FROM BAR.   FORGED.

FIG. 10.

for forging operations. If forging is done within this range, the internal structure of the material will be refined and improved. Too high a temperature will leave the metal weak and brittle, too low a temperature will result in internal stresses, and these may lead to distortion or cracking.

The following figures show the improvement in mechanical properties produced by the correct forging of mild steel.

	U.T.S., tons/sq. in.	Elongation on 2 in., %.	Red. in area, %.	Izod impact, ft. lb.
Original ingot . .	26	14	10	6
After forging . .	30	35	50	28

Rolling

The majority of mild-steel articles are made from rolled sections. The principal rolled-steel sections are : plates for ships, vessels and other riveted and welded structures; angles, tees, channels and joists for bridges and buildings; round, hexagon and square bars for forging and machining operations; sheets for vehicle bodies, household goods, such as gas and electric cookers and machinery guards; railway and tramway rails; and many other articles.

All the different types of rollings start as a cast-steel **ingot**. This is reduced in cross-section by a **cogging mill**, which consists of a pair of plain rolls made to rotate in either direction (see Fig. 11 A). The ingot is

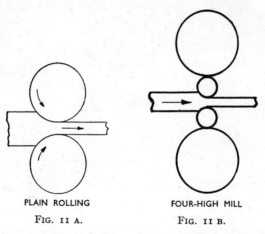

PLAIN ROLLING   FOUR-HIGH MILL

FIG. 11 A.   FIG. 11 B.

passed to and fro between the rolls, and a series of **blooms** are produced. The blooms may in turn be rolled down to produce **billets**, which are simply small blooms. If plate or sheet is to be produced, the bloom is rolled out by a series of flat rolls until the desired thickness is reached; but if bars or structural sections are being made, shaped rollers are used. These rollers revolve steadily in one direction, and the shape is produced by a series of " passes " through the rollers; each pass is through a shape nearer to the final cross-section. Long lengths are thus produced at high speed. A view of this type of mill is shown in Fig. 12.

As has already been mentioned, hot working allows the metal to be shaped more easily than cold working; larger sections can be shaped, the power absorbed is less and if the correct temperature is used the structure of the material is improved. Certain disadvantages must be noted. Hot metal oxidises readily, and the surface of a hot-worked article is dull and " scaly ", the size is also liable to vary. Immediately the temperature falls below the working range the part must be reheated ; this may be inconvenient owing to the size or shape of the part ; also the time and fuel expended in reheating will add to the cost.

Hot parts bend very easily, and sometimes it proves troublesome to

[*Machinery Publishing Co.*

FIG. 12.—A ROLLING MILL.

keep them straight when handling. Some materials are " hot short ", and may fly to pieces when hot worked ; steel, for example, which contains excessive amounts of iron sulphide is prone to hot shortness.

Casting

Casting is the oldest form of metal shaping, and is still the basic engineering process, since most metals are melted and cast from ores. Furthermore, iron, aluminium, gunmetal, zinc and brass castings are still very commonly used.

Patterns of wood or metal may be made and their shape reproduced in reverse in some suitable material such as damp sand. This mould is dried and molten metal is poured into it and allowed to solidify.

In the **die-casting** process the mould is made of metal, usually steel, and the molten metal is poured or forced under pressure into the mould. Die casting is suitable for mass production only, as the machines and dies are expensive; it is also limited to certain non-ferrous metals.

Metals vary greatly in their melting temperatures; this introduces certain limitations to the casting process, and some metals require special techniques. Furthermore, certain metals require careful heat treatment after casting before they are fit for use.

Cold-working Processes

Many metals have sufficient ductility to be worked cold. Cold working may vary from a simple bend to the great deformation produced by deep pressing and tube drawing: in all cases **work hardening** occurs to some extent, depending on the material and the amount of cold work. The phenomenon of work hardening—or plastic strain hardening, as it is sometimes called—is not thoroughly understood but Fig. 13 illustrates the structural change which can be seen with a microscope.

The structure of metals is crystalline, the size of the **crystal grains** being usually between $\frac{1}{100}$ and $\frac{1}{8}$ in. across. After cold working, this crystalline structure is deformed—the grains are elongated in the direction in which the metal is drawn out. The grain boundaries are still there, but each crystal grain has been flattened and lengthened.

NORMAL STRUCTURE   AFTER COLD WORK

A   B

FIG. 13.

The result of cold work is to increase the hardness and tensile strength, but to decrease the ductility and shock resistance: Fig. 13 B is typical of a cold-worked material. During cold work, therefore, the metal becomes more difficult to work and the danger of cracking increases. If the duty of the component is light and the cold working is not severe, the work hardening produced is unimportant, and in fact the greater strength and hardness may be an advantage. However, where considerable cold work is to be performed, the part may be **annealed** at some intermediate stage or stages of the work. For the moment it will be sufficient to understand that annealing consists of heating to a particular temperature, known as the recrystallisation temperature, and cooling at a suitable speed; the original crystal structure is thus restored and the metal regains its original softness and capacity for cold work.

It may be noted that in hot working the temperature is approximately the recrystallisation temperature, and therefore as fast as the crystal grains are deformed, they reform themselves; hence the statement that hot working refines the grain of a metal. The reformed crystals set up the "fibrous" structure illustrated in Fig. 10.

When annealing is necessary during cold work the cost of the article is increased, due to the time and fuel expended; also the heating introduces the scaling difficulty mentioned under hot working. A process known as **bright annealing** allows parts to be heated without scaling, but special furnaces are required.

In cold working, the surface of the material is very important, as scale may be worked into the finished article, with serious results. Pickling and other methods of surface cleaning are often used before cold working, and the cold-working processes themselves have their own highly specialised lubrication technique.

Cold Rolling

Strips and sheets are cold rolled in a **four-high** mill (see Fig. 11 B). The large rolls serve to " back up " the smaller working rolls and prevent any deflection and consequent change of thickness in the strip or sheet. The thickness can be maintained to very accurate limits; the surface is very smooth, and may even be polished.

Tube Drawing

The **billet** consists of a tube, cast or hot forged to a suitable length, bore and diameter; it is supported internally by a mandrel, and is drawn

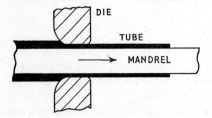

FIG. 14.—TUBE DRAWING.

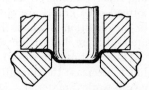

FIG. 15.—PRESSING.

through a series of hardened dies, each " draw " reducing the wall thickness and increasing the tube length. At suitable intervals a smaller mandrel is introduced, thus reducing the tube diameter. The process is shown in Fig. 14.

Rod and wire are drawn in a similar manner, but the mandrel is, of course, not required.

Pressing

This is a bending or forming operation in which the metal is stretched but not greatly reduced in thickness. Many elaborate press tools are made, as pressing is one of the most important mass-production processes. The pressing operation shown in Fig. 15 is of a very simple nature; the outer punch holds the blank firmly, whilst the inner punch forms the depression. On the same or a similar machine the blank itself may be blanked out (i.e., punched) from sheet. In some cases blanking and pressing are performed on one machine by sets of tools, and many complex shapes are produced.

Deep Drawing

This operation is similar to tube drawing, and Fig. 16, which shows deep drawing, resembles Fig. 14. Deep drawing, however, is done on a press, and is used for making cup-shaped articles. There is considerable reduction of the thickness of the blank, and heavy pressures are required. In the press-tool trade this reduction of wall thickness is termed " ironing ".

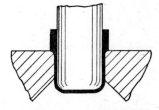

FIG. 16.—DEEP DRAWING.

Spinning

Hollow shapes with a cylindrical cross-section may be spun. This process is cheaper than pressing when a small number of thin parts is required, since a simple high-speed lathe and a wooden former are the apparatus used. Fig. 17 shows the method of making a simple shape.

The former rotates, and the sheet is held up against it by a " palette " in the lathe tailstock. The sheet is kept well lubricated with tallow,

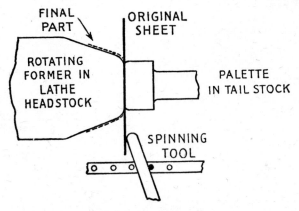

FIG. 17.—SPINNING.

and is gradually forced to the shape of the former with the tool. Spinning tools are about 3 ft. long and are pivoted on a round pin which can be placed in various holes in a rest at the front of the lathe. The pin is moved to " follow up " the shape. With a collapsible former made in a number of pieces components with a neck at the open end may be spun. With suitable tools various beads and ornamental edges can be formed.

Cold Heading

This is a method of forging heads on small and medium-sized screws, bolts, etc. The blank is usually a piece of wire of suitable length and cross-section; one end is cold forged in dies to form the desired shape of head. Annealing after cold heading may be required.

CHAPTER IV

IRON

Pig Iron

Pig iron is the first stage in the production of all ferrous metals. It is obtained directly from iron ore by heating the ore in the blast furnace with coke as the fuel, and limestone as a flux for removing some of the impurities. The iron is removed from the furnace in the molten state and run into suitable sand or metal moulds. The resulting castings are known as " pigs ", and weigh about 100 lb. each.

Pig iron varies considerably in composition, as it contains various amounts of carbon, silicon, manganese, sulphur and phosphorus. All these elements have an effect on the properties of the metal.

Carbon

Carbon is the most important alloying element in iron and steel. In cast iron, which is the general name for iron re-cast from pig iron, carbon is present in two forms: as free carbon or graphite; and as combined carbon or iron carbide (Fe_3C). The graphite is in the form of flakes (Fig. 18) of very low strength. It is these graphite flakes which impart the characteristic grey colour to fractured cast iron. The graphite is also responsible for the brittleness of cast iron and its " dirtiness " when being machined or filed.

GRAPHITE IN CAST IRON
Fig. 18.

The graphite flakes are discontinuities in the structure; they are a source of weakness if tensile forces are applied, but have little effect on the compressive strength of cast iron, which is quite good. The small cavities containing graphite have a damping effect on vibrations, and cast iron is anti-resonant—a very useful property in many applications.

Graphite is an excellent lubricant, and grey cast iron is easily machined, as the tool is lubricated and the chips break off readily. The freedom with which articles will slide over a smooth surface of cast iron is largely due to the graphite in the surface.

A great deal of research has been done to try to control the size and distribution of the graphite flakes in cast iron. When the graphite is in small particles and is evenly distributed throughout the iron, the metal is stronger and less brittle. Various techniques are used to obtain this desirable structure.

Iron carbide is a hard, brittle substance, and its presence greatly increases the hardness of cast iron. It is white in colour, and cast iron high in combined carbon and low in free carbon is white or very light mottled grey in appearance. Such white and mottled irons are very hard and almost unmachineable, but have certain special uses.

Silicon

Silicon is used as a **softener** in cast iron. Increasing the silicon content of the iron increases the free carbon and decreases the combined carbon.

Manganese

This important element is present in almost all ferrous metals. It has a strong affinity for sulphur, and readily forms the compound **manganese sulphide** (MnS). Sulphur is dangerous if present as **iron sulphide** (FeS), but fortunately is much less harmful as MnS, consequently sufficient manganese should always be present to take up the sulphur content. Manganese also tends to harden cast iron, as it promotes combined carbon. The hardness of grey cast iron depends chiefly upon the " balance " between the silicon and manganese contents.

Phosphorus

This element, like sulphur, is inherent in cast iron. It embrittles cast iron by forming **iron phosphide** (Fe_3P), but is less dangerous than sulphur. It is kept as low as possible except in certain light intricate castings, where it is encouraged, since it improves the fluidity of molten cast iron.

Sulphur

It has already been mentioned that sulphur is a dangerous element. Unfortunately, it is invariably present in cast iron, as it is picked up from the coke used in melting. The percentage is kept as low as possible. The primary difficulty with sulphur is the formation of iron sulphide, as has already been mentioned. Iron sulphide has a lower melting point than cast iron or steel, consequently when it is present it finally solidifies in the grain boundaries (see Fig. 13 A). Metals which have brittle grain boundaries are brittle themselves, and iron sulphide is very brittle. A further difficulty arises when steel containing iron sulphide is heated for hot working. At the correct hot-working temperature the iron sulphide in the grain boundaries is melting, and the steel flies to pieces when forging begins : this trouble is termed **hot shortness**. On the other hand, manganese sulphide has a high melting point and solidifies first in iron or steel, usually in small harmless pellets.

Foundry Cast Irons

In the iron foundry a balance has to be struck between the manganese and silicon contents so as to obtain a machineable but strong casting. The following are typical.

	Total carbon, %.	Silicon, %.	Manganese, %.	Sulphur, %.	Phosphorus, %.
1. Light castings .	3·2	2·0	0·5	0·1 (max.)	1·0
2. Heavy castings .	3·3	1·0	1·0	0·1 (max.)	0·3

The speed of cooling has a considerable influence on the final hardness of cast iron. Castings of light section cool more rapidly than heavy castings; this leads to the formation of more combined carbon (iron carbide) and less free carbon (graphite), with a consequent increase in hardness. For light castings, therefore, more silicon is required to encourage the formation of graphite.

The final composition is determined by charging the cupola with mixed pig irons and scrap cast iron in weighed quantities. These various irons have known quantities of the various elements. In a strong machineable cast iron the combined carbon percentage is about 0·5.

Chilling

In some castings it is necessary to have a hard durable surface—e.g., the slideways of machine tools. This is achieved by chilling. Iron plates are buried in the mould, and the metal coming in contact with these plates will be cooled rapidly, and will be harder than the rest of the casting.

In some cases the opposite effect is desired—i.e., even hardness throughout the casting is required. It has already been noted that heavy cast sections are softer than light sections; in a casting with various thicknesses the thicker parts will be softer, but with judicious chilling of these thicker parts, even cooling throughout can be obtained. This gives a casting of even hardness, and reduces internal strains set up by contraction of the metal.

Growth of Cast Iron

When subjected to temperatures above 700° C., particularly fluctuating temperatures, ordinary cast iron is subject to growth. The volume slowly increases and the tensile strength falls off. This is a nuisance in furnace castings and in other high-temperature parts. Certain alloy cast irons are less subject to growth.

Use of Iron Castings

Although there is a tendency to-day to replace iron castings by mild-steel welded structures, cast iron is still one of the commonest engineering materials. It can be cast into intricate shapes, and is equally useful for " one offs " to a wooden pattern, or for mechanical moulding with metal patterns in mass-production foundries.

The melting point (approximately 1200° C.) is low enough to allow reasonably easy pouring into sand moulds, and the internal structure, when cold, is good enough without annealing. This may be contrasted with steel castings, which, although finally stronger and more shock resistant than iron castings, require two annealings and a much more exacting moulding technique.

The cupola is a cheap apparatus for melting metal, and consequently the price of iron castings is low unless the shape is intricate. With the more recent types of iron casting, such as " Meehanite ", strengths comparable with mild steel can be obtained, but the price is higher than that of plain grey iron castings.

Except for the hard skin which is usually present, cast iron is easy to machine, and the graphite content obviates the use of cutting lubricants. No working processes, either hot or cold, except casting and machining, can be performed on grey cast iron.

The physical properties of cast iron vary considerably, but the U.T.S. is usually between 14 and 22 tons/sq. in.; the elongation is generally nil; the Brinell hardness number varies between 100 and 700, according to the proportion of free and combined carbon. About 450 is the highest Brinell number for machineable cast iron, and ordinary castings have a Brinell number between 120 and 180.

Malleable Cast Iron

The type of pig iron used in the foundry is termed " grey " iron, from the colour of the fracture ; this colour is derived from the graphite flakes which give the metal its characteristic brittleness and softness. However, **white** and **mottled** pig irons are produced. These have little silicon, and consequently little or no free carbon, but up to 3·5% of combined carbon. The metal is hard and unmachineable, but can be cast readily. Castings of many small articles are made in white or mottled iron, and are then softened and made malleable by special heat treatment.

In the **Whiteheart Process** the castings are packed in boxes with hematite iron ore and heated to a little over 900° C. for periods up to several days, according to thickness. The surface of the casting is **decarburised** (the carbon is removed), whilst in the interior much of the combined carbon is turned into graphite, not in the form of flakes, but in " nodules " or round particles. The resulting casting has a tensile strength of about 20 tons per square inch and an elongation of 10% ; it is readily machined and is fairly tough.

The **Blackheart Process** is very similar, except that the surface of the casting is not decarburised and the process is more akin to annealing.

Pipe and railing fittings are typical malleable iron castings ; they are made in quite intricate shapes and machined after heat treatment. They will stand up to rough usage without cracking.

Wrought Iron

Puddling is the original process for the manufacture of wrought iron, and is still employed. The manufacture of wrought iron was once a common process, but the introduction of the Bessemer process for the manufacture of mild steel rapidly ousted puddling, as mild steel is a much cheaper metal.

Grey pig iron and mill-scale (iron oxide) are melted in a reverberatory furnace, and the iron is moved about by long bars to bring it into contact with the mill-scale. Gradually, the silicon, manganese, phosphorus and carbon are removed by the oxidising action of the mill-scale. As the iron is purified, its melting point rises steadily, and eventually the furnace is not hot enough to keep the iron molten, and it becomes pasty ; it is then rolled up into balls. Only one impurity remains in appreciable quantity. This is iron silicate. It is usually termed " slag ". The balls are removed and forged into rough bars. These bars are cut up, fastened into bundles or " piles ", reheated and rolled out. The slag is elongated by these hot working processes, and is present as thin fibres in the finished bar, the direction of the fibres being determined by the direction of working. Fig. 19 shows a typical enlarged cross-section of wrought iron. The fibrous appearance of fractured wrought iron is due to the slag inclusions, and the fibres tend to let the metal crack slightly rather than to fracture outright, if overloaded, thus giving warning of danger. Wrought iron will stand repeated shock loads without becoming seriously embrittled, but occasional annealing is recommended.

Fig. 19.—Wrought Iron (enlarged section).

Chains and crane hooks are made in wrought iron, and bolts subjected to shock loads are sometimes preferred in wrought iron rather than mild steel. Water and low-pressure steam piping is nominally termed " wrought iron ", but is usually made from mild steel ; mild-steel piping does not lend itself to bending as easily as wrought iron.

The price of wrought iron is approximately three times that of mild steel.

Pure iron is difficult to produce, but certain grades of commercially pure iron, chiefly of Swedish and American origin, are used in electrical work for rotor stampings and transformer cores. A well-known grade is " Armco " iron.

There are also a number of other alloys of iron which cannot be termed steel, since they contain practically no carbon. Thus iron is alloyed with silicon up to 4% for certain classes of sheet, and " stainless iron " is essentially iron with 13% chromium.

c

CHAPTER V

PLAIN CARBON STEEL

PLAIN carbon steel is an alloy of iron and carbon. The essential difference between cast iron and steel is that the latter contains no free carbon. Iron carbide (Fe_3C) contains 7% of carbon, and the carbon in steel is always present as iron carbide. It is usual to state the amount of carbon present in a steel, and from this information the amount of iron carbide can be readily calculated by multiplying by $\frac{100}{7}$. Thus a $0\cdot3\%$ carbon steel contains $4\cdot3\%$ of iron carbide.

It has already been noted that it is the graphite in cast iron which gives the

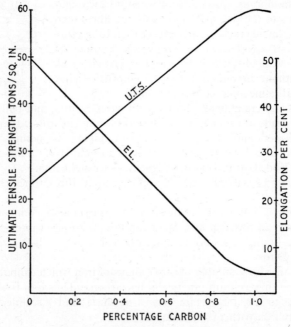

FIG. 20.—PROPERTIES OF STEEL.

metal its characteristic properties of brittleness and good machineability ; the absence of graphite in steel leads to greater strength and ductility if the combined carbon is low. However, with increasing carbon content, steel becomes harder and stronger, but less ductile and shock resistant. Fig. 20 illustrates the change in properties in steel as the carbon content increases.

Iron carbide is a hard, brittle substance, hence the changing properties of steel with increasing carbon content.

When discussing the manufacture of malleable cast iron, it was stated that white cast iron contains 3·5% of combined carbon and no free carbon. During heat treatment some of the combined carbon breaks down into free carbon, and the resulting metal is certainly not steel. The carbon in steel is limited to that amount which will all remain combined after any standard heat treatment. The theoretical limit is 1·7% for plain carbon steel : in practice 1·5% is rarely exceeded.

Steel-manufacturing Processes

Steel, like cast iron, is produced from pig iron, and steel-making processes are essentially methods of reducing the carbon content of cast iron, and if necessary, introducing known amounts of carbon, manganese and any other desired alloying elements. The terms **acid** and **basic** are frequently mentioned when steel is discussed, and the difference should be clearly understood. Phosphorus, which is present in quantities as high as $2\frac{1}{2}$% in some pig irons, must be reduced below 0·1% in steel ; in the basic steel-making processes the furnace used has a **basic refractory** lining, and such a lining is necessary if phosphorus is to be reduced in the iron, as it reacts with this element, and so removes it. The pig irons produced from high-grade hematite iron ore are low in phosphorus, and may be used for steel making in a furnace with an **acid refractory** lining ; this furnace does not reduce the phosphorus content.

The belief that " acid " steels are superior to " basic " steels is largely a fallacy ; the utmost that can be said is that careless work with a basic furnace may more easily lead to a poor quality of steel. On the other hand some authorities state that if the furnace working is correct, basic steel can be made slightly the superior of the two.

Open-hearth Furnaces

The great majority of steel in Britain is produced by the open-hearth method. The furnace hearth is shaped like a large saucer, and may be capable of holding up to 250 tons. The flames are allowed to play on the surface of the charge. The charge consists of pig iron or molten cast iron, scrap steel, iron ore and, in the basic process, limestone.

After a period up to fourteen hours the impurities have been removed and the molten metal is ready for pouring. In the acid process the furnace is tapped when the steel contains the desired amount of carbon, but in the basic process more carbon is removed, and then the metal is **recarburised** a little by adding anthracite coal when the metal is being poured. Additions of manganese and silicon are also made in the ladle ; these are necessary to **deoxidise** the steel.

The molten steel is cast into ingot moulds, and the hot ingots may then go forward to the rolling mills or forge, or, in the case of steel castings, the molten metal is poured into a suitable sand mould. From this it is apparent that all steel is cast steel : there is a tendency to use the term " cast steel " as applying to a particular type of tool steel ; this is unfortunate, since by far the greatest amount of steel casting is of mild steel. The full title of these tool steels should be **crucible** cast steels, to distinguish them from furnace cast steels. More will be said later about crucible steels.

The Bessemer Process

This is the oldest of the methods of producing steel in large quantities, and it was the invention of the process by Bessemer which cheapened steel far below the price of wrought iron. Mild steel quickly superseded wrought iron for most industrial purposes, and the manufacture of railway rails, ships' plates and boiler plates was given a tremendous impetus. It is not too much to say that the discovery of mass-production methods of steel making was the most important step of the Industrial Revolution.

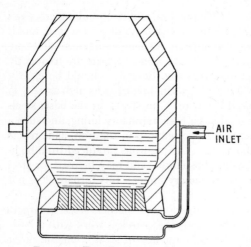

FIG. 21.—THE BESSEMER CONVERTER.

The converter (Fig. 21) can be tilted for charging and pouring. The charge is molten pig iron, and after the converter has been half filled it is turned up, and air under pressure blown through the metal from the bottom. The oxygen of the air combines with the silicon, phosphorus, carbon and manganese of the iron and burns them, thus producing the heat necessary to keep the charge molten (it will be remembered that the melting point of pure iron is higher than that of iron containing carbon). After about twenty minutes the " blow " must be stopped, otherwise the iron itself would start to combine with the oxygen to form iron oxide. Stopping the " blow " at the correct moment—the margin of error is a matter of seconds only—is one of the highly skilled operations of the process. The charge is then recarburised and deoxidised by the introduction of compounds of iron, manganese and carbon.

The Bessemer process may be acid or basic, according to the converter lining ; the acid process is used when the charge is very low in phosphorus.

The **Tropenas Process** is a more modern development of the converter principle. The air is blown across the surface of the molten metal. Tropenas converters are usually of not more than a few tons capacity.

Electric-arc Furnaces

The furnaces already described use coke or gas to produce the melting temperature, but electricity is also widely used. The common type of electric-arc furnace has two or more electrodes arranged above the metal, and the arc is struck between these electrodes and the metal of the charge. The cost of heating is higher than with gas-fired furnaces, but higher temperatures are obtainable, and the carbon content of the steel may be closely controlled. Also the deoxidising process can be done in the furnace. Most electric-arc furnaces have basic linings.

Blister Steel

Bars of practically pure iron are packed with charcoal and heated to a yellow heat for a number of days. Some of the carbon from the charcoal passes into the iron; the longer the heating continues, the greater will be the final carbon content of the metal.

The bars have a blistered appearance on removal from the furnace, hence the name. Blister steel is the raw material for tool steels.

Shear Steel

The bars of blister steel are heated and forged and then piled together; the piles are reheated to a white heat, at which temperature they will weld together, and are forged again to produce **single-shear** steel. In some cases the bar of single-shear steel is bent over on itself and re-forged to make **double-shear** steel. This is an expensive but extremely high-quality tool steel. It is an excellent example of the refinement of grain that is possible by correct and prolonged forging.

Crucible Steel

Small quantities of high-grade steel are produced by melting the raw materials in special fireclay crucibles. These crucibles may be heated by

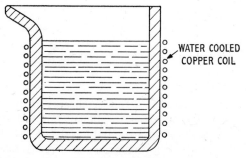

FIG. 22.—HIGH-FREQUENCY ELECTRIC CRUCIBLE.

coke, gas or oil firing or by electrical induction. The electrical method is the most efficient, and the method is shown diagrammatically in Fig. 22.

The crucible is surrounded by a copper coil, and alternating current of high frequency (over 2000 cycles per second) is passed through the coil. Water is circulated through the centre of the coil to prevent the copper being heated, but intense heat is generated in the charge itself. Once the charge has melted, strong circulation is set up by the magnetic effect, and any alloying elements are thoroughly mixed.

Since there is no fire, no fumes are present to contaminate the metal, and the whole operation can be carried out under the best conditions. Most high-grade tool steel is produced in this way, and is termed **crucible cast steel**. The raw materials must be of the finest, since sulphur, phosphorus, etc., are not removed. However, the steel is deoxidised in the crucible before pouring.

High-frequency crucibles can carry charges up to 10 tons, but 5-cwt. crucibles are usually the limit, and many smaller crucibles are in use. This may be contrasted with the older fire-heated crucibles, which had to be man handled, and were consequently limited to about 70 lb. maximum charge.

Carbon Content of Steel

Commercial plain carbon steels vary in carbon content from less than 0·1% to 1·5%, each variety having its own applications.

Dead Mild Steel

Carbon content up to 0·1%. This is the softest and most ductile steel. It is hot rolled into sheets, and is then suitable for cold-working processes, and is used for many light articles. It is also supplied in bar form for use as rivets, and as solid-drawn tube, which can be bent very readily. It has excellent welding properties and machines readily, except for a tendency to " tear " at the surface owing to its ductility. The mechanical properties are approximately as below :

U.T.S.	24 tons/sq. in.
Y.P.	12 tons/sq. in.
El.	32%
Red. in A	60%
Izod impact . . .	60 ft. lb.

Mild Steel

Carbon content 0·1—0·35%. This is cheaper than dead mild steel. Up to 0·2% carbon the properties are similar, but with 0·3% carbon the steel is definitely harder and stronger, but less ductile. A large proportion of the total steel produced is in the range 0·2—0·35% carbon ; rolled-steel sections for structural work, ship plates and boiler plates, bars for forging and general machining all fall into this group, and most large steel castings have a similar carbon content. The welding properties are good and the machineability is good. Typical mechanical properties are :

U.T.S.	.	.	.	.	. 30 tons/sq. in.
Y.P. .	.	.	.	.	. 16 tons/sq. in.
El. .	.	.	.	.	. 25%
Izod impact		.	.	.	. 30 ft. lb.

Medium-carbon Steel

Carbon content 0·35—0·65%. With increasing carbon content the strength and hardness increase further and the ductility falls off. Steel with 0·4—0·5% carbon is used for axles and other shafts which are heavily loaded and also have to withstand abrasion. Steel with 0·5—0·6% carbon is used for railway rails, owing to its abrasion-resisting properties. The welding properties and machineability become poorer with more than 0·4% carbon.

The U.T.S. reaches 50 tons/sq. in., but the elongation falls to 12%.

High-carbon Steel

Carbon content 0·65—1·5%. A number of different tool steels may be conveniently grouped together. They are used in the heat-treated condition, as their properties vary widely with the heat treatment given, but generally it may be said that the more abrasion resistance is required, the higher will be the carbon content; but this gain is made only at the expense of lower shock resistance. Welding is very difficult, and machining (except grinding) can be done only in the annealed state.

The following is a list of typical applications :

Carbon content, %.	Uses.
0·7—0·8	Springs, hammers, riveting punches, dies.
0·8—0·9	Punches, drills, shears, chisels.
0·9—1·1	Taps, drills, axes, tools for intermittent cuts.
1·1—1·4	Turning tools, small cutters.

CHAPTER VI

ALLOY STEELS

ENGINEERING parts are subjected to a number of forces in service. These forces may be accompanied by certain special conditions, such as heat in the internal-combustion engine or in steam plants, or chemical corrosion by liquids and gases. Tensile, compressive and shear forces may all be present at the same time; their intensity may vary slowly or rapidly, and may be produced by sudden shocks. Shear stresses may be produced by abrasion or wear.

It has already been noted that the yield point of mild steel is about 15 tons/sq. in. This figure is of great importance to the designer, who must work with a " factor of safety " and keep the stresses well within this figure. If heat, corrosion or abrasion is expected, then further allowances must be made.

A very wide range of alloy steels have been developed to meet these varying conditions, and it will only be possible to discuss a few of the more important types. Some alloy steels are complex, and contain a number of alloying elements; the reader may have noted slight variations between two apparently similar steels. These variations may or may not have importance, but it cannot be emphasised too strongly that the best guide to the manipulation and use of any particular steel is the instructions issued by the steel-maker. All reputable steel-makers are continually testing and trying to improve their products. In buying steel from such firms the wise engineer takes care to obtain the specialised knowledge which is so freely given.

Manganese

Manganese is present in all steels. It is required to counteract the bad effects of sulphur. Thus the minimum manganese content is determined by the sulphur content. It is greatest in mild steel, as the highly refined tool steels contain very little sulphur.

The manganese content of ordinary mild steel is usually about 0.5%. With 1.5% manganese, mild steel has a slightly higher yield point and a distinctly better shock resistance, and, since it is not much more expensive, it is often used as a superior form of mild steel.

Hadfields manganese steel contains $12-14\%$ manganese and 1.0% carbon. This alloy has very pronounced work-hardening properties. It can be hot forged, but is very difficult to machine, as cutting quickly leads to a hardened and almost unmachineable surface. For certain purposes where heavy abrasion is encountered this steel is unrivalled;

jaws for crushing machinery, dredger parts, railway crossings are all subject to heavy wear, and the abrasive forces merely serve to work harden the surface and increase the wear resistance of the steel.

Nickel

Mild steel containing 3% nickel is stronger and more shock resistant than plain mild steel ; it is rather more difficult to machine, and more expensive. Nickel has an unfortunate tendency to change carbide of iron into graphite when steel is being heat treated, and it is therefore only added to steel of low carbon content. One popular type is termed " case-hardening nickel steel " ; it contains 3% nickel and 0·15% carbon. The use of case-hardening steels will be discussed under heat treatment.

A steel containing 36% nickel and 0·2% carbon is called **Invar**. It is non-magnetic, stainless, and has a very low coefficient of thermal expansion, and is used in clocks and measuring instruments. It has the unfortunate property of increasing in length slightly over a period of time, and is therefore not suitable for standards of length (see Chapter XIII).

Chromium

Chromium and nickel are often found together in steel. The tendency of nickel to graphitise steel is counteracted by chromium which stabilises the carbide of iron. On the other hand, chromium tends to promote coarse-grain structure and increases the difficulty of heat treatment. This is counteracted by nickel, which refines the grain size and makes heat treatment easier. The proportion of nickel to chromium is roughly 4 to 1 : thus a steel with 3·5% nickel, 0·75% chromium and 0·3% carbon is readily machined in the annealed condition, and may then be heat treated to give the following figures :

U.T.S., tons/sq. in.	Y.P., tons/sq. in.	El., %.	R.A., %.	Izod impact, ft. lb.
60	54	22	60	60

A comparison may be made with mild steel. A particularly noticeable feature is the high yield point ; it is more than three times that of mild steel, and enables much higher stresses to be used. The high Izod impact figure shows good toughness. Heavily loaded shafts, high-tensile bolts, parts for aircraft or fast-running engines, where weight is important, are all made in this and similar types of steel.

Another nickel chromium steel has 4·25% nickel and 1·25% chromium. This can be hardened by heating and then cooling in air, and is used for some tools and for gear wheels. The U.T.S. in the hardened condition is about 100 tons/sq. in.

The carbon content of these steels is generally between 0·2 and 0·35%.

Stainless Steel

If not less than 13% chromium is added to steel, the corrosion resistance is greatly increased. A steel with 13% chromium and less than 0·1% carbon is used for stainless-steel turbine blades. Owing to the low carbon content it is sometimes called " stainless iron ". When chromium is present to such an amount as 13%, considerably less carbon is required to produce a hard steel. Consequently, the stainless cutlery steels contain 13% chromium and only 0·3% carbon, and can be hardened and then ground to a good cutting edge.

Another group of stainless steels are termed 18/8. These steels contain 18% chromium and 8% nickel. If heated and quenched they are quite soft and are very suitable for cold working of all descriptions. The cold working leads to considerable work hardening, but annealing can be repeated by heating and quenching. Many vessels and tools for chemical plants are worked up cold to shape in 18/8 steel.

Molybdenum

The steels containing nickel and chromium sometimes suffer from temper brittleness. This is a defect which arises if the steel is held at a temperature between 250° and 500° C. The tensile strength remains high, but the shock resistance becomes dangerously low. Since the temperature range mentioned is often found in steam plant, the danger is obvious. This trouble can be overcome by the introduction of 0·5% molybdenum. A typical alloy contains 3·0% nickel, 0·8% chromium, 0·5% molybdenum and 0·25% carbon. A steel used for steam piping at high temperature has 0·15% carbon, 0·7—1·2% chromium and 0·5% molybdenum.

Tungsten

When plain high-carbon steel is suitably heat treated it can be made very hard and will take a keen cutting edge ; unfortunately, heating to 300° C. or over will quickly soften it. Such temperatures are easily produced by friction at the cutting edge of tools used in machine tools such as lathes. If this softening is not to occur, cutting speeds must be kept very low and light cuts must be used. Efforts were made many years ago to develop a steel which had the property of red hardness—i.e., one which would retain its hardness at high temperatures. The first successful alloy was *Mushet* steel, introduced about 1860 ; it contained about 2% carbon, 4—6% tungsten, 1% silicon and 1—1½% manganese. Much progress has been made since the original *Mushet* steel was produced. The tungsten content has been increased, the carbon reduced, and other elements such as chromium, cobalt, molybdenum and vanadium have been added.

These alloys are termed high-speed or self-hardening steels. They may be heated to 600° C. without lowering the hardness, and in fact intermittent heating to this temperature tends to harden the material, hence the name "self-hardening" steel. The self-hardening property or **temper resistance** is only developed after correct heat treatment.

The following are typical high-speed steels :

	Chromium, %.	Carbon, %.	Tungsten, %.	Vanadium, %.	Molybdenum, %.	Cobalt, %.
1	5	0·6	14	—	—	—
2	5	0·6	18	—	—	—
3	4·5	0·7	20	1	1	10

Number 1 is the cheapest and No. 3 the most expensive ; all are dearer than plain carbon steel. No. 3 gives remarkable results in the machining of hard metals.

Between 1940 and 1943 a series of " substitute " high-speed steels were developed, particularly in the U.S.A. These steels were developed in order to conserve tungsten, which was in very short supply. Molybdenum was substituted for most of the tungsten, and a typical substitute steel contains 6% molybdenum, 6% tungsten, 5% chromium and 1% vanadium. Such a steel has similar cutting properties to a steel with 20% tungsten, since 1% molybdenum is equal to about 2½% tungsten in determining the cutting properties.

Die Steels

In certain applications, such as dies, it is important that the part should not change in size when hardened—a very common defect in plain high-carbon tool steels. A typical " non-shrinking die steel " contains 1·0% carbon, 0·9% molybdenum, 0·5% tungsten and 0·75% chromium. Owing to the small amounts of the various alloying elements, the steel is not very expensive.

CHAPTER VII

FORMS OF STEEL

STEEL as a raw material for the various engineering processes can be bought in many forms, and the more common forms are as follows :

Bar

Black mild and medium-carbon and alloy steel bar is a common rolling-mill product. It may be obtained in round, square, rectangular and hexagonal sections. Round bar from $\frac{1}{4}$ in. diameter to 10 in. diameter ; rectangular bar from $\frac{3}{8}$ in. $\times$ $\frac{1}{2}$ in. to 2 in. $\times$ 12 in. ; square and hexagon sections up to 6 in. across are typical ranges. The surface of black scale is due to oxidising of the steel by the atmosphere during hot rolling. Generally, the corners of all black bar are slightly rounded.

Another form very similar to bar is the supply of **billets** for forging down ; small billets are merely suitable bar cut off to length, but larger sizes are rolled to the size requested by the customer.

Bright-drawn Bar is obtained by cold drawing mild-steel bar through shaped dies ; the finish is smooth, and in sections other than round ; the corners are sharp. The size and shape may be guaranteed within 0·002 in. This accurate size and bright finish are often a great advantage. Capstan, turret and automatic lathes are sometimes fitted with a collet chuck which feeds the bar forward as required, this is a self-centring chuck, and can be used only with accurate round-bar stock. Many engineering parts have a considerable length of parallel cross-section, and if other portions are to be machined down, bright-drawn bar of the appropriate section may be used with a considerable saving in machining time. A component which must have a hexagonal or square portion, but the remainder cylindrical, may be turned from the hexagon or square bar ; similarly, nuts are drilled, tapped and parted off to length from hexagon bar.

The drawing operation work hardens the surface of bright-drawn bar, the depth of this hardening depending on the severity of the drawing. This is sometimes a disadvantage ; if the bar is heated (as in welding), distortion will probably occur, and the same difficulty may arise if the work-hardened surface is machined away at certain points. Where distortion must be avoided, the bar may be annealed, and if the bright surface is to be retained, bright annealing may be employed. It should be noted that bright-drawn bar will be stronger but less ductile than black bar.

Bright-drawn **free-cutting steel** bars are used for many small mass-produced parts. It has been noted in Chapter IV that sulphur in iron

44

and steel is much less harmful if combined with manganese. Manganese sulphide occurs in steel in the form of small particles which break up the chips in machining in a similar manner to the graphite flakes in cast iron. Free-cutting mild steel has about 0·3% sulphur, and can be machined about 50% faster than ordinary mild steel. Another type of free-cutting steel has a small percentage of lead instead of manganese sulphide.

It should be noted that the high-sulphur steels have a lower shock resistance than plain mild steels, and are difficult to weld, but lightly stressed parts machined from bar can be produced more cheaply from free-cutting steel, despite the higher cost of the material.

High-carbon and alloy tool steels can also be obtained in round and square bar for machining and for forging into tools of various shapes. Of particular interest is the **precision centreless ground** high-carbon steel bar. This has a very smooth ground finish, and is truly cylindrical and correct to size within 0·0002 in. It is used for dowels and guide-pins, particularly in jig and press tool work.

Rolled Sections

The commonest black-rolled sections are angles, channels and joists with a carbon percentage of about 0·25. The sizes produced range between ½ in. by ½ in. angle and 24 in. by 7½ in. joist. The principal use is in structural steel for buildings, bridges, etc., but many engineering parts which formerly were cast in iron are now being built up by welding from rolled sections and plate.

Sheet

Hot-rolled sheet is obtainable in various carbon steels and many alloy steels. The thinner sheets are usually of dead mild steel, to give good cold-working properties. The surface finish of sheet varies with the application. Tin-coated sheet has a thin coating of tin on each side, and is much used for food canning and small semi-ornamental articles such as fancy retail goods. The finish is rust-proof with normal usage, and joints may readily be soldered—a useful point for sealed food cans. **Tin-terne** sheets have a coating of tin–lead alloy, and are cheaper than pure tin-coated sheets; **lead-coated** sheets are cheaper still. The lead-coated sheet is used for machinery guards and much fairly large press work; it can be painted or enamelled after the part is shaped, as it is free from rust.

Galvanised sheet has a coating of pure zinc. It is the most suitable type for outdoor use. If much work is done on galvanised sheet, or heat is applied for bending, welding or riveting, the galvanised surface will be damaged; consequently, for such articles as water-tanks, the bending, riveting or welding is done on ordinary mild-steel sheet, and the whole article is cleaned and dipped in a bath of molten zinc.

Cold-rolled sheet and strip with a smooth bright finish is produced in mild steel and some alloy steels, notably 18/8 stainless. Very attractive cold-worked articles are produced from it. It is usually supplied " close " or bright annealed and carefully flattened.

Plate

Mild-steel plate is hot rolled in thicknesses from $\frac{1}{8}$ in. to 3 in. The thickest plate normally stocked is, however, about $1\frac{1}{4}$ in. Plates are used in shipwork, boilers, heavy tanks and vessels of all descriptions, and, as already mentioned, they are being increasingly used as a substitute for cast iron. The plate is cut and bent to shape and then welded.

Tube

Tube is produced in three ways : solid drawn, for heavy duties ; seam welded ; and close jointed. The solid-drawn mild-steel tube is used for hydraulic, high-pressure steam and oil services. The seam-welded tube is made from low-carbon-steel strip of suitable width, which is hot drawn to circular form, and the joint, which may be lapped or butted, is pressure welded. It is used for water and gas services at moderate pressures. Electric conduit is made from a thinner strip which is brought to a circular form and the joint well closed, but not usually welded.

Wire

Wire is usually cold drawn through dies. If it is required for bending to shape, a low-carbon steel is used, and the wire is finally annealed. Steel-wire ropes for cranes, lifts and haulage work are made from steel of high carbon content and are **patented** before cold drawing. This is a special heat-treatment process which gives the metal a suitable structure for the severe cold work. These high-tensile wires are cold drawn to give a tensile strength of 80—100 tons/sq. in. and an elongation of 6—8%.

Forgings

These may be purchased unmachined or rough machined. Large shafts, engine connecting-rods, and high-pressure boiler drums are typical forgings. Many small parts of high strength are produced as plain carbon or alloy steel drop forgings.

Castings

A casting of much higher strength can be produced in mild steel than in grey cast iron, but these mild-steel castings are more expensive. Furthermore, the castings must be annealed before use. The following figures illustrate the change in mechanical properties after annealing.

	U.T.S., tons.	Y.P., tons.	El., %.	Red. A., %.	Izod impact, ft. lb.
As cast . . .	28	15·5	6·5	11	10
Annealed . .	31	19·5	25	30	26

CHAPTER VIII

NON-FERROUS METALS

Copper

Pure copper is a soft, ductile metal of high electrical conductivity. The best quality of copper for wires and other electrical conductors contains only faint traces of other elements. It is termed **electrolytic copper**, from the method of refining. **Best select** copper is less pure and has a lower conductivity, but is cheaper and finds many uses. **Arsenical** copper has up to 0·5% arsenic and smaller amounts of other elements; it is stronger than pure copper, and is used for heater tubes, rivets, etc.

Copper is resistant to a number of corrosive liquids, and is used in chemical works, food and brewing plants; its ductility allows heavy cold work, and sheet copper is spun, pressed and drawn into many shapes. The mechanical properties of annealed copper are: U.T.S. 11 tons/sq. in., elongation 50%; there is no definite yield point.

Zinc

Pure zinc is used to coat mild-steel sheets in the galvanising process to prevent rusting. An alloy containing 4% aluminium, 2½% copper and 93½% zinc is used for die castings, a well-known application being the small toy vehicles which are mass produced by a number of firms; this is the only common zinc-base alloy.

Zinc is alloyed with copper to form **brass**. Since zinc is cheaper than copper, the larger the amount of zinc, the cheaper the alloy; but the properties of brass vary considerably with the zinc content, and with more than 37% of zinc there is a rapid fall in the ductility of brass (see Fig. 23). Three types of brass are of particular importance. The alloy known as 70/30 contains 70% copper and 30% zinc. It is very ductile, and is produced in various cold-drawn and cold-rolled sections such as tube, strip and sheet. It is annealed by heating to 600° C. and then cooling at any desired speed; generally cooling by quenching is used to save time.

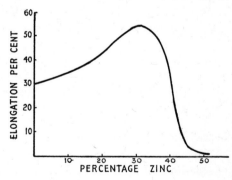

FIG. 23.—DUCTILITY OF COPPER–ZINC ALLOYS.

The amount of cold work done on the metal after the last anneal has a considerable effect on the mechanical properties ; sheet brass is supplied in three qualities : hard for cutting to shape, half hard for simple cold work such as bending, and soft for heavy cold work such as drawing. Hard brass has a Brinell number of 200, whilst annealed brass has a number of 60.

70/30 brass has many applications ; one particular application has earned for it the title **cartridge brass**. Steam condenser tubes are made from **Admiralty** quality. This has the composition 70 copper, 29 zinc and 1 tin. This is more expensive, as tin is a very dear metal, but the corrosion resistance is improved.

Basis brass has the composition 63 copper, 37 zinc, and is cheaper than 70/30, but is less ductile. It is quite suitable for reasonable cold working. There is an Admiralty quality with the composition 62/37/1.

Season Cracking

When either 70/30 or 63/37 brass has been severely cold worked, season cracking may occur. This happens when the article is brought into contact with mild corrosives, such as slightly salty water, or air containing traces of acid. Cracks suddenly appear, sometimes after years of service. Owing to the internal stresses set up by cold working, these cracks may be wide. The remedy is to anneal at 280° C. after cold working. This treatment relieves internal stresses, but has little effect on the hardness.

Muntz Metal

The brasses already mentioned are for cold working ; Muntz metal has the composition 60/40 and is suitable for hot working by rolling, stamping or extruding ; it may also be cast.

70/30 is an unpleasant material to machine, as the swarf comes away in long ribbons with sharp, jagged edges, and the machined surface is usually torn and rough. 63/37 is better, but 60/40 machines readily, and bars for machining are made in 60/40.

Leaded Brass

The machining properties of brass are greatly improved by the inclusion of small amounts of lead. Extruded brass rods with the composition 56 copper, 41 zinc, 3 lead can be machined at very high speeds. The lead is in the form of small globules distributed throughout the brass, and its action is to break up the chips into short pieces and to act as a lubricant. The tensile strength is almost unchanged, but the shock resistance of the brass is lower ; however, many small capstan and automatic lathes use large quantities of leaded brass bar to produce small lightly loaded components.

Special Brasses

Various metals are added to brass to improve particular properties such as corrosion resistance in specific circumstances, tensile strength, hardness or shock resistance. The following is a brief summary of some of these special brasses.

If 1·5% iron and 0·75 manganese are added to 60/40 brass, the tensile strength and resistance to salt water corrosion are both increased. The alloy is usually called **manganese bronze**, but is really a brass. It is used for underwater shafts and fittings.

Manganese, aluminium and iron are added to 60/40 brass to give a tensile strength of 40 tons/sq. in. A number of proprietary alloys are based on this composition.

Nickel is added to brass to give a silvery appearance which does not tarnish readily. **Nickel silver** contains 20% nickel, 30% zinc and 50% copper. It is used for ornamental work on motor cars, shop and house fittings, because of the fine white polish it will take. Since nickel is fairly expensive, cheaper grades have lower nickel contents.

Tin

This is the most expensive of all the common engineering metals, the price usually being several times that of copper. Tinned mild-steel sheets have already been mentioned. The tin coating is kept extremely thin.

Bronze

The simplest type of bronze is an alloy of copper and tin. Bronze containing 95% copper and 5% tin is very ductile, but work hardens more rapidly than 70/30 brass. The tin content of simple bronzes oxidises very quickly when the metal is hot, forming tin oxide (SnO_2). This makes the bronze brittle and "scratchy". Various deoxidisers are added, the most common being zinc or phosphorus.

Gunmetal contains zinc as a deoxiser. Admiralty gunmetal contains 88% copper, 10% tin and 2% zinc. This alloy gives strong corrosion-resistant castings, and is used for small valves and fittings for water services. Owing to the high price of tin, cheaper gunmetals are used— e.g., 90% copper, 3% tin and 7% zinc—but these alloys have poorer casting qualities. Free machining gunmetal contains 85% copper, and 5% each of zinc, tin and lead.

Phosphorus is a powerful deoxiser and **Phosphor-bronze** contains up to 12% tin and a little phosphorus. The phosphorus hardens the bronze, and two distinct phosphor bronzes may be mentioned. With 5—10% tin and not more than 0·5% phosphorus, alloys are suitable for rods for machining and for valve-castings. With 10—12% tin and up to 1% phosphorus an alloy suitable for gear wheels and heavily loaded bearings is

D

produced. These bearing metals are very rigid and have no plasticity, the shaft must be carefully aligned in the bearings and requires a ground finish. The high-tin phosphor-bronzes resist acid corrosion very well.

Plastic bronze is a bearing metal which will work under less rigid conditions than the foregoing. A typical composition is copper 65—70%, lead 25—30%, tin 5%; small quantities of nickel are usually added to ensure even spreading of the globules of lead.

Cupro-nickel

Alloys of copper and nickel are rather expensive. Zinc is slightly cheaper than copper, but the price of nickel is several times that of copper.

The alloy containing 80% copper and 20% nickel has excellent ductility and malleability. It is sometimes used for steam condenser and heater tubes, as it is not subject to season cracking, and is also highly corrosion resistant. It is more expensive than 70/30 brass. Small quantities of manganese are usually present in 80/20 cupro-nickel. The tensile strength (annealed) is 25—30 tons/sq. in. and the elongation 40—50%.

Another alloy has 60% copper and 40% nickel. This has a very fine appearance and is ductile and malleable. The extra nickel further increases the cost.

Monel metal contains about 68% nickel and 28% copper with small amounts of iron and manganese. The composition varies slightly, as monel metal is refined directly from an ore. It can be cast and hot forged as well as cold worked, and it also has considerable strength at temperatures which would completely soften most non-ferrous metals.

A number of highly corrosive acid and alkaline substances have little or no effect on monel metal, and consequently the alloy is used in many industrial chemical processes for special pumps, vessels, utensils and tools.

Aluminium Bronze

Two copper-base alloys containing aluminium are important. With 5—7% aluminium an alloy which can be worked hot or cold is obtained. It has a fine golden colour, and is resistant to a number of corrosive substances.

With 10% aluminium a castable alloy is produced; it can be heat treated in a manner rather similar to a medium-carbon steel.

Aluminium

Pure aluminium is a weak but ductile metal; its most important property is its light weight—roughly one third that of iron. The development of aluminium as an engineering metal has been an essential part of the aircraft industry. Intensive research has produced a wide range of alloys, each with its own properties and consequent uses.

Duralumin

The main alloying element is 4% copper, but other metals are present in small quantities. It should be understood that there are a number of alloys which have slight variations in composition, but all have fairly similar properties. One very important property is that of **precipitation** or **age hardening.**

Duralumin, after heating to about 490° C. and quenching in water, is soft and will cold work readily, but after a few hours the hardness increases appreciably, and will continue to do so for several days; at the same time, the ductility falls off rapidly. This process can be retarded by holding the alloy at a very low temperature. Duralumin parts are softened and immediately cold worked, and are then put on one side to age harden. Where duralumin rivets are in use, they may be annealed and kept in a refrigerator. They should never be left about the shop to age harden and then be used. The change of properties is shown below:

	U.T.S., tons.	El., %.	B.H.
Before age hardening . . .	17	20	62
After age hardening . . .	26	20	98

Duralumin is supplied in sheets, strips, rods and many rolled shapes such as tees and angles. Sheet made from duralumin with a thin coating of pure aluminium at each side is sold, and is more corrosion resistant than duralumin alone.

There are a number of castable alloys of aluminium. Some are complex alloys containing nickel, copper and magnesium; these alloys do not age harden naturally, but some can be age hardened by heating at a temperature between 100° and 200° C. Other castable alloys include 12% copper and 88% aluminium; alloys containing aluminium, copper and zinc; and one containing 13% silicon and 87% aluminium. This last alloy is used in automobile work, as it casts well into intricate shapes; it has a tensile strength of 13—14 tons/sq. in.

Anodising

The corrosion resistance of aluminium depends largely on a thin film of hard oxide, which gradually builds up and inhibits further corrosion. This film can be produced artificially by anodising, and is then thicker and more even than the natural film.

The parts to be treated are polished and sand blasted, and are then placed in a bath containing chromic, sulphuric or oxalic acid. The parts form the anode when electricity is passed through the bath. The film thus produced may be dyed in any one of a number of colours; the smooth, coloured surface is hard wearing and has a pleasing appearance.

Aluminium has a coefficient of linear expansion over twice that of cast iron or steel, and this fact sometimes requires special precautions in design.

An aluminium piston in a cast-iron cylinder requires considerable clearance when cold, and this may lead to piston " slap " unless special designs of piston are used.

Bearing Metals

Phosphor-bronze, plastic bronze and various brasses have already been mentioned. The plastic bronzes have a **duplex** nature—i.e., they consist of soft globules of lead surrounded by a network of hard bronze. This duplex structure is typical of many bearing metals. The hard constituent takes the wear, whilst the soft constituent acts as a cushion and allows the bearing surface to " give " to slight misalignment ; furthermore, the soft spots on the surface are always slightly below the hard spots, and thus form minute oil reservoirs.

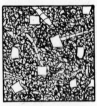

FIG. 24. — MICRO-STRUCTURE OF WHITE METAL.

For heavy loads and moderate speeds the leaded bronzes are very suitable. For light loads, a cheap lead-base alloy will suffice, but for high speeds and heavy loads a more expensive tin-base alloy is necessary. A typical lead-base alloy contains 80% lead, 15% antimony and 5% tin. A tin-base alloy used for high-speed bearings contains 86% tin, 10·5% antimony and 3·5% copper. The microstructure of this latter alloy is shown in Fig. 24. The cubes consist of a chemical compound of tin and antimony (SnSb) whilst the " threads " are CuSn (copper–tin). In casting the metal the CuSn locks the cubes of SnSb and ensures their even distribution throughout the bearing metal.

Solder

Solder is an alloy of tin and lead, to which a little antimony is often added. The melting temperature of an alloy is often lower than that of either of the two metals of which it is made. Fig. 25 is a simplified

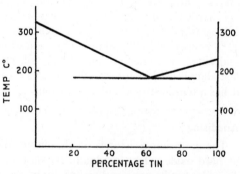

FIG. 25.—EQUILIBRIUM DIAGRAM LEAD–TIN ALLOYS.

diagram illustrating this point. The melting point of lead is 330° C. and that of tin is 232° C. In each case the melting or freezing occurs at this temperature, and the whole mass remains substantially at this fixed point until melting or freezing is complete. In the case of lead–tin alloys the melting point decreases with increasing tin content, reaching a minimum of 183° C. with 62% tin and then increasing again. With 62% tin the whole mass freezes at 183° C., but for any other composition there is a freezing range.

In Fig. 25 it will be noted that a horizontal line is shown. Below this line, which is at 183° C., all lead–tin alloys are solid; between this line and the upper V-shaped line is the freezing range. Common solder contains equal proportions of tin and lead, and has a range from 210° to 183° C.; it solidifies fairly quickly. Plumber's solder has 70% lead and 30% tin and freezes from 250° to 183° C.; consequently it has a long, "pasty" stage. This enables the plumber to "wipe" a joint. Tinman's solder has about 40% lead and 60% tin, and consequently solidifies rapidly, as the freezing range is very short.

CHAPTER IX

HEAT TREATMENT OF STEEL

WHEN iron is heated from room temperature and careful observations of the temperature are made, a rather strange phenomenon is noted. The temperature rise, after proceeding steadily, is suddenly arrested, and for a time the metal remains at practically the same temperature. During this period the metal absorbs heat, but the heat brings about certain changes in the metal, instead of raising the temperature. After the change is complete further heating causes a rise in temperature as before. The temperatures at which these changes occur are termed " arrest " or **critical points**.

Critical points also occur in steel, but the temperatures at which they occur alter with the carbon content of the steel. In mild steel there are four critical points, but it will only be necessary here to consider two of them, as the remaining two are not important in the present discussion.

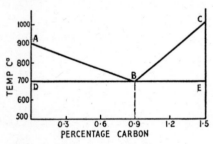

FIG. 26.—CRITICAL POINTS OF PLAIN CARBON STEEL.

Fig. 26 is a diagram showing the approximate critical points for steel of various carbon contents. The line ABC shows the **upper critical points**, and the straight, horizontal line DBE shows the **lower critical points**.

From the diagram we see that all plain carbon steels have the same lower critical point—i.e. 700° C.—whilst the upper critical falls from 900° C. with no carbon to 700° C. with 0·9% carbon. Thus 0·9% carbon steel has only one critical point, but all other steels have an upper and a lower critical. The temperature range between the upper and lower critical points for any steel is termed the **critical range**. Steel with 0·1% carbon has a wide critical range; steel with 0·8% carbon has a narrow critical range.

Annealing

Steel is annealed by heating it to slightly above the upper critical and then allowing it to cool very slowly. When a steel is heated slightly above the upper critical, its structure consists of small, unstrained crystals (see Fig. 13 A). If the steel has been cold worked or deformed, these internal strains will have been removed when the upper critical is passed :

further heating merely increases the size of the crystal grains, and thus tends to weaken the metal when it returns to the cold state.

In the case of some non-ferrous metals, the speed of cooling has no effect on the final structure, but for steel with more than 0·25% carbon the cooling rate is very important. To obtain the metal in its softest state, the cooling should be done as slowly as possible; for small pieces, after heating above the upper critical, the part may be buried in hot ashes, but for large components it is customary to cool the steel by gradually lowering the furnace temperature. With very large sections, forty-eight hours cooling may be necessary to allow the heat of the interior to escape gradually. After annealing, the steel is in its softest and most ductile state, and is generally suitable for all kinds of work, either hot or cold.

Normalising

If a steel is heated slightly above the upper critical and allowed to cool freely in still air at room temperature, it is said to have been normalised. It will be stronger and harder than annealed steel; it will be less suitable for cold working, but generally will be more suitable for putting into service. Hot-rolled plates and sections are worked at about the upper critical, and then allowed to cool off under conditions approximating to normalising. Forgings are often cooled off in the same way.

Normalising is cheaper and quicker than annealing, as the part may be removed from the furnace after heating, but the cooling rate cannot be so carefully controlled.

Structural Changes in Cooling Steel

The changes occurring in a steel when it is being cooled from above the upper critical to room temperature are complex, and cannot be fully discussed here, but the following explanation may be helpful.

When the steel is held at a temperature slightly above the upper critical point, the structure is homogeneous (similar in all parts) and the size of the crystal grains is at the minimum for the particular type of steel. Any strains due to previous working will have disappeared; the steel is said to be **austenitic.** The carbide of iron will be **in solution**—i.e., it will be dissolved in the steel just as sugar may be dissolved in water, but it is **solid** carbide of iron dissolved in **solid** iron. If the hot steel could be examined, it would appear as shown in Fig. 13 A; the carbide of iron would be invisible.

If the steel is now cooled fairly slowly, as in annealing or normalising, the carbide of iron will come out of solution—i.e., it will be **precipitated**. If the cold steel is suitably prepared and examined under a microscope, it will appear as shown in Fig. 27. The dark crystal grains consist of the precipitated carbide of iron mixed with iron; the light grains contain iron only. With increasing carbon content there will be more dark grains, and with 0·9% carbon all the grains will be dark; Fig. 27 shows a steel with about 0·2% carbon. This precipitation of carbide of iron occurs during the critical range and is completed at the lower critical point. Steel with 0·9% carbon has no critical range; all the carbide of iron is precipitated at 700° C., and this steel shows a very pronounced heat arrest at that temperature.

If steel is heated, the reverse process takes place; carbide of iron begins to dissolve in the iron when the steel passes the lower critical point, and the solution is complete at the upper critical point. As may be surmised, if steel is held in the critical range, part only of the carbide of iron will be in solution.

Fig. 28 shows a piece of steel as seen under a very powerful microscope. The particular portion shown is at the junction of several dark crystal grains. The dark lines are the carbide of iron, and the light spaces are iron. This structure is termed **pearlite**, and the appearance is typical of

Fig. 27.—Mild Steel.   Fig. 28.—Pearlite.   Fig. 29.—Martensite.

annealed and normalised steels. Pearlite is considerably harder and stronger than pure iron; hence the increase in strength and hardness of steel with increasing carbon content.

Stress Relieving

This is the best name for a process sometimes termed " sub-critical annealing ". If a piece of steel has internal stresses due to cold work or due to the strains of welding or other local heating, it may have these relieved by heating to 650° C. This stress relief is due to the fact that the elastic limit of steel (see Chapter I) is lowered by heat, and at 650° C. it is low enough for the stresses to pull the softened metal into the shape which releases them. There is no solution of the iron carbide in heating to 650° C., which is below the lower critical, and consequently no precipitation on cooling again. Therefore this heating and cooling bears no resemblance to annealing; it is much better to call it **thermal stress relieving.**

Martensite

The formation of pearlite occurs whilst the steel is cooling through the critical range, and an appreciable time is required for austenite to break down into pearlite. If steel is cooled very quickly through the critical range—i.e., if it is quenched in a liquid—then pearlite cannot form in the short time, and instead, another structure, termed **martensite**, is produced from the austenite. The appearance of martensite under the microscope is shown in Fig. 29. It was first noted by A. Martens, the German metallurgist.

In this condition steel is extremely hard and brittle. The Brinell number will be about 700, the tensile strength will be up to 100 tons/sq. in., but the ductility will be zero. It must be understood that martensite is produced due to the presence of carbide of iron; pure iron cannot be hardened by heating and quenching. When the carbon content exceeds 0·3% the hardening effect becomes pronounced, and increases rapidly with higher carbon contents.

To obtain martensite, the cooling must be done very quickly, particularly with plain carbon steel; hence the necessity for drastic quenching, usually in cold water. For any steel there is a **critical hardening speed**, and this speed must be exceeded if martensite is to be produced. It may be noted that many alloy steels have fairly low critical hardening speeds and may be quenched in oil, or even in an air blast to yield martensite.

If a piece of steel is heated and then quenched in water, the outer skin will be cooled very quickly, but if the steel is to be hardened throughout, then heat must be extracted from the centre at a speed exceeding the critical hardening speed. This becomes impossible with plain carbon steel if the section is more than 1 in. across, and larger sections have a hard surface but a softer interior : this is termed **mass effect**, and 1 in. is the **limiting section** of the material.

Certain alloying elements, particularly nickel and chromium, may be added to steel, and will decrease the critical hardening speed, so that large sections up to 6 in. may be hardened throughout. A further advantage of these alloy steels is that the low critical hardening speed allows oil to be used for quenching, thus minimising the risk of cracking and distortion.

Tempering

Cutting tools made from fully hardened high-carbon steel are extremely hard, but are too brittle to be of any use. Some of this brittleness, which is due to internal stresses set up by drastic cooling, may be removed by suitable tempering. The shock resistance of the tool will be increased considerably, whilst the hardness will be lowered very little.

Cutting tools are tempered by heating to some temperature between 220° and 320° C., and then cooling off. The higher the temperature, the better will be the shock resistance, but the lower the hardness; the usual practice is to use the lower temperatures for smooth-cutting tools so as to retain the cutting edge as long as possible, whilst cold chisels and similar tools are tempered at the higher temperatures to give good shock resistance.

Gauges and other precision measuring instruments are often hardened to improve their wearing properties; unfortunately they are then liable to alter in length over a period of months or years—a process known as **secular change**. This change can be almost eliminated by **stabilising,** which consists of tempering several times at about 150° C.

The processes described above are usually termed **low-temperature tempering,** and are intended to retain most of the hardness of the quenched steel, but there is another tempering range from 450° to 650° C.; this range is used when steels are required to be tough rather than hard. Plain carbon steels from 0·3% to 0·6% carbon are often quenched and then tempered in the upper range. They are harder and more shock resistant than the same steel in the normalised state, but are still machineable. Many alloy steels, particularly those containing nickel and chromium with low mass effects, only show their best properties after hardening and tempering, and furthermore, by choosing suitable tempering temperatures, the final properties can be varied over a wide range of hardness and strength values.

It should be noted that all tempering is done below the lower critical point. Generally, it is not advisable to hold steel at a temperature within the critical range.

Hardening and Tempering Practice

In the workshop carbon-steel tools are often hardened and tempered with the aid of a small gas-fired furnace or the blacksmith's hearth. They are heated to about 800° C. (the temperature being judged by the colour) and then partially immersed in water, the cutting point being held downwards to ensure its being quenched. Part of the tool shank remains red hot, and on removal from the water the heat from the shank flows back to the cutting point and tempers it.

This method is only possible due to the peculiar oxidisation of the steel. When the cold cutting point is removed from the water it is quickly polished and watched carefully. At about 220° C. a faint yellow oxide film forms on the surface of the steel. This colour slowly turns to brown, then to purple and finally to blue at 300° C. In the case of an orthodox cutting tool the effect produced is that of a band of colours, headed by yellow, passing slowly down to the point of the tool. When the desired colour reaches the tool point, the whole tool is quenched out in water. The following list gives the tempering colours and typical articles tempered.

Temper colour.				Actual temperature, °C.	Articles.
Pale yellow	.	.	.	230	Planing tools, brass turning tools.
Deep yellow	.	.	.	240	Drills, milling cutters.
Brown	.	.	.	250	Taps.
Brown–Purple		.	.	265	Punches.
Purple	.	.	.	275	Chisels.
Blue	.	.	.	300	Springs.

The method outlined above is not suitable for parts which require hardening throughout their length. In such cases the part may be quenched out in water, and then held over a heated iron plate until the tempering colour appears. By skilled manipulation an article of irregular section can be tempered in this way. The surface temperature only is indicated by the colour, but a good craftsman, tempering the tools and observing the results in service, can produce good work by hot-plate tempering.

By far the most accurate method of tempering is to immerse the article in liquid at the tempering temperature. Various liquids are used, such as molten mixtures of tin and lead (solder), various salts of low fusibility, and even hot oil.

When steel is to be tempered in the high-temperature range, colour tempering cannot be used, and the part is either immersed in liquid or a furnace is held at the desired temperature.

Case Hardening

Many articles such as pins and rollers require a hard surface to resist wear, but must have a tough, strong core. This dual structure is obtained by case hardening. The component is made from a steel containing 0·15% carbon, and is finished with the possible exception of a small amount of grinding. It is then placed in a gas-tight box and surrounded by materials rich in carbon, commonly a mixture of charcoal and barium carbonate, and is heated in a furnace to 900° C. for a number of hours. The low-carbon steel absorbs further carbon into its surface, and after six or eight hours the surface may have a carbon content of 0·9% to a depth of 0·040 in., and will thus respond to heat treatment.

Referring to Fig. 26, it will be realised that the **carburising process** just described had been done at a temperature higher than the upper critical point of the 0·15% carbon steel core, and very much above the upper critical of the 0·9% carbon steel case. Consequently, the grain structure of the steel will be coarse and needs refining. The part is taken from the carburising box, cleaned and reheated to 870° C., which temperature is slightly over the upper critical point of the core. The core is thus refined and the part is quenched, usually in oil. The quenching does not harden the core very much, owing to the low carbon content, but the case will have a hard but coarse martensitic structure. The article is slowly reheated to 600° C., and then quickly brought up to 760° C. Just long enough is allowed to heat the case to this temperature, and thus bring it above its upper critical point. Quenching follows, and the component should then have a strong core and a hard fine grained case. If desired, the case can be tempered at 150° C.

Cyanide Salt Baths

Small parts are often given a shallow, hard case by a heated bath of cyanide salts. The bath usually contains a mixture of sodium cyanide

(NaCN) and soda ash (NaCO$_3$) at a temperature of 920° to 950° C. The parts are cleaned and immersed for a short time. They come out clean and carburised to a depth of about 0·008 in., and are usually quenched immediately, this completing the treatment. The process is very suitable for small mass-produced parts. An unfortunate drawback to this process is that the bath gives off poisonous fumes, and the workmen must be carefully protected from them.

Nitriding

Special alloy steels are immersed in ammonia gas (NH$_3$) at 500° C. for periods up to eighty-eight hours. Iron nitride—an extremely hard substance—is formed in the case, and no quenching is necessary. Since the treatment is carried out below the lower critical point, and no quenching is required, the structure of the steel is unaffected and there is no distortion, cracking or scaling. Parts may be finish ground before nitriding. Gauges and bushes for drill jigs are often nitrided.

Heat Treatment of Alloy Steels

The various alloy steels containing nickel, chromium, molybdenum, vanadium and other alloying elements are usually hardened and tempered to develop their best qualities. The critical points vary considerably with different compositions, and the only satisfactory method of heat treatment is to follow carefully the instructions supplied by the maker. Usually they are quenched in oil, except certain air-hardening steels, which are merely heated and allowed to cool in the atmosphere. The slow quench, and the absence of mass effect, make them very useful for all types of duties where heavy stresses or hot conditions are encountered, as they are of even hardness throughout, and free from distortion.

High-speed Steel

The high-speed steels are heavily alloyed, principally with tungsten; they are dense steels of low heat conductivity, and the changes from austenite to martensite, etc., occur sluggishly. Correct heat treatment is most essential if the best results are to be obtained. There are no sharply defined critical points, and the diagram (Fig. 26) for plain carbon steels does not apply at all. Each steel must be treated according to the maker's instructions, but the following is a rough general guide.

Annealing is done by heating at about 850° C. for four hours, followed by very slow cooling. To obtain full hardness, the tool is heated slowly to 850° C., usually in the low-temperature chamber of a two-chamber furnace; it is then transferred to the high-temperature chamber, and quickly heated at the point to 1250° C. or over, removed, and quenched in a blast of dry air; the tool is then reheated to 600° C. and again cooled. This last reheat is termed **secondary hardening**, as it improves the wearing qualities when cutting. It is not a tempering operation, as might be imagined from the temperature used, but serves to fully develop the martensite. In the machine shop a high-speed steel tool sometimes puts up a poor performance when first used and quickly requires regrinding ; after regrinding, however, the performance is quite satisfactory. In such cases it is probable that the tool point has been heated up by excessive friction to about 600° C., thus performing the " secondary hardening " in a crude but effective manner. Freezing high-speed steel to temperatures of −150° F. also helps to develop a very hard martensitic structure.

High-speed steel is liable to " scale " when heated—i.e., a soft, scaly surface is produced—and this must be ground off before the tool can be used. This scale is due to oxidisation, and arises from an incorrect mixture of gases in the furnace. The question of furnace gas mixtures will be dealt with later.

Heating Steel

If a piece of steel is heated in any of the usual furnaces, the heat must penetrate from the outside. If steel at 20° C. is placed in a furnace at 1000° C., the outer skin will quickly heat up and expand whilst the interior is still cold. This expansion will set up severe internal stresses, and may cause internal cracks. Slow heating is therefore required, and for large sections the temperature of the furnace must be raised steadily, after the component has been placed inside. Small parts may be preheated, either in a separate furnace or on the sill of the furnace.

The upper critical point of most steels is below 900° C., and consequently the furnace temperature should not greatly exceed this figure, otherwise grain growth will occur at the surface of the steel and in thin sections. When the steel is approaching the furnace temperature, heating will slow down considerably, and thus parts of any thickness require considerable soaking. The soaking time will depend on the thickness and also on the thermal conductivity of the steel. Most alloy steels have low thermal conductivity, and the internal structure changes more slowly than plain carbon steel ; they therefore require longer soaking times.

The steel must be evenly heated. This is partly a question of furnace design, and will be discussed later ; but in a simple furnace care should be taken in placing the component. Thin parts should be kept away from the direct flame, as this is the hottest part of the furnace. It is a bad practice to open the furnace door at frequent intervals to observe the charge ; for cold air may be drawn in across some part of the work. Distortion of articles is usually blamed on the quench, but it must not be forgotten that red-hot steel is comparatively soft, and will sag if not properly supported. The hearth of a furnace is often allowed to get into a very rough state, making it difficult to support the work in a satisfactory manner. The careless use of cold tongs on hot steel causes distortion ; for delicate parts, it is better to make iron clips rather than to use tongs. The judgment of temperature by the eye is not efficient, for even the most experienced workman is influenced by the dullness of surrounding articles and by his state of health. There are many systems of temperature measurement, some of which are described later. The following table, which gives some idea of the appearance of steel at various temperatures, is useful only for very simple forging operations.

Colour.					Temperature, °C.
Very dull red	.	.	.	.	500— 600
Dark blood red	.	.	.	.	600— 700
Cherry red	.	.	.	.	700— 800
Bright red	.	.	.	.	800— 850
Pinkish red	.	.	.	.	850— 900
Pinkish orange	.	.	.	.	900— 950
Orange	.	.	.	.	950—1000
Yellow	.	.	.	.	1000—1100
Yellowish white	.	.	.	.	1100—1200
White	.	.	.	.	1200—1300
Brilliant sparkling white	.	.	.	over 1300

Cooling Steel

If steel is to be annealed or normalised it must be cooled slowly, and some of the precautions mentioned under the heading " heating of steel " will apply. In annealing, the furnace temperature must be lowered at a speed suitable to the size of the component. This point is of great importance when the steel is being cooled through the critical range. Alloy steels will require slower cooling than plain carbon steels.

Quenching Media

The order of severity of the various quenching media is as follows : brine, water, oil, dry air. The least severe medium that will give full hardness should always be used, in order to minimise the danger of distortion or cracking. The one to be used is that which will just cool the steel a little faster than the critical hardening speed, hence the importance of knowing the properties and correct hardening technique of each steel used.

The condition of brine and water calls for little comment, except that each should be clean and particularly free from grease or soap. Quenching oil must have a high flash point, and ordinary lubricating oil is quite unsuitable. Even the best quenching oil is subject to change : certain lighter portions are evaporated by the hot metal, thus increasing the viscosity and lowering the cooling properties. Furthermore, a sludge consisting of carbonised oil and scale from the quenched metal is gradually formed. Many compressed-air systems do not yield dry air, and precautions should be taken to dry the air if it is to be used for quenching purposes.

The method of immersing a component in the quenching bath requires forethought. The hot steel will vaporise some of the liquid, and bubbles of vapour may cling to the surface of the steel or be trapped in blind holes.

If long components are dipped at an angle or horizontally, distortion is more probable than if they are dipped vertically.

In many cases the article is immersed and moved about in the bath, but in modern installations jets of oil are directed on to the component at suitable points, the component being placed over the bath. In other cases the liquid in the bath is arranged to have a steady flow by means of pumps or rotating paddles. There are also arrangements whereby the oil is constantly withdrawn and passed through a cooler to maintain an even temperature.

Influence of Design on Heat Treatment

The designer can provide unnecessary problems for the heat-treatment department. Sharp corners and unsymmetrical or abruptly changing

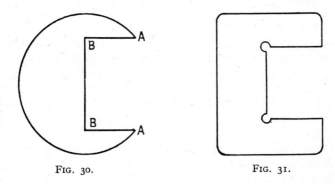

FIG. 30.   FIG. 31.

shapes should be avoided. Consider the two flat gauges shown in Figs. 30 and 31. In Fig. 30 cracks might be set up at *B* during quenching, and the thin corners at *A* would readily overheat in the furnace. Fig. 31 shows the same gauge modified to overcome these difficulties; it is the usual form of the ordinary workshop " snap " gauge.

Certain other difficulties have already been mentioned. Blind holes should be avoided if possible, and long, thin parts are a nuisance, since a deep bath is required if they are to be quenched vertically. Hardened parts sometimes appear to have certain holes drilled in them unnecessarily, but on examination it becomes obvious that these holes have been drilled to thin down certain bulky sections, and to give the component a more even thickness throughout.

CHAPTER X

HEAT-TREATMENT FURNACES

Furnaces are available for all the usual heat-treatment processes and for a wide range of components. The use to which the furnace will be put decides the design. Not only the size and shape require designing, but also the source of heat, the method of temperature control and observation, the size and disposition of the door or doors, and, in the case of large furnaces, the lay-out of the whole heat-treatment department must be carefully planned.

Gas-fired Furnaces

In modern practice coal-gas-fired furnaces are the commonest type. In order to appreciate their use, a little knowledge of combustion is required. Coal gas after purification, as supplied in the usual town's gas main, consists almost wholly of the elements hydrogen (H) and carbon (C). Hydrogen and carbon combine chemically in a number of **hydrocarbons**. One typical hydrocarbon is methane (CH_4), and this gas is present in all town's gas.

When the hydrocarbons burn they do so by combining with oxygen (O), thus liberating great heat and forming a new series of gases. The principal gases formed are carbon monoxide (CO), carbon dioxide (CO_2) and water vapour (H_2O). The relative amounts of carbon monoxide and carbon dioxide depend on the amount of oxygen provided; if enough oxygen is present, all the carbon will form CO_2, but if there is a deficiency of oxygen, then some CO will remain.

The usual source of oxygen is the atmosphere, which consists mainly of a mixture of four parts of nitrogen (N) to one part of oxygen; consequently the combustion is accompanied by large quantities of nitrogen. This nitrogen contributes nothing to the combustion, but nevertheless is heated up to the same temperature as the other gases. Each pound of hydrogen gives out about 60,000 British Thermal Units when burnt to H_2O; each pound of carbon gives out about 9000 B.Th.U. when burnt to CO or about 20,000 B.Th.U. when burnt to CO_2. These two gases provide all the heat; the oxygen which is essential to the combustion process, and the nitrogen which is incidental to it, provide no heat—in fact, they have to be heated by the heat energy released by the hydrogen and carbon, and in consequence they lower the final gas temperature very considerably. In order to burn coal gas completely, not less than four volumes of air are required for each volume of gas: it will be obvious to the reader that the volume of nitrogen is very great.

When a hot flame is required, pure oxygen is provided for mixing with the combustible gas, which is usually acetylene (C_2H_2) or pure hydrogen. Since hydrogen has a higher calorific value than carbon, the oxy-hydrogen flame is hotter than the oxy-acetylene flame, but both are much hotter than the air–coal-gas flame, due to the absence of nitrogen.

In the ordinary coal-gas furnace, if plenty of air is provided, the products of combustion are N_2, CO_2, H_2O and O_2. Of these gases, the last three, and particularly the free oxygen, will quickly oxidise hot steel, and at the same time extract carbon from the surface of the metal. In consequence, they are termed **oxidising** or **decarburising** gases, and the furnace is said to have an oxidising or decarburising **atmosphere.** Steel heated in such an atmosphere will **scale** rapidly. This scale consists of a layer of iron oxide, under which there will probably be a further layer of decarburised steel. Such a scale may have disastrous consequences. The oxide layer acts as a heat insulator, and prevents quick heat dissipation when the hot steel is quenched ; the low-carbon-steel layer cannot be hardened, and the result is that the component has a soft, scaly surface, and may be improperly hardened throughout. Many components have to be ground after hardening, but if they have been allowed to scale, they may require so much grinding as to leave them undersize and useless.

If the air supply to the furnace is cut down there will be a deficiency of oxygen, and the products of combustion will be : N_2, CO, H_2O and some CO_2, with some unburnt hydrocarbons such as CH_4. The hydrocarbons and the carbon monoxide are **reducing** or **carburising** gases—that is, they tend to extract oxygen from the steel and to deposit carbon. In these circumstances the furnace is said to have a reducing or carburising atmosphere. The scaling will be much less than with an oxidising atmosphere, but it will not be eliminated ; this can be accomplished only by removing the H_2O.

With either a reducing or oxidising atmosphere, the highest possible temperature is not attained. With the former the unburnt hydrogen and carbon are wasted, with the latter the excess oxygen and nitrogen are heated unnecessarily. By careful control a **neutral** atmosphere may be obtained ; this has neither excess hydrogen nor oxygen. Such an atmosphere is difficult to hold, and in practice the atmosphere is given a reducing bias to ensure that it will never be oxidising.

In the completely non-scaling atmosphere which is used for close or bright annealing and similar operations, the H_2O is eliminated as follows. The steel is enclosed in a gas-tight chamber or **muffle.** The atmosphere for this muffle is provided by burning coal gas and air in a separate chamber and passing the products of combustion through a condenser. In the condenser the H_2O changes from vapour to liquid and is drained off. In burning the coal gas the amount of air is deliberately restricted, and to ensure that the gas is reducing, some unburnt coal gas is added after the condenser. The atmosphere thus created is passed to the muffle, and there

E

surrounds the steel. The heating of the muffle is done externally by gas, oil or coal, whichever is most convenient. Fig. 32 illustrates the principle of this system.

In another type of furnace the muffle is flooded with " cracked "

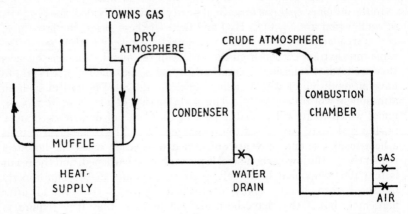

FIG. 32.—DIAGRAMMATIC ARRANGEMENT OF CONTROLLED ATMOSPHERE FURNACE

ammonia which has been partially burnt. The gas ammonia (NH_3) is treated to separate the two constituents, and the hydrogen is partially burnt in air, thus adding further nitrogen. The H_2O produced is removed by condensation, and the atmosphere for the muffle consists solely of nitrogen with a small proportion of unburnt hydrogen. This method is rather expensive, owing to the price of ammonia, but the atmosphere can be re-circulated and " freshened up " with a little new ammonia.

The Bunsen Burner

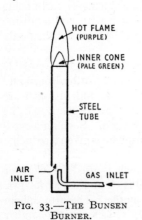

FIG. 33.—THE BUNSEN BURNER.

The Bunsen burner is the apparatus used for providing the flame in the coal-gas furnace. The principle is illustrated in Fig. 33. The gas is introduced to the bottom of a thin iron tube and the **primary** air enters at the side. The gas flow is controlled by a valve on the gas-inlet pipe, whilst the air orifice may be equipped with an adjustable shutter. The air and gas mix thoroughly as they rise up the tube, and they burn at the top with a duplex flame. The air surrounding the flame provides the oxygen required to complete the combustion and is therefore termed **secondary** air.

A very important point about the Bunsen flame is its cleanliness. If pure coal gas is allowed to pass up a tube it will burn at the top, obtaining its air from the surrounding atmosphere.   However, if a metallic surface is placed in the flame it will be covered in soot from the flame in a few seconds.   This soot is, of course, carbon deposited by the gas.   In the case of the Bunsen flame no soot will appear, but the surface will oxidise, as has already been described.   Oxidisation is, however, quite a slow process compared with the sooting up caused by the pure gas flame.   If the gas-tap is opened on a Bunsen burner and the air is not allowed to enter, a long, yellow flame will result, but immediately air is admitted the flame shortens greatly and narrows, burning to purple.   The gas, already charged with air, burns in a much smaller space, and the heat is much more concentrated.

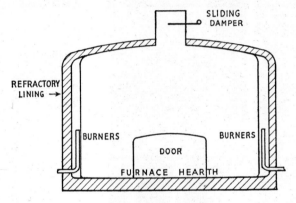

FIG. 34.—SIMPLE COAL-GAS FURNACE.

The simplest type of gas-fired furnace consists of a box-shaped oven, the inside being lined with fire-bricks or other heat-resisting material; this is termed the **refractory** lining.   The heat is provided by one or more Bunsens let into the furnace.   One arrangement is shown in Fig. 34.   The burners are placed vertically in recesses or flutes in the vertical sides of the furnace.   The flames rise up each side and play on the roof before passing up the chimney.   A considerable amount of the heat is obtained by radiation from the arched roof.   The chimney is provided with a sliding damper which is opened when the furnace is lit, but is subsequently partially closed, thus conserving some heat.   The front of the furnace is provided with a counterweighted door which slides up to give access to the inside.   Many furnaces have elaborate heat controls, but the ordinary workshop furnace is often controlled by simply adjusting the gas-taps by hand.

The size of these simple furnaces varies widely, and may be very large, but the most popular types have hearth sizes from 2 ft. × 2 ft. to 5 ft. × 3 ft.   The temperature attained is up to 1000° C., therefore plain carbon and many alloy steels can be given any standard heat treatment. Fig. 35 shows a typical natural draught furnace fitted with an automatic temperature controller.

For the hardening of high-speed steel, temperatures of 1300° C. are required; furthermore, slow heating to about 850° C. followed by rapid heating to the quenching temperature is essential. For this work special double-deck furnaces are manufactured. Fig. 36 shows a typical furnace for high-speed steel. The air is supplied at a pressure of about ½ lb. per

[*Manchester Furnaces, Ltd.*

FIG. 35.—NATURAL DRAUGHT FURNACE.

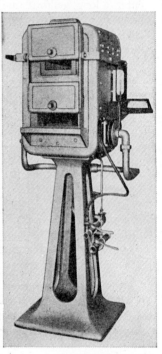

[*Manchester Furnaces, Ltd.*

FIG. 36.—TOOL HARDENING FURNACE.

sq. in., usually by an air blower, whilst the gas is supplied at the usual mains pressure. The mixture of air and gas is projected at high speed into the lower chamber and as this is quite small, with a volume of little more than a cubic foot, and is heavily heat insulated, the temperature of 1300° C. is quickly attained. The hot gases rise from the lower chamber round the sides of the upper chamber, which is partially protected from the direct flames, and has a temperature of about 900° C.

High-speed steel tools are warmed at the sill, soaked in the upper chamber, and finally transferred to the lower chamber. The air and gas mixture is controlled by an automatic valve.

Fig. 37 illustrates an automatic air–gas proportioning valve, and also three methods of admitting the flame to the furnace. The gas inlet cock is simply opened full out and the size of flame is controlled by the position of the air-cock. The gas governor automatically admits the correct amount of gas according to the air pressure, several burners being controlled by one governor.

The three burners shown would not normally be used on one furnace, but each has its own application. The one on the right is arranged to direct the flame on to a heap of broken refractory. The large surface

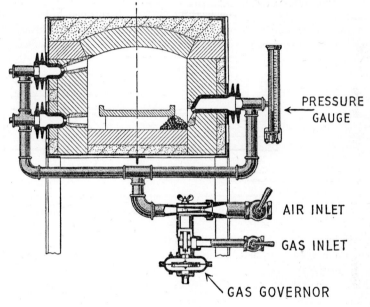

[*British Furnaces, Ltd.*

FIG. 37.—AIR-GAS PROPORTIONING.

accelerates the completion of combustion and radiates an enormous amount of heat. The "tunnel" burners shown on the left are usually fitted in the side wall of the furnace. The flame may play on the furnace arch, or can be directed under the hearth to provide "bottom" heat where this is required.

The muffle furnace has been mentioned earlier. Simple muffles are frequently made in the workshop by capping the ends of a suitable piece of wrought-iron pipe and placing the steel inside the pipe before insertion in the furnace. It should be realised that a certain amount of air is present inside the muffle, and the results obtained are not equal to those produced in a proper muffle furnace, with a controlled atmosphere. However, uneven heating and excessive scaling are minimised.

The Continuous Furnace

The furnaces already described soon attain a fixed temperature, depending on the amount of air and gas admitted. If a part is to be heated or cooled at a certain rate, the furnace must be heated or cooled with the component. The continuous furnace is long compared with its width; the temperature is kept low at the entrance and rises steadily along the length. If annealing is to be done, the temperature falls towards the exit, if hardening is required, the temperature is kept high up to the exit. If prolonged soaking is required, a suitable length of the furnace is held at that temperature. It only remains to traverse the components at the correct speed and the heating cycle is performed automatically. This traversing may be done by pushing the components through the

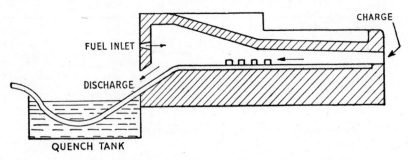

FIG. 38.—CONTINUOUS FURNACE WITH QUENCHING TANK.

furnace by mechanically operated rods (the pusher furnace) or by carrying them on a conveyor belt made of heat-resisting metal (the travelling hearth furnace).

Fig. 38 shows diagrammatically a continuous furnace and quenching bath for the mass heating and quenching of small parts.

The Salt-bath Furnace

These furnaces, which may be heated by gas or electricity, consist essentially of a suitably shaped container with molten salt in which the components are immersed. The mixture of salts used is varied according to the working temperature. The salt-bath furnace has several advantages : the heating of the components will be rapid and even, due to their being surrounded by a liquid ; no oxidising will take place, as air is excluded from the work ; very accurate temperature control is possible ; distortion of the hot component is unlikely, as it can be suspended or held in a suitable metal basket. Disadvantages are : they are rather expensive ; the component cannot be seen ; some salt will cling to the component and will drip off during subsequent handling, or will contaminate the quenching bath. Fig. 39 shows a self-contained salt-bath furnace for the heat treatment of tools.   The salt is heated by electrodes which pass a heavy current of low voltage through the salt.   The bath can

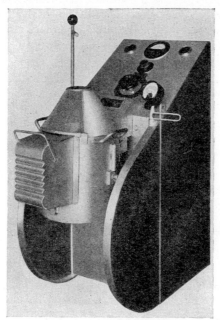

[*Wild-Barfield Electric Furnaces, Ltd.*

FIG. 39.—SALT-BATH FURNACE.

be tilted for emptying purposes.   The anti-splash guard should be noted, also the neat arrangement of the electrical controls.

Electric Furnaces

The electric furnace is a chamber of refractory material supported by a suitable steel casing on the outside, and heated inside by heating elements which work on the same principle as the ordinary domestic electric fire, giving their heat to the charge by radiation.   The heating elements are commonly made from an alloy of nickel and chromium which has great heat-resisting powers.   In small furnaces these elements are made from wire, but in larger equipment, strip, rod or tube is bent to a suitable shape. These elements may be placed on the side walls, base and roof, and arranged to give even heating of the furnace charge.   Fig. 40 shows the disposition of the elements in a box type furnace.

In the gas-, oil- or coal-fired furnace the flame is actually inside the chamber, and thus decides the atmosphere content; there is also danger that the flame impinging on the component may cause local overheating. Also flues must be arranged to carry away the products of combustion.

In the controlled-atmosphere furnace heated by gas, coal or oil the charge must be placed in a separate gas-tight muffle which is surrounded by the heating flames. In the electric furnace the atmosphere consists simply of the air of the atmosphere, or, if this is detrimental, a suitable atmosphere is manufactured and fed directly into the furnace chamber.

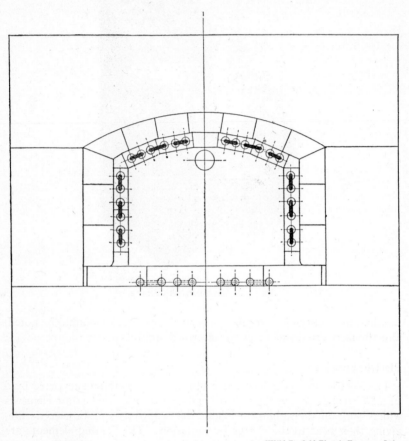

[*Wild-Barfield Electric Furnaces, Ltd.*

FIG. 40.—HEATING ELEMENTS IN ELECTRIC FURNACE.

The disadvantages of electric furnaces are that for very high temperatures the heating elements have a rather short life and are liable to be damaged by careless work. It is also usually stated that gas-fired furnaces cost less to run, due to gas being cheaper than electricity in most towns ; but this is a controversial subject, as electric furnaces would appear to have a higher thermal efficiency per unit of energy supplied. Either type can be accurately controlled as regards temperature.

Induction Heating

In Chapter V (Fig. 22) the high-frequency induction furnace was sketched and described. The same process is used to heat metal for other purposes than melting. For example, a long bar can be passed quickly through a high-frequency induction coil and immediately quenched in a spray of oil or water (see Fig. 41).

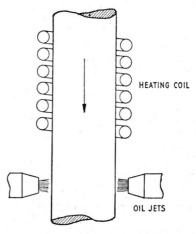

The process may be described as that of passing metal parts through a coil of wire which carries an alternating current. The greater the number of cycles per second, the smaller the distance the heat penetrates, but the more rapid will this heating be. Components or bars of medium-carbon, high-carbon or alloy steel can be heated and quenched at the surface whilst remaining normalised at the core. The number of cycles varies from 1000 to 500,000 or more per second, the lower frequencies being used for " through " heating of fairly large components. The advantages of the system may be summarised as follows :

FIG. 41.—INDUCTION HEATING.

1. The heat can be applied exactly where it is required for the correct length of time.

2. The surface heating of a component may require only two or three seconds, and thus the oxide film formed is infinitesimal. However, the process can be performed in a reducing atmosphere if necessary.

3. The interior of the material may remain cold and rigid, thus minimising distortion.

4. The method lends itself to mass production, and in fact this heat-treatment process is not very different from a machining process ; hence it can take its place in the production line.

The principal disadvantage is the rather expensive electrical equipment required.

Besides the " through " and surface heating of parts, induction heating is suitable for heating for brazing, as in the " tipping " of machine cutting tools.

CHAPTER XI

PYROMETRY

TEMPERATURE observation and control is of great importance in heat-treatment processes. In some cases an error of 20° C. can lead to serious defects in the heat-treated component. There are a number of instruments for the measurement of temperature. Most of them give a scale reading, whilst some produce a chart which gives a record of temperature over a period of twelve or twenty-four hours. The furnace illustrated in Fig. 35 is fitted with an automatic recorder. Certain special instruments not only record the temperature of the furnace, they also control the temperature by governing the amount of fuel fed to the furnace.

Pyrometry is the term used for the technique of temperature measurement. However, before considering the various types of industrial pyrometer, it will be advisable to consider the various temperature scales.

Temperature Scales

The **Fahrenheit** scale, which is the oldest, has little to recommend it except custom. It is still widely used in steam engineering, but in the heat-treatment shop the **Centrigrade** scale, which is much simpler, is generally used. In the Centigrade scale the freezing point of water is marked 0°, and the boiling point is marked 100°. The interval between the two marks is termed the **fundamental interval**. The fundamental interval is divided into one hundred equal parts.

Lord Kelvin devised a temperature scale known as the " gas scale " or **absolute scale** of temperature. This scale was deduced from the behaviour of certain gases, of which hydrogen is the most important. The zero of the absolute scale is equal to −273° on the Centigrade scale.

Temperatures on the absolute scale are often indicated by the letter K. Thus the freezing point of water is 0° C. or 273° K., whilst the boiling point of water is 100° C. or 373° K.

Liquid Mercury Thermometers

There are the familiar mercury-in-glass thermometers, which can be used up to 500° C. and also the mercury-in-steel thermometers. The latter, which operate a pressure-gauge mechanism, can be used as indicators or, by means of a revolving chart, can operate as recorders. Furthermore, the fine-bore tube connecting the mercury bulb to the pressure gauge may be up to 100 ft. in length. When the pressure-gauge mechanism is operated by expansion of liquid mercury the maximum working temperature is about 600° C.

Vapour-pressure Thermometers

These thermometers use mercury vapour instead of liquid mercury. They have a steel bulb which is immersed in the hot substance and is connected by fine-bore tubing to the pressure gauge. The pressure gauge, which is calibrated in ° C. or ° F., may be placed in any convenient position up to 100 ft. distant from the bulb. Vapour-pressure thermometers may be used up to a temperature of 800° C.

With mercury-in-steel thermometers it is essential that the bore of the connecting tube should be very small relative to the mercury bulb. When this precaution is taken the connecting tube may be heated to some extent without affecting the reading appreciably.

Fusible Cones

These cones are about $\frac{1}{2}$ in. in diameter at the base and about 1 in. high. They are made from various salt mixtures, each of which has its own melting temperature. The cone is mounted on a small porcelain or fire-clay dish and placed in the furnace—preferably on or near the part being heated. The cones are marked with the melting temperature. Incipient fusing can be detected as the cone starts to bend over from the apex.

If a certain temperature is to be attained, say 780° C., then two cones are inserted, one with a melting point of 750° C. and another with a melting temperature of 800° C. The 750° C. cone is melted, but the 800° C. cone is left intact. One serious limitation of this method is that no continuous record of furnace temperature is obtained. The only information gained is that at a certain time the furnace temperature was between two limiting values and that at no time was the upper limit exceeded.

Thermo-electric Pyrometers

Most of the furnaces in the heat-treatment shop are fitted with this type of pyrometer. If two dissimilar wires are brought into intimate contact at one end (by twisting together and welding) and this end is heated, then a small electric potential is set up across the contact. Such a pair of wires is called a **thermo-couple**. The electrical circuit is completed by a millivoltmeter, as shown in Fig. 42. We owe this discovery to Le Chatelier, who used

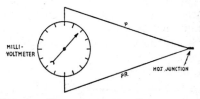

FIG. 42.—THERMO-ELECTRIC PYROMETER.

one wire of pure platinum and another of platinum alloyed with 10% of rhodium. Since that time, the platinum alloy has been altered to one containing 13% rhodium.

The platinum/platinum–rhodium thermo-couple is satisfactory up to a temperature of 1400° C. It is known as the **rare-metal** thermo-couple and is expensive. For temperatures up to 1100° C. **base-metal thermo-**

couples are quite satisfactory. Since the metals used are fairly cheap, the wires can be of thick section, thus giving a more robust instrument. The rare-metal wires are usually $\frac{1}{20}$ in. diameter, whilst the base-metal wires are commonly $\frac{1}{8}$ in. diameter. In the case of the iron/constantan base-metal couple a constantan rod may be welded at one end to the base of a closed iron tube ; this is a very stout construction.

The common base-metal couples are the copper/constantan (up to 500° C.), the iron/constantan (up to 900° C.), and the chromel/alumel (up to 1100° C.).

Referring to Fig. 42, it is usually impracticable to connect the milli-voltmeter directly to the wires of the thermo-couple, as it would be heated up by the furnace. Such heating would upset the reading, since it is the temperature **difference** between the hot and cold junctions which determines the readings. Consequently the milli-voltmeter and the cold junctions are installed in a place which does not suffer from wide variation in temperature. The modified circuit is shown in Fig. 43. It will be

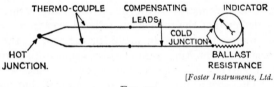

[*Foster Instruments, Ltd.*

FIG. 43.

noted that **compensating leads** have been added. If copper leads were used, the junctions between the copper wires and the wires of the thermo-couple would themselves introduce additional thermo-couples, and heating of these extra junctions would upset the reading. Consequently, the compensating leads must be made from suitable alloys of copper and nickel which will not cause a potential difference across the junction of the lead and the thermo-couple wire. The instrument is calibrated after the compensating leads have been fitted. It will be appreciated that the leads must not be shortened when the pyrometer is fitted to the furnace. To obtain the most accurate readings the cold-junction temperature should be kept constant. This may be done in several different ways, one of which is by bringing the cold junctions to a depth of several feet in the earth under the building. However, in industrial plants the milli-volt-meter can usually be placed at some point where the temperature variation is not very pronounced in relation to the high temperature to be measured.

The milli-voltmeter may then be set to read correctly with the cold junction at room temperature—say 20° C. If the cold junction is likely to suffer from excessive temperature variation, then an automatic compensating device can be fitted to the milli-voltmeter.

The reader will have noted the **ballast resistance** shown in Fig. 43. The resistance of the thermo-couple circuit changes with temperature, but the ballast resistance is made from material which has a constant resistance. The ballast resistance has a value of at least four times the resistance of the rest of the circuit.   Consequently, changes in resistance of the circuit are " swamped " by the ballast resistance, which is sometimes termed a **swamp resistance.**

The inclusion of this large extra resistance reduces the amperage of the thermo-couple circuit.   The milli-voltmeter used must, therefore, be an extremely sensitive instrument.   Fig. 44, which is a plan view, is a diagram illustrating the working principle of the milli-voltmeter.   A permanent magnet (not shown) produces a magnetic field in the air gap between two pole pieces M and a central core O.   A moving coil C,

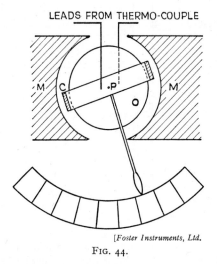

LEADS FROM THERMO-COUPLE

[*Foster Instruments, Ltd.*

FIG. 44.

which can rotate about the central core, has pivots P at top and bottom. The leads from the cold-junction terminals are brought to the coil C by light hair-springs.   Changes in electro-motive force cause the coil to rotate.   This rotation is registered on a temperature scale by a finger attached to the coil.   In practice, the scale would be vertical to the paper.

There are many interesting problems involved in the design of these instruments, but they are too complex to be discussed here.   The reader is referred to specialist books on the subject.

Fig. 45 shows a thermo-couple mounted in the wall of a furnace.   The two wires are protected by a porcelain sheath made from special fireclay which is impervious to the furnace gases.   They are insulated from each other by being passed through beads with twin holes.   The wires are brought to two terminals in the head of the instrument.   The compensating leads are fixed to these terminals.   The head of the instrument should be some little distance from the furnace wall so that the compensating leads are at a temperature lower than 100° C.

The thermo-couple shown has a single sheath of refractory material. For temperatures up to 1100° C. the refractory sheath may itself be

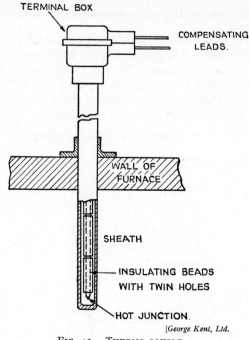

FIG. 45.—THERMO-COUPLE.

enclosed by a nickel–chromium-alloy sheath, which protects the refractory sheath from accidental damage. A disadvantage of this double sheath is that the response of the pyrometer to temperature change is slowed down.

Recorders

Many thermo-electric pyrometers are fitted with a recorder. The recorder moves a paper chart under a pen which periodically makes an ink dot on the chart. Over a period of time a line is made on the chart, which has a suitable temperature scale ruled upon it. The usual method of conveying the pyrometer reading to the chart is as follows.

Let us suppose that the last mark on the chart is at 900° C. Subsequently, the milli-voltmeter reading has risen to 910° C. Two clamps grip the finger of the milli-voltmeter for a short time whilst two prongs move together and " find " the new position. The movement of the prongs operates an electrical relay system, which, in turn, moves the pen to the new correct position and dips the pen to make a fresh mark on the chart. The finger of the milli-voltmeter is now released by the clamps so that it can move in accordance with any further temperature change.

Electrical Resistance Thermometers

When a conductor made from a pure metal such as nickel or platinum is heated, its electrical resistance varies. The principle of the resistance pyrometer is based on this phenomenon.

The measuring device for the pyrometer is based on the **Wheatstone** Bridge. As shown in Fig. 46, this device consists of four resistances, R_1, R_2, R_V and R_X, a galvanometer and a battery which supplies current to the circuit. The resistances R_1 and R_2 are of known value, whilst the value of R_V can be varied as required. The value of R_X is unknown.

The galvanometer is a sensitive instrument which records any difference in electrical potential between the points A and B. If A and B are at the same potential, the galvanometer reads zero, and the bridge is said to be " in balance ".

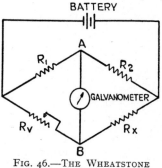

FIG. 46.—THE WHEATSTONE BRIDGE.

When the bridge is in balance, the following relationship holds good :

$$\frac{R_1}{R_V} = \frac{R_2}{R_X}$$

or

$$R_X = \frac{R_2 R_V}{R_1}$$

In using the Wheatstone Bridge the resistance R_V is varied until the bridge is in balance.

Knowing the values of R_1, R_2 and R_V, it is possible to calculate the value of R_X. If R_1 and R_2 are equal to each other, then $R_X = R_V$. Alternatively, R_2 might have a value of, say, $10R_1$, in which case $R_X = 10R_V$. The relative values of R_1 and R_2 determine the relationship of R_V to R_X. The Wheatstone Bridge can be used therefore to determine the value of an unknown resistance, whether the value is large or small.

The application to the electrical resistance pyrometer is shown in Fig. 47.

As before, we have the known resistances R_1 and R_2, which, in this case, are of equal value, and also the variable resistance R_V. The platinum coil R_p now forms the unknown resistance.

The compensating leads are platinum wires with a length equal to that of the leads to the platinum coil. The coil leads and the compensating leads, which are insulated from each other, are enclosed in the porcelain sheath which contains the platinum coil. This sheath is exposed to the hot substance, such as the atmosphere of a furnace.

When the furnace temperature rises the resistance of the platinum coil, and of the two pairs of leads, increases. As regards the four leads, since two are on each side of the bridge, their change of resistance has no effect, but the increasing resistance of the coil unbalances the bridge and deflects the galvanometer. The slider of the variable resistance is now moved

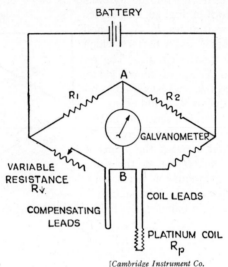

[*Cambridge Instrument Co.*

FIG. 47.—THE RESISTANCE PYROMETER.

until the bridge is in balance. The change in resistance of R_V is equal to the change in resistance of the platinum coil.

The relationship between change of temperature of a platinum wire and change of resistance is complicated, but it need not concern us. In the industrial type of resistance pyrometer the scale for the slider of the variable resistance is marked in degrees.

This method of restoring a zero reading on an instrument is termed the **Null method.** It usually leads to very accurate readings. The resistance thermometer, which may be used at temperatures up to 1200° C., is a very accurate instrument. It is sometimes used to calibrate thermo-electric pyrometers.

Radiation Pyrometers

All the instruments previously described must be exposed to the hot substance whose temperature is to be measured. None of them is suitable for continuous use at temperatures exceeding 1400° C. However, the heat or light emitted by the hot body may be used to measure its temperature.

Before proceeding further, we must consider the emission of heat by hot bodies.

All hot bodies at the same temperature do not radiate the same amount of heat energy per unit area. The heat energy radiated by carbon at a particular temperature is about twice that emitted by polished platinum at the same temperature, when both are in the open. In other words, the condition of the radiating surface influences the amount of heat energy radiated.

It is very common to speak of " black-body " conditions when discussing the emission of heat energy. A perfect black body is one which radiates the maximum amount of heat energy at a particular temperature. As noted in the last paragraph, platinum in the open is far removed from a perfect black body. The same remarks apply to other metals when viewed in the open. If the quantity of heat radiated by a certain surface area is taken as a measure of temperature, allowance must be made according to how far the particular metallic surface deviates from the ideal " black-body " surface.

In heat-treatment practice the main concern is with temperatures inside

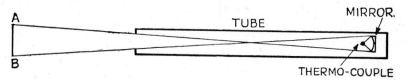

FIG. 48.—THE RADIATION PYROMETER.

an enclosed space. It can be shown that a metallic surface when completely enclosed (e.g., by a furnace) radiates energy under conditions which approach those of a black body. Even more important is the fact that the inside wall of a furnace is almost equal to a perfect black body as regards the radiation of heat energy.

It can be shown that the heat energy received by a cool body from a hot body varies as the difference between the fourth powers of the absolute temperatures. In heat-treatment furnaces the temperature of the furnace is very much higher than that of the receiving body, i.e., the radiation pyrometer. Consequently, small changes in temperature of the pyrometer are unimportant.

The radiation pyrometer is usually arranged to collect the heat energy passing through the peep-hole of a furnace. In other words, the instrument " views " that part of the inside wall of the furnace which is opposite the peep hole.

Fig. 48 illustrates the principle of the **variable-distance** instrument. Heat from the hot body AB enters the tube and is focused by a concave mirror on to a small sensitive thermo-couple. The temperature of the thermo-couple will be much lower than that of the hot body, but its temperature will vary in accordance with variations in the hot-body temperature. The milli-voltmeter attached to the thermo-couple is

F

calibrated in terms of the temperature of the hot body. Temperatures up to 2000° C. may be measured in this way.

The line AB represents a circular portion of the hot surface being viewed. Now the heat collected by the mirror from unit area of the hot surface diminishes in proportion to the square of the distance between the hot body and the mirror. On the other hand, the area of the body from which the mirror is receiving heat (i.e., the area " seen " by the mirror) increases as the square of the distance. Consequently, within certain limits, the distance of the mirror from the hot body is immaterial. It is essential that the area of the hot body " covers " the mirror. Since most

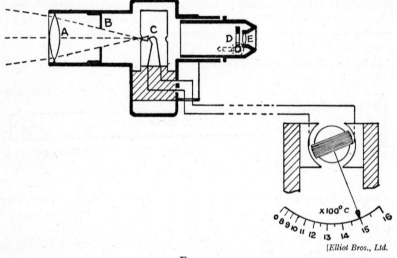

[Elliot Bros., Ltd.

Fig. 49.

of the observations are made through a peep-hole in a furnace, this sets a practical limit to the distance at which the instrument can be used.

A lens-focus instrument is shown in Fig. 49, together with the necessary moving-coil galvanometer or milli-voltmeter. This instrument is normally set for use at a distance of about 2 ft. 3 in. from the hot body, but can be set for other distances when required. These instruments are fixed at a set distance from the furnace peep-hole. If necessary, the peep-hole can be fitted with a short search-tube and a mica screen. The pyrometer is then calibrated with the screen in place.

It will be noted that the radiation from the hot body is focused by the lens A, is passed through the orifice plate B and falls on the thermo-couple unit C. Four thermo-couples, which are enclosed in a glass envelope, are provided. These are coupled in series in order to increase the sensitivity of the instrument. The glass envelope is filled with inert gas. The radiation is focused on to small plates of blackened platinum attached to the thermo-couples. On looking through the eyepiece E and the absorption screen D (which is used only for high temperatures), the view is as shown in Fig. 50. The dark strips are the thermo-couples. The white circle, which is an image of part of the hot surface, must completely surround the thermo-couples.

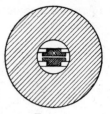

In addition to the instruments which can be adjusted for distance, *fixed* distance instruments are made. These instruments are fixed permanently to the wall of the furnace. A water-cooled tube protrudes through the furnace wall; the tube of the pyrometer is fixed to the outer end of the wall tube.

Fig. 50.

Optical Pyrometers

There are two distinct types of optical pyrometer. The more important type, which is called the **disappearing-filament** pyrometer, will be described first.

Light from the hot body is compared with the light emitted by the filament of a lamp. The brightness of the lamp filament can be varied. The operator alters the current flowing through the lamp until the filament has the same brightness as the hot body. The temperature is then read off the scale of a rheostat which is calibrated in degrees of temperature.

The optical principle is shown in Fig. 51. Light from the hot body is

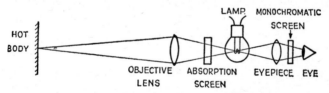

[Foster Instruments, Ltd.

FIG. 51.—DISAPPEARING-FILAMENT PYROMETER.

picked up by the objective lens. After passing through an absorption screen, it is focused on the lamp filament and passes to the eyepiece lens. The light then passes through a monochromatic screen which reduces the dazzle and eliminates colour difference between the hot body and the filament. The operator looks through the eye-piece and sees the dark filament of the lamp against the bright background of the hot body (see Fig. 52). The lamp current is now increased, and eventually the lamp filament shows bright against the background. The current is adjusted until the filament disappears. This is the correct setting. The absorption screen behind the objective lens reduces the intensity of light from the hot body. In consequence, the filament brightness has only to equal the apparent brightness of the hot body. This allows the lamp to be run at reasonable temperatures, thus increasing the life of the filament.

An external view of the pyrometer is shown in Fig. 53.   The knurled ring controls the filament temperature : the reading is taken on the curved scale near the top of the instrument.   The twin leads are connected to a small accumulator.

The electrical circuit is shown in Fig. 54.   It will be noted that a Wheat-

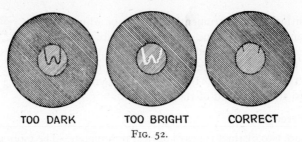

TOO DARK   TOO BRIGHT   CORRECT

FIG. 52.

stone Bridge is used.   The resistances A, C and D are adjusted so that the bridge is in balance, and the milli-voltmeter M is at zero when the lamp filament is at, say, 800° C.   The rheostat R, taking current from the accumulator B, is adjusted so as to raise the filament temperature.   The resistance of the lamp filament will increase with increasing temperature, but resistances A, C and D remain unaltered.   Consequently, the milli-ammeter will register an increasing out of balance of the current flowing

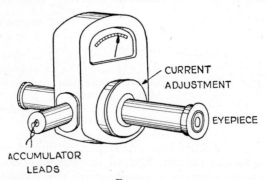

CURRENT
ADJUSTMENT

EYEPIECE

ACCUMULATOR
LEADS

FIG. 53.

through the bridge.   The " ballast " resistance E is put in when cali-brating the instrument ; it is also used as a " swamp " resistance against temperature changes of the whole of the instrument.   The lamp and resistances can be detached at points w, x, y and z, and removed as a single unit from the body of the instrument.

The disappearing-filament pyrometer is suitable for temperatures between 800° and 3000° C.

The **Wanner** optical pyrometer, which is named after its inventor, may also be noted.   This instrument is not very widely used, and a brief description will suffice. The light from the hot body is optically matched with the light from a constant-comparison lamp. The light from the lamp is polarised in one plane, and the light from the hot body is polarised in a plane at right angles to the first plane.

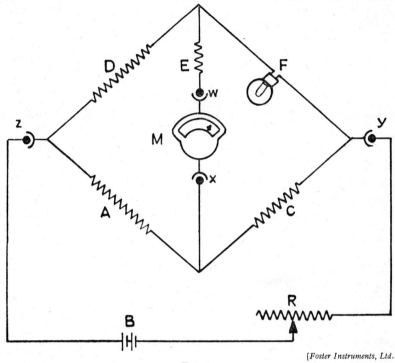

[*Foster Instruments, Ltd.*

FIG. 54.

The two beams are passed through a Nicol prism which is rotated. Rotation of this prism causes an apparent increase in light from one source and a diminution of light from the other source. The prism is rotated until the two beams appear to give light of equal intensity. The device for rotating the prism has a scale marked in degrees of temperature. The maximum temperature which can be measured is 4000° C.

Choice of Pyrometer

The choice of pyrometer for a particular application is dependent on several factors. Direct-contact instruments are limited to about 1400° C. The accuracy of reading required must be taken into account. Instruments of a high degree of accuracy are more expensive. The grade of attendant employed must be considered. Where the labour is unskilled, a recording instrument is most suitable. When the temperature must be kept constant within close limits the pyrometer should be connected with a fuel-control system. In this connection it should be noted that the optical pyrometer cannot readily be coupled to a recorder or a fuel-control system.

Since there are a number of firms who specialise in the field of temperature measurement, it is wise to consult them before purchasing a pyrometer for a particular purpose.

CHAPTER XII

WELDING

THE welding of two pieces of metal is the permanent joining of them. The oldest method of welding is to heat the metals to a soft and " sticky " state at the proposed joint and hammer them together to form one homogeneous piece. This ideal was not always realised in practice : the joint often remained a source of weakness, due to the work being done at too low a temperature or to the inclusion of metallic oxides in the joint.

Before the introduction of cheap steel, wrought iron was the common material for forged parts. Wrought iron is a very suitable material for

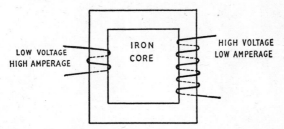

LOW VOLTAGE
HIGH AMPERAGE

IRON
CORE

HIGH VOLTAGE
LOW AMPERAGE

FIG. 55.—DIAGRAM OF TRANSFORMER.

forge welding. The blacksmith prepares the ends to be joined and heats them white hot. The heated ends are fluxed with clean sand and thoroughly forged together. Wrought iron has a high melting point, and the full heat of the blacksmith's furnace is just sufficient to bring the metal to the welding temperature.

The limitations of this method are obvious. It is not possible to weld long edges, such as two plates, whilst tubes and shaped sections present very serious difficulties. Metals which do not have a " sticky " stage cannot be joined. The whole process calls for considerable skill and is slow.

For metals which will stick together when heated to a suitable temperature the various **resistance** welding processes have largely superseded the blacksmith's methods. When an electric current is passed through a metal conductor, the resistance to its passage depends mainly on the surface area of the conductor and the electrical conductivity of the material. If the resistance is high, the metal will be heated. The commonest example of this is the fine wire which forms the filament of an electric lamp. This is heated to whiteness when the current is switched on. However, unless the conductor is of very small size or the current extremely great, the resistance will be almost negligible, and little heating will occur. The conditions become quite different if there is a discontinuity in the conductor. For example, if two metal parts are touching, there will be a distinct break at the point of contact, and if electric current is passed through them, considerable resistance will occur at the joint and great heat will quickly develop at this particular place.

[Electric Welding Machines, Ltd.

FIG. 56.—BUTT-WELDING MACHINE.

The electricity supply in most works is alternating current at about 200 to 400 volts. This is a dangerous voltage to use on bare metal parts which may be touched accidentally by the workers. Furthermore, these high-voltage currents have not the best heating value. For any normal welding process 100 volts is ample for all purposes, and for the resistance welding processes 10 volts is usually quite sufficient. Accordingly, resistance welding machines usually incorporate a step-down **transformer**. The principle of this device is shown in Fig. 55. The high-voltage current is brought to a soft iron core by insulated cables. The cable passes a large number of times round one arm of the core. The take-off side of the transformer consists of another cable which has a few turns round the opposite arm of the core. When the high-voltage mains current is switched on a low-voltage current is induced in the cable at the opposite side of the core. The ratio of the two voltages is determined by the ratio of the number of turns round each of the arms. The practical transformer is more complicated than this, but it works on the principle outlined.

The energy value of an electric current is measured in watts and watts = amps. × volts. With the exception of certain losses, the fall in voltage at the outlet of a transformer brings about a proportionate rise in the amperage output. It is the amperage which largely determines the heating value of an electric current when it passes along a conductor.

The **flash-butt welding machine** shown in Fig. 56 is designed for butt-welding bars, tubes and similar sections. The machine has two compressed-air-operated jaws for gripping the parts to be joined; the

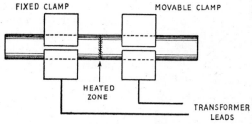

FIXED CLAMP   MOVABLE CLAMP

HEATED
ZONE

TRANSFORMER
LEADS

FIG. 57.—BUTT WELDING.

jaws are plainly seen at the front of the machine. The jaws are connected by cables to the output side of a transformer. One jaw is fixed and the other is movable, mounted on a slide through which the forging pressure is applied. The components to be welded are mounted in the jaws, and the ends are brought lightly in contact with each other; simultaneously the current is switched on. An arc is struck between the parts, and intense heat develops rapidly at the joint. The two end faces soon begin to melt, but a " creep " action of the movable jaw keeps them close. The current is switched off, and instantly the creep movement is transformed into a sharp blow, this action forging the two weldable ends together into a homogeneous joint. The jaws and the two components are shown diagrammatically in Fig. 57.

There is a typical " flash " round the finished joint where overheated metal has been forced out by the final blow. The actual welded zone is at about 150° F. below the melting temperature. The flash serves the purpose of protecting the weld from the atmosphere at the instant of welding, and contains the overheated metal unsuitable for welding.

The advantages of this method are as follows. The whole process is automatic, and can be done at a very high speed with comparatively unskilled labour. Except at the joint, the metal is cold, and thus not distorted. It is not necessary to take great care in preparing the faces to be welded; they may be sawn off, for example, and during the "creep" action they will be melted away uniformly. In this connection it should be noted that the faces to be joined should have an equal cross-

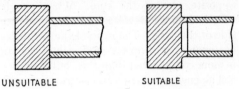

UNSUITABLE   SUITABLE

FIG. 58.

section. The solid plate and tube shown in Fig. 58 would be unsuitable for the process; instead the plate should be prepared with a spigot as shown. It would then be quite suitable. Solid pieces of equal size can, of course, be welded quite easily. Many very intricate components can be made in simple parts, and the whole brought together by flash-butt welding, thus saving a complicated forging operation. Sheet steel pressings (such as motor-car body-work) are made in convenient pieces and are then assembled rapidly by flash-butt welding.

Fig. 59 shows a **spot-welding** machine, and Fig. 60 shows the working principle. Spot welding is used to join two plates together at their joint surface. The transformer takes A.C. current at the mains voltage, and provides a high-amperage, low-voltage current to the two electrodes. When the plates are in place and the two electrodes are seated firmly on them, the current is switched on. Care is taken to have the electrode tips in close contact with the outsides of the plates; consequently the principal resistance is on the insides, and it is here that most of the heat is developed. When the

[Holden and Hunt, Ltd.

FIG. 59.—SPOT-WELDING MACHINE.

spot in the middle reaches welding temperature the current is switched off and the electrode pressure is simultaneously increased. The plates are pressed firmly together and a weld made at this spot. To prevent heating of the electrode tips, cooling water is circulated through the core of each electrode.

Spot-welding machines work on an adjustable time cycle. The top electrode is moved upwards to allow the plates to be inserted, and is then brought down; at the same time the current is switched on and the welding completed; the top electrode then moves upwards again and releases the plates. The complete cycle is performed by the operator

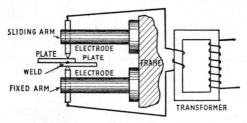

FIG. 60.—SPOT WELDING.

pressing a foot pedal. The heating period is automatically given, and is pre-set for the particular type of component.

The spot weld is an excellent substitute for a rivet on light plates. There is no hole to drill or rivet to fit, and apart from a very slight mark left by the electrode tip, the outer surface is quite smooth.

A variation of spot welding is **seam welding.** The plain electrodes are replaced by rollers. The plates pass between the rollers at a fixed speed, and the time cycle of current, heat and weld pressure goes on automatically producing spot welds as long as the plate is fed along. If more than about

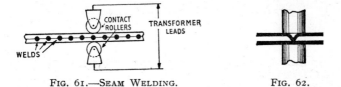

FIG. 61.—SEAM WELDING.   FIG. 62.

ten welds per inch are made the weld edges will overlap and produce a continuous seam. Fig. 61 illustrates the principle of seam welding.

When it is desired to weld a fairly thick object to a thin plate—say a nut to receive a screw—**projection spot welding** may be used. One or more projections are made at the points where a weld is desired (see Fig. 62).

When the welding current is switched on, the projection collapses under the heat and pressure, and a weld is made at this point.

The processes described above consist of heating metals to the " sticky " stage and forging them together. The **fusion-welding** processes are based on the principle of melting the edges to be joined and adding further molten metal to form a pool joining the two edges. The pool is then allowed to solidify and form a joint. <u>Fusion welding, therefore, is a melting and casting process</u>. The metal recast may have a different composition from the parent metal. In fact, one of the important points in fusion welding is to provide a filler metal best suited to make the joint. It is obvious, of course, that the filler metal must be capable of alloying with the two parent metals. In welding, certain constituents may be fused out under the intense heat. These can be replaced by having an excess in the filler metal.

[*Murex Welding Processes, Ltd.*

FIG. 63.

Fig. 63 shows a weld made between two plates. The undisturbed structure can be seen, and the recast metal shows plainly. The original shape of the plate edges is obvious; but the pool has not been confined within these edges; it has penetrated the parent metal at both sides. This factor of **penetration** is of great importance. A sound welded joint should have even penetration into both the parent metals. The skill of the welder influences the penetration obtained; poor penetration is often due to bad workmanship, such as unequal heating of the plates to be joined.

Three common plate welds are shown in Fig. 64. There are many variations on these welds; principally it is a question of plate preparation.

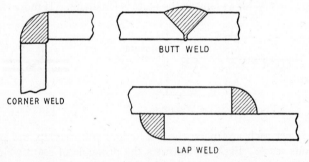

FIG. 64.

Four different preparations are shown in Fig. 65. The U shape requires less filling metal than the V shape, and the double U and double V are necessary on thick plates to prevent distortion, minimise the amount of filler, and ensure good penetration throughout the weld. Fig. 66 shows a plate welded from both sides and a plate welded mainly from one side, but with a " sealing " run on the opposite side. The various shapes are

generally prepared on a special plate edge planing machine or by
" gouging "—a process which will be described shortly.

Except for light work, it is not possible to fill up the joint with a single
pass of the welding apparatus.   A number of " runs " are made super-

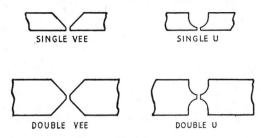

SINGLE VEE   SINGLE U

DOUBLE VEE   DOUBLE U

FIG. 65.

imposed on each other.   Fig. 67, which is actual size, shows a weld made
in a number of runs.   This method has certain advantages.   The first
layer of molten metal cools rapidly, and is liable to be hard and brittle.
However, each succeeding run re-heats the lower ones, which will then be

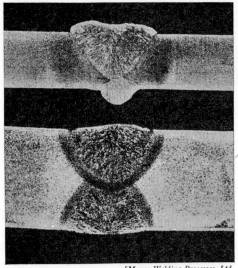

[*Murex Welding Processes, Ltd.*
FIG. 66.

insulated from the atmosphere and will cool more slowly.   It is important
to clean the weld surface before each fresh run is made, otherwise dirt may
be trapped in the weld, and will be a source of weakness.

Owing to the intense local heating, welded structures are liable to be
distorted when complete.   This distortion can be minimised by " tacking "

components together at selected spots by short runs and then filling in the intervening spaces judiciously. It is also common to provide fixtures for holding the work whilst welding proceeds. These hold the components in the correct relative positions, and may also be able to turn round so as to present the working faces to the welder at a convenient height. Fixtures that can revolve or swivel are sometimes called " manipulators ". In the best class of work the finished welded structure is placed in a furnace and is given a thermal stress-relieving process to remove internal strains.

Distortion and cracking in welded work are sometimes prevented by **pre-heating**. This is particularly important when broken iron castings are being repaired by welding, since cast iron has very little ductility. If a portion of a casting is expanded due to heat, the rest of the structure is cold and rigid, and will warp or crack. However, if the whole structure

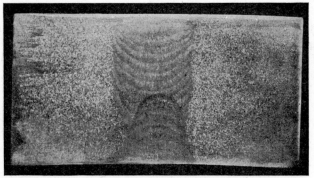

[*Murex Welding Processes, Ltd.*]

FIG. 67.

can be heated, the broken portion can be welded, and the whole casting can cool and contract together.

Besides the repair of castings, worn parts, such as shaft journals, are often built up by welding. A deposit of suitable depth and hardness is put on the worn place and then machined up to the original dimensions.

However, the principal field of fusion welding is in the building up of structures from mild-steel plates and other sections. These are cut and bent to shape and welded up. Welding has largely replaced riveting on vessels of all descriptions, from small water-tanks to ocean-going ships, and is now quickly eating into the field covered by the iron-casting process. The question is partly one of economics. There is a serious shortage of skilled foundry workers. Many structures which might well be cast are welded instead, simply because young men like to be welders, but dislike being iron founders. The trouble is that many iron foundries are old, dirty and technically obsolete, and little is done about it.

The two main methods of fusion welding are the **electric-arc** process and the **gas-torch** process.

The principle of the electric-arc process is shown in Fig. 68. An electrode of suitable material is brought close to the parent metal. Current of low voltage and high amperage passes across the gap, thus forming an electric arc from the electrode to the parent metal. The metal on the circumference of the arc is rapidly melted by the intense heat developed. Globules of metal from the electrode are forced across the arc and join the pool of molten metal, thus providing the filler already mentioned. As the electrode moves along the work, the pool solidifies. Bare electrodes may be used, but the deposit is liable to be hard and brittle. For the best work covered electrodes are used, and it is a covered electrode that is shown in Fig. 68. It will be noted that the coating projects beyond the tip of the electrode, thus protecting it from the atmosphere. The coating produces

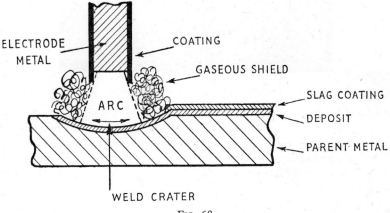

FIG. 68.

a gas which shields the arc and prevents air reaching the molten pool; it also contains a flux which cleans the joint and leaves behind a slag-coating on top of the solidifying metal. This slag-coating protects the metal from oxidation and slows down the cooling process. The slag must be brushed off with a wire brush before another " run " is made, so that it will not be trapped in the weld. Welds made with covered electrodes are stronger, tougher and more ductile than welds made with bare wire electrodes.

To start up the arc, the electrode end is lightly scratched on the work; a pressure of about 70 volts is required to break down the resistance and start the arc. This is termed the **striking voltage.** Once the arc has been struck, the voltage falls to about 20 to 30. This **working voltage** depends on the length of the arc, but modern welding machines are designed to compensate automatically for slight variations in the distance of the tip from the molten pool. Roughly, the correct distance is $\frac{1}{10}$ in. to $\frac{1}{4}$ in. It must be realised that since the tip is melting, this distance cannot be maintained all the time, even by a good operator. If the electrode actually dips into the molten pool, the resistance will be almost nil and the system will be short circuited. At this point maximum current will flow. It may be up to 400 amps. at almost zero voltage. No harm will be done, as the welding machine is designed to cover this contingency.

The operator is provided with a face-shield which has a dark glass through which he can watch the process. The electrode is held in the

[*Murex Welding Processes, Ltd.*

FIG. 69.—ELECTRODE AND HOLDER.

insulated holder as shown in Fig. 69. One wire is brought to the base of the electrode holder ; the circuit to the machine is completed by a second wire, which is clipped to the work and returns the current to the machine.

D.C. current may be used for arc welding. It is provided by a special generator with a **drooping characteristic**. Fig. 70 shows a typical

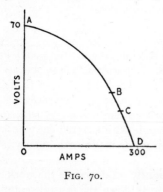

FIG. 70.

characteristic curve. When the generator is on open circuit—i.e., when no current is passing—the amperage is nil and the voltage is at a maximum. This is point A on the curve. When the arc is struck, the voltage falls almost instantaneously to the part of the curve marked B—C. If the electrode end contacts the metal being welded, then the short-circuit position D is reached. It is important that the generator should steady itself very quickly in any of these positions, as they may arise very frequently when welding is being done ; if the changes cannot be accommodated in a few hundredths of a second, the welder will have difficulty in working steadily.

The D.C. generator may be driven by a D.C. or A.C. motor, by petrol or heavy oil engine. A portable, engine-driven D.C. plant independent of a supply of electricity can be constructed, and such sets may be mounted on trailers or railways trucks, if desired. In the workshop the commonest type is the A.C.-motor-driven set, which may be mounted on wheels or more or less fixed in one position, according to circumstance. Fig. 71 shows a typical A.C.-motor-driven D.C. generator set. The A.C. motor with its starter is on the right and the D.C. generator with its switchboard on the

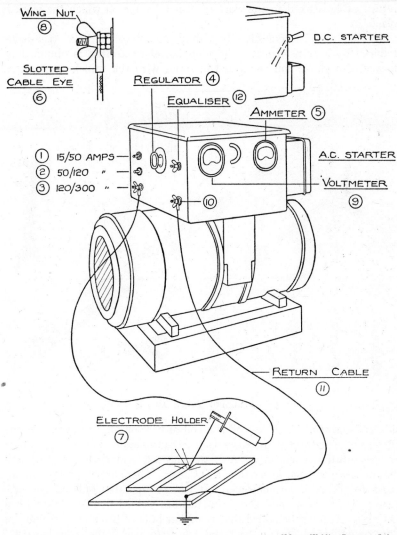

[*Murex Welding Processes, Ltd.*]

FIG. 71.—MOTOR-DRIVEN WELDING SET.

left. Three current ranges are available, from 15 to 300 amps., by connecting to terminals 1, 2 or 3, and the regulator (4) permits fine adjustment within each range. The actual amperes used are registered on the

G

ammeter (5). The lower current ranges are used for thin electrodes and light plates, although the type of metal being welded also has an effect on the correct current value. The terminal (10) is the negative pole of the generator, and the return cable (11) is fixed to this. The other end of the return cable is fixed to the work or a metal table on which the work is placed.

Welding may be done directly with an A.C. current, the voltage being reduced by a transformer. The drooping characteristic is obtained by means of a choke coil connected in series with the transformer output

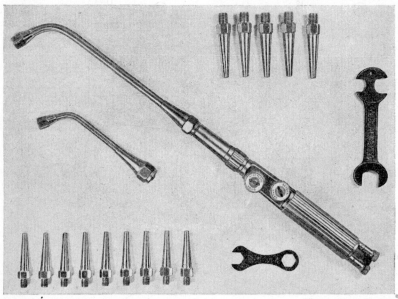

[*British Oxygen Co., Ltd.*

FIG. 72.—WELDING TORCH AND NOZZLES.

side and the arc. A choke coil is a coil of wire on an iron core. As the current passing through increases, the coil causes a drop in voltage. There are no rotating parts in an A.C. welding set, and both first cost and maintenance cost are lower than a D.C. set. There are certain disadvantages to the A.C. set, however. It can be operated only where A.C. current is available, and certain metals are welded more readily with a D.C. set. It must be added that the great bulk of production welding is done on mild steel, and on this metal A.C. welding is quite as good as D.C., providing the correct type of electrode is used. Most types of automatic arc welding are now done with A.C. current. In damp situations the D.C. method is often preferred, chiefly because the maximum striking voltage of the A.C. method is about 100 volts, against the 70 volts of the D.C. system.

Oxy-acetylene Welding

It has been pointed out (see page 63) that the oxy-acetylene flame is much hotter than the air-acetylene flame, owing to the absence of nitrogen. If oxygen and acetylene under a slight pressure are properly mixed and burnt

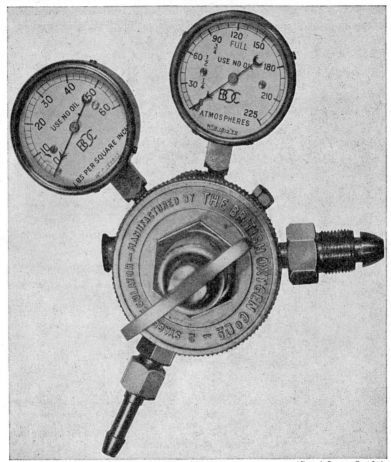

[*British Oxygen Co., Ltd.*]

FIG. 73.—HIGH-PRESSURE BOTTLE HEAD.

at the outlet of a suitable nozzle, the flame produced has a maximum temperature of 3,100° C., and will quickly melt the surface of any of the normal metals, or alloys, encountered in engineering. The oxy-acetylene welding torch is shown in Fig. 72. A nozzle is fixed to the outlet end of the torch, and the bore of this nozzle determines the gas consumption and the size of the flame. A selection of nozzles is shown, and also the spanners for changing nozzles. The larger the flame the quicker will melting proceed. The two gases are brought to the two connections by separate rubber tubes, and are thoroughly mixed in the torch. A neutral flame is obtained by supplying the correct gas proportions to the nozzle. The regulating knobs can be seen quite plainly in the photograph.

The oxygen and acetylene are stored under high pressure in steel " bottles ". In the case of acetylene, the bottle contains a liquid called acetone in which acetylene dissolves very readily. As the pressure is

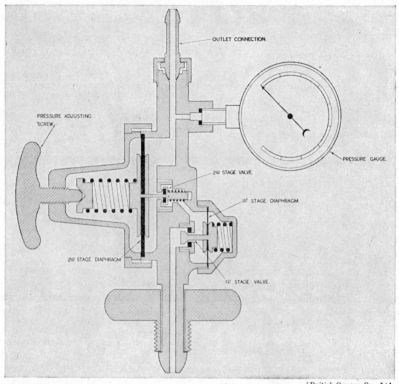

[*British Oxygen Co., Ltd.*

FIG. 74.—PRESSURE REGULATOR.

increased, more acetylene will be dissolved : for example, 1 volume of acetone will absorb 25 volumes of acetylene at atmospheric pressure, but at 15 atmospheres pressure 375 volumes may be dissolved. It follows, therefore, that as acetylene is withdrawn from the bottle and the pressure falls, more of the gas will emerge from solution. To assist in even distribution of acetylene in the acetone, the bottle also contains " Kapok " fibre, which gives a cellular construction to the chamber. The cellular construction also prevents too rapid a discharge of gas.

Fig. 73 shows a bottle head. The first pressure gauge shows the bottle pressure. The gas passes through a reducing valve, and the reduced pressure is shown on the second gauge. It then passes into the rubber tube, which conveys it to the torch. Fig. 74 is a section through the regulator; it will be noted that the first reducing valve is automatically controlled, and the second or hand regulator is thus rendered more sensitive.

The parts to be welded are prepared in the manner already described. The torch-flame is adjusted and played on the joint, at the same time the

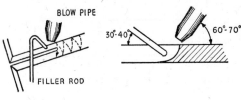

LEFTWARDS WELDING

FIG. 75.

end of a welding rod is held in the flame. The edges to be joined and the welding rod are melted simultaneously, and a pool of molten metal is formed. The operator moves steadily along the joint building up a weld between the two parent metals. Two methods are practised. **Leftwards** welding consists of holding the rod steady and oscillating the flame slightly.

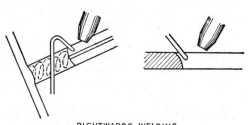

RIGHTWARDS WELDING

FIG. 76.

In **rightwards** welding the flame is kept steady and the end of the rod is given a circular motion. The two methods are illustrated in Figs. 75 and 76. It will be noted that in the rightwards method the flame is directed on to the newly deposited metal, thus giving better control of the cooling rate.

As in the electric arc process, there are many different types of welding rod to suit the various metals to be joined. The rod is not of quite the same composition as the metals to be joined; for example, it is usual to add a deoxidising agent, such as silicon, to improve the quality of the weld metal.

Flame-cutting

Plates are often cut to shape by means of the oxy-acetylene flame. The part to be cut is first heated to a high temperature known as its "ignition point", and a jet of pure oxygen is then played on to the hot surface. Violent oxidation or burning immediately commences, and will continue as long as oxygen is supplied. A narrow groove is formed, the force of the jet blowing out the burnt metal in a shower of brilliant white sparks. The speed at which the groove is formed depends on the plate thickness. The following speeds are typical of mild steel plate.

Plate thickness (inches)					1	3	6
Speed of cutting (feet per hour)			.	.	70	44	28

The flame-cutting nozzle is rather different from the welding nozzle. The oxygen and acetylene for the heating flame emerge through an

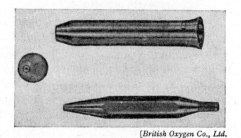

[British Oxygen Co., Ltd.

FIG. 77.—FLAME-CUTTING NOZZLE.

annular nozzle which surrounds a central nozzle through which the pure oxygen of the burning jet is discharged. Fig. 77 shows the component parts of the nozzle and a "muzzle view" of the assembled nozzle.

Hand torches may be used for flame cutting, but much work is now done on special cutting machines. These have a well-balanced double-jointed arm, on the end of which is placed the torch, directed vertically downwards. The path of the torch may be guided by hand round a template or along a straight-edge mounted above the head of the torch and contacted by a roller. Other machines are equipped with rollers which automatically traverse the torch around the template at a pre-set speed. A machine is shown in Fig. 78, with a cut plate. The top arm is carrying a radius cutting attachment.

The flame-cutting machine is extremely useful in shops where plate is welded up into various components. It is also very convenient for cutting large holes in plates. Previous to its advent this was a laborious business, involving the drilling of many holes and the subsequent breaking out of the unwanted piece, often with hammer and chisel. Even when this was done, the scalloped edge left by the holes had to be trimmed up either by boring or further hand chipping and filing.

[*British Oxygen Co., Ltd.*

FIG. 78.—FLAME-CUTTING MACHINE.

A special flame-cutting nozzle called a " gouger " may be used to cut the U-shaped plate edge shown in Fig. 65.

Inspection of Welds

The view afforded to the welder through the darkened window of his shield or goggles is far from perfect. One defect which occurs is that of " undercutting "; this is shown in Fig. 79. Metal from the vertical plate is brought down into the pool, and is not replaced by deposited metal. The actual size of the fillet may not be correct, or may vary along its length. This defect can be checked with radius gauges. Other visible defects are burnt metal—caused by undue " dwelling " at one spot—cracking and porosity of the weld surface.

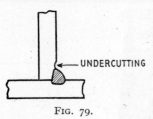

FIG. 79.

Internal faults, such as slag inclusions, can only be detected by X-ray photography. The apparatus required is expensive, and the technique of interpreting the photographs requires skill and experience. For all important work such as vessels and pipes carrying high-pressure steam the X-ray test is essential.

The way to get good welded work is not to rely entirely on inspection to separate the good from the bad. The type of welding rod must be stated, the method of working should be laid down and the worker must be properly supervised. Above all, the young worker must be trained. It is not sufficient to place a novice with a skilled man and tell him to " pick it up ".

The prime requisites of a craftsman are patience and a firmly rooted belief in logical cause and effect. This latter may be termed " mechanical common sense ". These basic virtues must be implanted in the young worker. Technique is important, but it is merely the shape imposed on the human material; it can and should be modified over the years as new products and new methods arise.

CHAPTER XIII

IRON FOUNDING

In its simplest form the production of a casting consists of making a hole in a suitable substance, pouring the molten material to be cast into the hole, and allowing it to cool and solidify. The cooled casting is then removed from the hole.

In the production of iron castings the mould or cavity is formed in a suitable type of sand ; pig and scrap iron are melted in a furnace called a **cupola** and brought to the mould by means of a ladle ; the metal is poured into the mould and allowed to solidify. Subsequently, the sand mould is broken up and the casting removed. Since the mould is expended each time a casting is made, the rapid making of moulds is a very important matter. In many foundries it does not get sufficient attention.

The craft of Iron Founding is neglected by many engineers. If this neglect continues, the whole engineering industry will eventually suffer. This author is not competent to teach the craft, and is concerned chiefly with emphasising its importance. There are some excellent books on this subject which can be read with profit by all engineers. However, to understand the basic principles underlying foundry practice, it is necessary to know the common methods employed in the iron foundry. Some examples of moulding will therefore be described.

Making a Simple Bracket

Fig. 80 shows a wooden pattern which is almost a replica of the shape of the casting desired. However, the mould made from the pattern will contain molten metal at approximately 1200° C., which will then contract in cooling. Accordingly, the pattern-maker uses a **contraction rule** in preparing the pattern. This type of rule has all lengths increased in the proportion of $\frac{1}{8}$ in. to 1 ft., thus making the pattern slightly bigger than the desired casting size. The castings will therefore be of the correct volume after contraction has taken place, but not necessarily the correct shape. Castings are often pulled out of shape due to certain thin portions solidifying quickly and subsequently being distorted by the thick portions which cool and contract later.

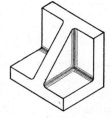

FIG. 80.

In making small and medium-size castings it is convenient to have the sand mould in a **moulding box** or flask. A two-part box is shown in Fig. 81. The top part is called the **cope**, and the bottom part is called the **drag**.

The cope and drag are registered by having dowel pins fastened on the ends of the drag. These pins fit in holes in projections on the side of the cope. So that the cope cannot be turned 180° relative to the drag, the pin and its hole at one end of the box are made larger in diameter than at the other end. It is necessary to be able to fasten the two parts of the box firmly together, otherwise the top part is liable to "float off" when the

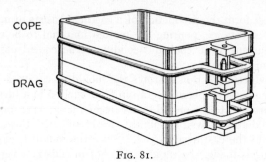

COPE

DRAG

FIG. 81.

mould is full of molten metal. The two halves may be clamped together with special clamps or, alternatively, the top part may be weighted down before the mould is filled with metal.

The pattern is placed on a flat board, called a **turnover** board, and the drag is placed upside down on the board. If desired, the dowel pins can be removed temporarily. The pattern is now covered over with **facing sand**. This is specially prepared sand of good quality which must take a clean, smooth impression. During the casting process it will be in con-

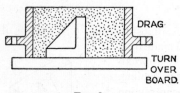

DRAG

TURN OVER BOARD.

FIG. 82.

tact with the molten metal. When the pattern is well covered with facing sand, the drag is filled up with **backing sand**. Backing sand is the ordinary sand of the moulding-shop floor. Much of it will be old facing sand which has been knocked out of previous moulds. The backing sand is rammed up fairly tightly over the pattern and more tightly round the sides of the box to make a good solid mould. The drag, rammed up, is shown in Fig. 82. The top surface has been levelled up by passing a straight-edged board known as a **strickle** over the top. This levelling process is often termed "strickling off".

The drag and board are now turned over, and the board is removed, but the pattern is left in place. The dowel pins are replaced in the drag and the cope is put in position (see Fig. 83). The top surface of the sand and the flat surface of the pattern are level with the joint of the drag and cope. This surface, which is called the parting face, is the datum for filling the cope. As the cope must be removed at a later stage, **parting sand** is sprinkled on the parting face. Parting sand has no cohesion, and the two bodies of sand will always part at this face. Two taper sticks are placed in the cope, one directly over the pattern, and the other to one side, clear of the pattern. The cope is now rammed up, a layer of facing sand being followed by backing sand until the cope is full. The top of the cope is smoothed off, and the rammed mould is as shown in Fig. 84.

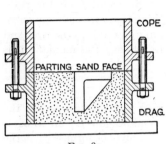

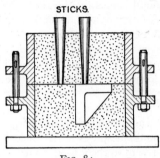

FIG. 83.

FIG. 84.

The cope is now lifted off the drag. On removing the two sticks two slightly tapered holes are left in the cope. The hole over the pattern is to serve as a **riser** through which air and gases will escape when the mould is filled with metal. The other hole is to serve as a **runner**. The runner in the cope is connected to the mould in the drag by means of a **gate**. This arrangement prevents the metal from dropping straight down into the mould and damaging it. The cross-sectional area of the gate must be smaller than that of the runner, so that a full runner will always supply metal under a slight pressure to the gate.

The pattern is now removed from the drag. A wood screw is screwed into the top of the pattern, or for small work a sharp steel spike is lightly driven in. The sand round the edge of the pattern is damped with a few drops of water. The screw or spike is lightly rapped in all directions to loosen the pattern slightly, and the pattern is carefully withdrawn.

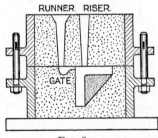

FIG. 85.

Slight damage to the mould can be repaired with hand tools. The " gate " is cut in the bottom half-mould. The top of the runner is opened out to a convenient funnel shape.

To assist in producing a clean face on the casting, the face of the mould is given a light coating of plumbago, this will prevent the sand fusing with the hot metal.

The cope may now be replaced. Sand is considerably lighter than molten cast iron and therefore it will be necessary to prevent the cope from lifting when the mould is first filled. Taper cotters may be driven into the slots in the box pins, or, alternatively, suitable weights may be placed on the cope to hold it down. The mould will appear as shown in Fig. 85, and is ready for casting. The pouring process consists of adding molten metal to the top of the runner, which is kept full. The molten metal is brought to the mould in a hand " pot " and poured into the runner until metal comes up the riser. The metal in the riser will act as a reservoir. and the first shrinkage will be compensated by metal from the riser. Where heavy sections are involved, the neck of the riser may be prevented from too rapid solidification by inserting a thin iron rod into the riser and moving it up and down, taking care not to damage the mould. This churning action is called " **feeding** ".

Venting

In most moulds the escape of gas via the riser is not certain to free the mould of all gases. It must be realised that in addition to the air which is present in the mould cavity, steam and other gases will be formed when the

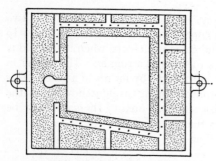

FIG. 86.—VENT CHANNELS.

hot metal touches the mould faces. Much gas is generated in the body of sand immediately adjacent to the mould face. Moulding sand must have some porosity to allow this gas to escape without actually entering the mould cavity. Unfortunately, the act of ramming consolidates the sand and reduces porosity very considerably. The sand mould is, therefore, usually **vented**. A **vent wire** is pushed into the rammed sand at various points to open up the structure. The wire is pushed through almost to the mould face. Venting thus allows more solid ramming, a necessary feature of deep castings, where the pressure of the molten metal would bulge a lightly rammed mould.

The vent wire is **never** allowed to make a hole straight through to the mould face, otherwise metal would enter the vent hole and effectively seal it up.

In many cases other methods of venting are also practised. The centre joint of the mould offers a suitable place for some types of venting. Fig. 86 shows a typical application. Whilst the pattern is still in position in the mould, a number of channels are cut, these being about $\frac{3}{8}$ in. wide and roughly semicircular in section. The sand round the pattern is then vented by pushing a vent wire vertically downwards from the base of the surrounding channel into the sand. From this vent channel, other channels are arranged to carry the gases away to the edge of the box.

A rather more complicated casting may now be considered.

Split Patterns and Cores

Fig. 87 shows the pattern for a straight pipe with flanged ends. The pattern is split longitudinally, the two halves being dowelled together. It will be noted that the pattern has a cylindrical projection at each end. These projections, which are called **core prints**, have a diameter equal to the bore of the pipe; their use will be apparent at a later stage of the discussion.

The half-pattern with the dowel holes is laid on a turnover board with the flat face to the board. A drag of suitable length is laid on the board. The drag has a number of transverse ribs, as shown in Fig. 88, the ribs being cut away to clear the pattern. In boxes of any size these ribs are

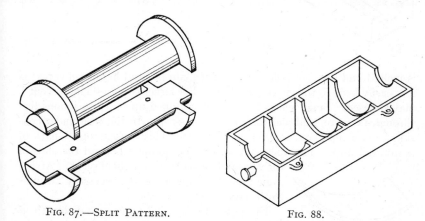

FIG. 87.—SPLIT PATTERN.   FIG. 88.

essential, as they " key " the sand of the mould and prevent its dropping out when the box is being turned over. As ramming proceeds, the sand is carefully forced under each rib so as to leave no spaces. When the drag is rammed and strickled, it is turned over, and the other half-pattern with the dowel pins is placed over the first half. Parting sand is applied to the joint face; the cope is placed in position and rammed up. The mould may then be parted and the half-pattern removed from drag and cope.

Usually, the runner will be arranged to feed a gate which enters one of the end flanges on the horizontal centre line. A riser will be provided on top of each flange.

Whilst the moulder has been preparing the mould, the coremaker will have prepared the core. The core is made in a core box, as shown in Figs. 89 and 90. Fig. 89 shows one half of the box, and Fig. 90 shows a section through two half-boxes with the dowel pins in position. To stiffen the core a **core iron** is rammed up on the core axis. Since the core will be almost surrounded by molten metal, the venting problem is acute. Accordingly, a special oil–sand mixture is used for the core, which is subsequently dried out thoroughly in an oven. After the baking process the structure of the core will be strong and porous. Further venting of the core is usually arranged. One method is to bury a vent wire in the core and draw it out after the core has been rammed up. Another method is to insert wax string in the core. During the baking process, the wax

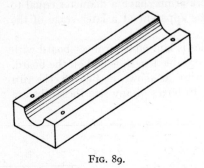

FIG. 89.

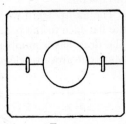

FIG. 90.

is melted and leaves a hole. Wax string can be used in curved cores, as it is easily bent to the curves required. For larger cores a " cinder vent " may be used. Small pieces of coke are rammed up in a continuous line through the core, and will form a vent passage. In the case under consideration a pipe vent is used for the core. This consists of a length of perforated pipe. The open ends of the pipe project beyond the ends of the box and provide an excellent vent. At the same time, the pipe gives the necessary stiffness to the core.

FIG. 91.—PIPE CHAPLET.

The pipe core has the same overall length as the pattern; consequently the ends rest in the prints left by the projections on the end of the pattern. The vents, which have been brought to the ends of the core, must then be led to the edge of the box. It is important to know the width of the space between the core and the face of the mould, as this will be the final metal thickness. Small dabs of clay are secured on the mould face at various points, and the mould is then assembled with the core in place. The clay is squashed to the thickness available. If this thickness is not satisfactory, then adjustment is made. Before final assembly of the mould, the clay is removed.

It has been mentioned before that sand has considerable buoyancy in molten cast iron. The ends of a long core may be secure in the prints, but there will be a strong tendency for the core to bend upwards in the middle. This lifting tendency is prevented by placing one or more chaplets in the top part. A pipe chaplet is shown in Fig. 91. It is made from iron and carefully tinned so that it cannot rust, as rusting would prevent it from welding to the molten metal. The chaplet is installed as shown in Fig. 92. The saddle rests on the core, whilst the end of the stem is firmly anchored by placing a bar across the top of the box and wedging

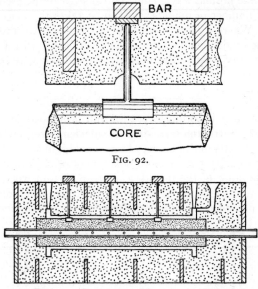

FIG. 92.

FIG. 93.—COMPLETED MOULD FOR PIPE.

the end of the stem under the bar. The bar may be weighted or clamped down, but in either case it must bear on the box edges, not on the mould.

The assembled pipe mould is shown in section in Fig. 93. The runner and gate have been shown, though in practice these would be on the edge of the flange rather than on the face.

Odd-side Moulding

In the example just described, the use of a turn-over board and a split pattern ensured that the mould was split across a diameter. It is essential to split a mould so that the pattern can be removed without damaging it. If a circular pattern is buried rather too deeply in a half-mould, it cannot be released from the box without breaking the mould away. To embed a solid pattern so that the face of the mould coincides exactly with a diameter on the pattern is not easy, as it cannot be rammed up in the normal way. To overcome the difficulty **odd-side** moulding may be used.

A suitable cope is rammed up lightly, the right way up, and strickled off. The shape of half the pattern is then cut out of the mould and the pattern tried in : further cutting of the mould and bedding of the pattern is done until the pattern lies solidly in the top part with the maximum diameter exactly level with the joint face. The drag, with the centre joint downwards, is then placed in position and rammed up. The two half-boxes are clamped together, and the whole mould is turned over. The cope is now removed—this is the " odd side ". Another similar cope is then put on the drag which contains the pattern, and the mould is rammed up and completed in the normal way. The " odd side " may be used to place the pattern for a number of moulds; in fact, it takes the place of the turn-over board. Where a large number of castings are required, the " odd side " may be made semi-permanent by using sand with a special bond which will set very hard. Alternatively, an odd side may be made up in Plaster of Paris.

Floor Moulding

For large castings it becomes very difficult or impossible to turn over a rammed drag. Furthermore, a drag of sufficient size may not be available. Consequently, most of a very large mould is made in the floor sand; with a little ingenuity two or more boxes may be used to form the cope. To register the joint of the mould, a number of stout wooden stakes are driven firmly into the sand. These guide the cope to the correct position. The problem of venting is sometimes troublesome in floor moulds; to over-

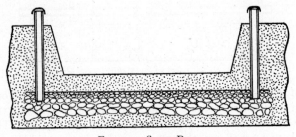

FIG. 94.—COKE BED.

come the difficulty a **coke bed** is often used. A coke bed is shown in Fig. 94. A hole is dug out in the sand; the bottom is rammed as hard as possible. Alternatively, an iron plate may be laid on the bottom of the hole as a foundation. These iron plates may be prepared for bolts which help to clamp the assembled mould together.

The coke is laid on the solid foundation, large pieces being placed down first, followed by smaller pieces. At the sides **vent pipes** are arranged to lead away the gases. These are $1\frac{1}{2}$ in. or 2 in. bore, mild steel pipes, placed so as to clear the cope. Rag caps are tied over the vent-pipe tops to prevent loose sand falling down and choking the vent. A thin layer of straw is placed over the roughly levelled coke; floor sand to a depth of about 9 in. is rammed fairly tightly over the straw; the surface is levelled with straight edge and spirit level, and the whole body of sand is thoroughly vented down to the coke bed. To close the upper end of the vent holes against the metal, a layer of facing sand is now spread, lightly rammed and strickled off level. The work of ramming up the pattern can now proceed. The sides of the mould can be vented in the usual manner by passing the vent wire down near the sides of the pattern and leading the gases away by channels cut in the joint face, as shown in Fig. 86.

Drawbacks

A common problem in floor moulding is a buried flange or other projection in the mould. Such a projection will prevent the pattern being drawn out. In this case a **drawback** may be used. Drawbacks are mounted on iron plates. To strengthen the body of sand, iron rods project upwards from the bottom plate. Rods with lifting eyes are also required for the drawback. Fig. 95 shows a drawback, and Fig. 96 shows the method of using the drawback, which, in this case, forms one end of the mould. The weight of the drawback is taken by the crane, and the drawback is carefully pulled away horizontally until the pattern is cleared. The pattern can then be lifted out, and the drawback replaced. Sand is then rammed up behind the drawback to hold it in place. Alternatively, an iron backing plate may be buried behind the drawback, which may be wedged firmly in place from the backing plate.

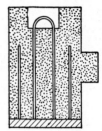

FIG. 95.—A DRAW-BACK.

The drawback is wider than the mould, so that it abuts against a face

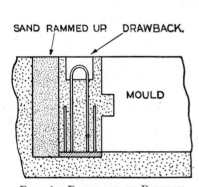

SAND RAMMED UP. DRAWBACK.

MOULD

FIG. 96.—DRAWBACK IN POSITION.

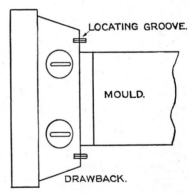

LOCATING GROOVE.

MOULD.

DRAWBACK.

FIG. 97.—LOCATING A DRAWBACK.

which locates it in position in one plane. To ensure location in the other plane, grooves are cut in the joint face (see Fig. 97). The cope may then be placed in position to close the mould.

Skeleton Patterns

Where a single casting of large size is required the cost of a complete pattern may be prohibitive. There are several ways of minimising the pattern cost. **Skeleton patterns** may be used. A skeleton pattern formed

H

by light wooden ribs is made, and the shape of the mould is worked up from this.

Loam Moulding

Many large castings are produced by the **loam moulding** process. The principle of loam moulding is that of building moulds with bricks, loam is used as mortar and also for facing the mould. Loam is blacksand mixed with water and a binding agent to make a stiff paste. The moulding of a large pipe, say 6–8 ft. in diameter and of a similar length, is typical of this class of work. Such a pipe is shown in Fig. 98. It will be noted that a " header " is shown chain dotted at the top of the pipe. This is cast on the pipe and subsequently parted off by machining. The purpose of the

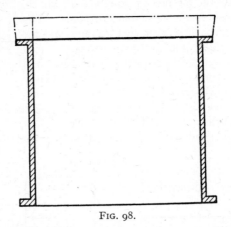

Fig. 98.

header is to act as a reservoir for molten metal, and to leave a place in which gases and impurities can collect harmlessly.

A saddle plate is buried level with the floor ; a heavy cast-iron ring of the type shown in Fig. 99 is used as a base. This base ring is placed in position concentric with the saddle plate. The saddle plate has a small central hole into which the tapered end of a spindle fits.

The base ring is placed in a convenient position relative to the wall of the shop. A spindle which is supported from a wall bracket is greased and mounted in the hole in the saddle plate. A course of bricks is now laid on the base ring, the loam between the bricks being about ¾ in. thick. This is followed by a similar thickness of loam all over the brick course. A second course of bricks is laid and is followed by a further coating of loam. The top of the loam is strickled off with a board mounted on the spindle (see Fig. 100). The plate and base are now removed to a large stove and thoroughly dried out, after which a coating of " blackwash " is applied. This is a mixture of plumbago, water and a binding substance. The dried blackwash will form a parting face.

The cope or outer portion of the mould is then built up. A cast-iron cope ring is laid on the bottom part· this ring has a central hole rather larger than the bottom flange of the pipe. The cope is now built up with firebricks and loam, using the revolving board as a guide. Cast-iron

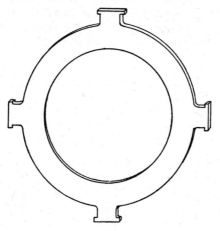

Fig. 99.—Base Ring.

" building rings " strengthen the structure. When the cope has been built up, the strickle board is brought in 1 in. A 1-in. thickness of loam is plastered on the inside of the cope and is strickled up to a true cylinder. It will be noticed that an extra thickness of loam is allowed under the top

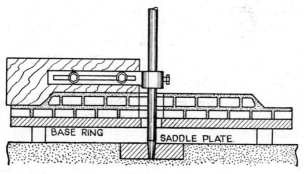

Fig. 100.

of the casting. This is to allow some " give ", as the pipe casting shrinks downwards in cooling (see Fig. 101).

The cope is removed bodily by means of the cope ring, and is placed in the drying stove.

The core is now built directly on to the bottom part, being swept up

with the strickle on the outside as shown in Fig. 102. The finished outside radius of the core will be less than that of the cope by the thickness of
the metal. In making the core, some bricks are left out and loam
" bricks " are substituted. When the mould has been cast up these loam
bricks will " give " as the casting begins to contract. The core is dried
out in the stove, and the outer surface blackwashed.

A top plate will be necessary to close the mould. Since loam will be
required to hang downwards from the top plate, "dabbers" are cast on

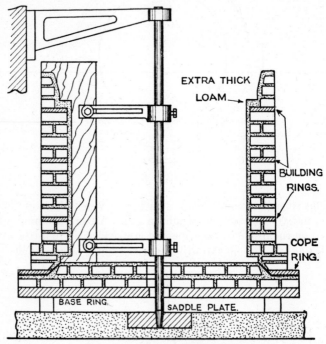

FIG. 101.—BUILDING THE COPE.

the top plate to key the loam firmly. Dabbers are short fingers projecting
from the working face of the plate. The top plate also has a series of holes
for the usual runners and risers. A layer of loam is plastered on the top
plate and smoothed off, and a runner and riser added, as shown in Fig. 103.

The bottom plate and core are now lowered into a pit in the shop floor.
Generally the top of the core projects slightly above the top of the pit.
The cope is lowered into place over the core and the whole pit outside the
cope is rammed up with sand. The lower layers require tight ramming to
support the cope when the pressure of the molten metal is trying to burst
it outwards. Long bolts are fixed in the bottom plate and pass right
through to the top. The top plate is clamped down on the bolts, thus
fastening the whole mould together.

The mould is now cast up. After a few minutes certain " key " bricks are removed. The casting in contracting crushes the core inwards, the loam bricks giving way gradually.

The method outlined is part of a very flexible technique. Flat surfaces

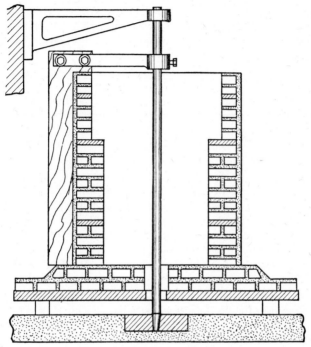

FIG. 102.—BUILDING THE CORE.

can be generated by guiding a strickle over two straight edges. The pattern shop can prepare contoured guides for various shapes of strickle. Ribs can be introduced by burying wooden battens, which are removed when the loam is ready for drying. Other features can be prepared as

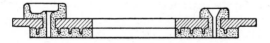

FIG. 103.—THE TOP PLATE.

separate moulds and attached at the appropriate places. Skeleton patterns may be used for irregular shapes. Cores and drawbacks may be added just as in sand moulding.

Core stripping is often practised in the loam-moulding shop. The core is first prepared by means of a skeleton pattern, by strickling or by a combination of both methods. It is then dried and blackwashed. Clay or wooden strips of a depth equal to the thickness of metal are placed on the core, which is then built up all over with loam to the metal thickness. After drying and blackwashing of the core the cope is built up over the core. The cope may be jointed as necessary so that it can be drawn off. When completed, the cope is drawn off and dried. The "thickness" of loam is now broken off the core; the thickness strips are removed and the true core surface repaired and blackwashed afresh. After stripping the thickness it is usual to replace the cope over the core, trying the thickness at various points with dabs of clay, as has been described. If the "metal" is thin, the core is rubbed down, if it is too thick, the face is built up with a little loam.

The mould can then be reassembled ready for casting. Venting is just as essential in loam moulding as in sand moulding. Vent pipes and cinder vents are sometimes used, but dried loam itself has excellent venting properties. Bricks, of course, have no venting properties. Consequently, a good thickness of loam is required between the bricks.

Thickness stripping from loam cores is also practised in the sand foundry. The making of a small pipe from a conventional split wooden pattern and core box has been described previously. For larger pipes, which are not likely to be repeated, a loam core is made. For straight pipes, with straight branches, the cores are built up on **core barrels**. These are perforated pipes as shown in Fig. 93, but of larger diameter. The core barrel is laid in vee blocks and a handle fitted at one end. Straw rope is wrapped on the barrel and a good thickness of loam added. The core barrel is longer than the core. Consequently the roughly built core may be rotated in the vee blocks whilst a flat strickle is held up against it to bring the surface to a true cylindrical shape. The size is tried by calipers and the length is measured off. The core is then dried out and blackwashed. More straw rope followed by a layer of loam is used to produce the "thickness". Wooden flanges are added and the "pattern" is used to make a sand mould; it is then removed from the mould; the thickness is broken off; the wooden flanges are removed and the "pattern" becomes a core again, ready for placing in the mould.

A very similar technique is used for bent pipes, but the core cannot be rotated. Instead the pattern shop provides curved templates for the core and pattern surfaces. With unusual shapes of pipe, the pattern-maker acts in a supervisory capacity, checking the core and pattern for correct shape and size. The pattern-maker is usually more adept than the moulder at this type of work, which involves the reading of drawings.

Plate Moulding

The moulding processes considered so far have all been concerned with the making of a few articles only. When large numbers of parts are required, other methods are often used. In Figs. 80–85 the moulding of a small bracket was illustrated. If considerable numbers of this bracket were required, then the loose wooden pattern could be fastened to the turn-over board by screws. After the drag has been turned over, the turn-over board and pattern are withdrawn together. This entails a truly vertical lift, which may be aided by having guide bars. It is best performed by a mechanical lifting and vibrating device, working in vertical guides.

When the mould is part in the drag and part in the cope, then a board can be made for each half-mould with a half-pattern attached. The cope and drag can now be rammed up separately and brought together. With this procedure, one difficulty which must be overcome is that of ensuring that the two half-moulds coincide at the parting face. Each board must be dowelled to the half-box on which it is used, so that the mould is always made in exactly the same place. Alter-natively, a double-sided board may be used, with one-half of the pattern fixed to each side. The board is then placed between the cope and drag, which are rammed up at each side of it. The pins of the two half-boxes may then be used to register the half-moulds. It is necessary, of course, to make sure that the two half-patterns are fixed in the correct positions on each side of the board.

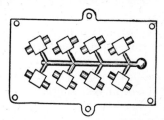

Fig. 104.—Plate Pattern.

Wooden patterns wear rapidly when continually rammed up in sand. Instead of a wooden board and pattern, the moulding shop can prepare a metal " plate " pattern. Originally, these plate patterns were invariably made in cast iron, but modern practice is to use aluminium, on account of its lightness. With small castings a number of patterns may be mounted on a single plate, which also carries the shape of the " gates " or " sprues " through which the metal is to run from a single runner. Fig. 104 shows a plate for producing half-moulds for a small casting. Plate moulding in the modern foundry is essentially a machine process; it will be considered more fully in Chapter XV.

Investment Mouldings

This is often termed the **lost wax** process. It is used for the manufacture of small articles to precision limits in materials which are unsuitable for die casting. Many of the new heat-resistant alloys are difficult to machine and, owing to their high melting point, they cannot readily be cast in the metal moulds used for die casting. Articles otherwise suitable for die casting may be required in small quantities which do not justify the use of metal dies. These also are suitable subjects for investment moulding.

A plaster replica of the desired part is made, due allowance being made for the shrinkages and expansions which occur at various stages of the process. A metal mould is now made by pouring a low-melting-point alloy round the plaster replica. Wax patterns can be " cast " in the metal mould.   On removal they are kept in cold water until used.   An alternative to a metallic alloy as a wax mould is a flexible plastic material. This can be " twisted off " the plaster replica, and allows small undercuts in the article.   Similarly, the mould is worked off the wax pattern.

A number of wax patterns are joined by suitable wax " feeders " to a wax " main runner ", the various parts being welded together by a hot metal spatula.   The pattern assembly is then sprayed with a suitable coating and placed in a rectangular box.   It is surrounded by a refractory mixture of a soft cement-like consistency.   The mould is now inserted in an oven which bakes the mould and melts out the wax.   Subsequently, the oven temperature is raised sufficiently to " fire " the mould to a dry, hard state.

The completed moulds go forward to the casting station, and are there cast up with the appropriate metal.   After cooling, the mould is broken off the finished casting.

Investment moulding is a very old process.   It seems to have been forgotten and re-discovered several times.   The accuracy attainable is of the order of 0·003 in., but the process may be cheapened where an accuracy of 0·01 in. will suffice.

Shell Moulds

In making a mould the flasks in common use are round, square or rectangular, according to the shape to be cast.   Usually the space occupied by sand greatly exceeds the actual mould space.   If the weight of the flask is added to the weight of sand in it, it will be realised that a mould is a heavy article.   Owing to the comparative weakness of sand structures, care is necessary when moving a mould.   Consequently, all but the smallest moulds are made and cast up in one place.   Apart from turning over, they are not moved.   The pattern and core boxes are used and then put at one side, possibly for days, whilst the mould is smoothed, built up, cored, cast up and broken away.

In the mechanised foundry expensive conveying machinery is installed for moving the moulds to the casting station, and a continuous " flow " of moulds is required.

These difficulties can be reduced considerably by the use of " shell " moulds.

The metal pattern is placed in a convenient place and heated to a suitable temperature.   It is sprayed with a mixture containing sand and a suitable plastic binder.   When a thin shell has been built up, it is baked and hardened, and the pattern is then removed.   The shell mould can now be stored until required.   Obviously the shell must be capable of being stripped from the pattern.   Many shell moulds are made in a number of pieces, which are built up prior to casting and held together with binding tape or suitable steel clamps.   If required, the mould can be partially buried in sand when being cast up to give support against the pressure of molten metal.

The shell mould is quite permeable, so that air and gas can escape readily and there is little risk of porosity in the finished casting. When the casting has solidified, the shell mould is easily broken away from the casting.

Shell moulding requires only a small fraction of the sand used in conventional moulding. The moulds, which are light, can be easily transported to the pouring station, instead of the molten metal being carried to the moulds in ladles, as is the practice in most moulding shops.

Centrifugal Casting

This process is used for the production of straight pipes of all sizes and of " stacks " of various alloy cast irons. These stacks are used for the manufacture of piston rings and similar articles. Non-ferrous alloys are sometimes cast centrifugally.

The molten metal is poured into a rapidly rotating cylindrical mould, and is held against the mould by centrifugal force, so that no core is needed. On cooling, the casting is complete, and may be removed from the mould. The moulds are generally made from steel, but sand-lined metal cylinders are also used. The moulds may require heating or cooling according to the process.

Centrifugal castings are generally denser and more homogeneous than ordinary sand castings. The process is obviously limited to simple shapes and fairly large quantities.

Defects in Castings

In most engineering processes a mistake can be seen as soon as it is made. Unfortunately, this does not always apply in the moulding shop. The moulder is often faced with a defective casting, but can only conjecture how the defect has arisen. He must then proceed by trial and error, guided by his previous experience. Here lies much of the skill of the craft of moulding. It must be emphasised that the approach of the average moulder is anything but scientific, and prejudice is allowed too much scope. An elementary knowledge of physics is a great virtue in a moulder ; it is a pity that it is so rare.

Blowholes are caused by gas trapped in the metal. They are smooth round or oval holes with a " shiny " surface. Trapped gas is caused by insufficient venting of mould or cores ; the incorrect placing of risers ; too great a moisture content in green-sand moulding or insufficient stoving in dry-sand moulds. It is sometimes caused by bad pattern and corebox arrangements, which lead to trapping of gases in " blind " places in the mould.

Scabs are formed when sand breaks away from the mould face, thus leaving a rough lump on the surface of the casting. They may be caused by slack ramming, or metal washing heavily on the mould face. The hidden danger in scabbing is the fact that the loosened sand is **washed into the metal**, and may turn up at some other point when the casting is machined. Smooth lumps on castings are due to the pressure of metal forcing out the mould face where the ramming has been slack.

Fins are due to badly fitting mould parts or cores which do not fit snugly in the core prints. They are easily removed, but the result is unsightly in places where a smooth cast surface is desired.

Displaced Cores are generally due to the buoyancy of cores in molten metal. Cores must be firmly anchored. In long cores bending must be guarded against by using stiff core irons and seeing to the correct placing of chaplets.

Misplaced Cores are due to the moulder not checking up the various thicknesses when finally assembling the mould and cores. Both displaced and misplaced cores can be extremely dangerous, as the checking of thicknesses in the finished casting may be difficult. Fatal accidents have occurred due to castings having a thin side and a thick side, when everyone thought that the thickness was equal all round.

Drawing is a defect associated with the contraction of the metal in the mould. It is prevalent in thick bosses which remain liquid after the surrounding metal has solidified. Drawing may take the form of minute or fairly large holes with a black surface. The remedy is to " feed " such places, or to chill the metal to speed up the rate of cooling to that of the rest of the casting.

Distortion of the casting is due to contraction stresses, and is a symptom that should not be ignored. Designs which lead to distorted castings require modification.

Cold Shuts usually occur in thin places where two streams of metal meet. The cooling action of the mould lowers the temperature and makes the metal sluggish, so that it fails to unite.

CHAPTER XIV

MOULDING SANDS

MOULDING sand may be left " green " or damp; this is the common practice for castings of reasonably plain shape without complicated cores. For complicated castings the mould may be dried out in a stove, and is then called a " dry sand " mould. Large moulds made in the shop floor are " skin dried " by coke braziers or hot-air blowers. These varying methods call for sands of rather different composition; for example, the " green strength " is important in the first type, whilst " dry strength " is important in the two latter types.

The essential properties of moulding sand are as follows.

1. **Permeability.** The sand must allow the steam and other gases generated by the heat of casting to escape freely. If there is insufficient passage through the body of sand, then the gases will try to bubble through the solidifying metal and will leave holes in the casting. The moulder has some control over permeability; hard ramming lowers the permeability, but this is relieved by liberal venting.

2. **Plasticity.** The ability to take up an intricate shape, such as a figured face. Fine-grained sands have better plasticity than coarse-grained sands, but the plasticity of a sand is chiefly a question of the content of clay, which retains moisture when the sand is damped.

3. **Flowability.** This property is allied to plasticity. It is the ability of the sand to take up the desired shape.

In ramming up, the blows of the rammer must be transmitted through the body of sand, which should respond readily to the packing action.

4. **Cohesion.** The sand must hold together when the pattern is withdrawn and the mould is moved about. Cohesion must be retained when molten metal enters the mould and washes the heated mould surface. This property is often termed **bond strength**. According to the type of mould, green bond strength or dry bond strength may be required. The bond strength of moulding sand is determined largely by the alumina (clay) content. The clay should be present as a thin, tenacious film on each grain of sand. Generally, angular grains with a roughened surface are the best base for the alumina film; " sharp " sands have smooth oval grains, and are not so easily bonded. Clay, when slowly baked to a reasonable temperature, gives up the free water with which it is associated, but retains the water with which it is chemically combined. In this state, which is that of a dry sand mould, the cohesion remains. However, at high temperatures the chemically combined water is driven off. The **burnt sand** which remains has no powers of cohesion, and is of no further

use as moulding sand, since the clay cannot be induced to take up water again.

5. **Refractoriness.** The sand should resist the heat of the molten metal without fusing. It is the silica content of the sand which has the best refractory properties, the clay being the first to fuse. To prevent the metal from making too close contact with the sand face, coal dust up to 10% is added to facing sand. The first effect of the molten metal is to burn this coal dust, which forms a gaseous " blanket " between the metal and the mould face. In addition, the finished mould face is coated with plumbago, so that the sand cannot fuse on to the casting face and produce a rough, hard skin.

Composition of Sand

Certain natural sands have suitable compositions for use as moulding sand: Erith, Mansfield, Belfast and Clyde are typical. However, there is a growing tendency to add artificial bonding agents, thus producing what are termed " synthetic " sands. In these, part or all of the bonding agent may be added to the sand. **Bentonite** is one of the best known of the binders added to the sand used in iron founding. This is a natural clay which is pulverised to a colloidal state. It then has an extremely fine particle size and remarkable water-holding properties. Fireclay is also used in the pulverised condition.

Core sands are almost invariably made up with an artificial binder. Core sand is usually a clean, sharp, silica sand to which is added a compound binder. These binders usually contain dextrin (a starchy substance) and linseed oil, sometimes mixed with other oils and water. The core is made and dried out by stoving. It is then hard and strong, and will stand rough usage, but has very high permeability. Permeability is a most important property, since cores are often almost entirely surrounded by molten metal. When it has served its purpose the core must be easily removable from the finished casting and, therefore, must disintegrate readily when " picked ".

The principal constituents of moulding sands are as follows: Silica (SiO_2) 86–90%; Alumina (Al_2O_3) 4–8%; Iron oxide (Fe_2O_3) 2–5%; with smaller amounts of the oxides of titanium, manganese and calcium and some alkaline compounds. Coal dust and water are, of course, added substances.

The water content of moulding sand needs controlling. Green-sand moulding requires to be done with sand of low moisture content (3–5%), but in dry-sand moulding more water may be present when making the mould, as this is beneficial in promoting dry bond strength after stoving.

The Testing of Sand

This has become an important side of the foundry metallurgist's work. There are instruments for testing all the main properties of sand.

Grain size may be tested by washing the sand free from clay and impurities, and then passing it through a series of sieves of different mesh, thus obtaining the proportion of the total amount which falls into each range of particle size. Another test for grain size is by **elutriation.** The sand is acted on by a rising column of water, the velocity of which can be controlled. With low velocities, only the smaller particles will rise with the water, and these are collected. The water velocity is then increased in steps, and larger particles are collected in a series of grades.

Green and dry strengths are tested by preparing a cylindrical specimen, 1 sq. in. cross-sectional area and approximately $2\frac{1}{4}$ in. long. The ramming is done under standardised conditions. In the case of dry specimens, suitable stoving is necessary. The specimen is then placed on end in a machine which applies a gradually increasing compressive load until collapse occurs. The crushing load is read from a scale attached to the machine; this figure is also the compressive strength in lb. per square inch. It may be noted that green strength rarely exceeds 8 lb. per square inch.

Permeability is determined by noting the time, in seconds, which is required to pass a known volume of air through a standard test piece; the air being maintained at a standard pressure.

CHAPTER XV

FOUNDRY PLANT AND MACHINERY

The Cupola

A SECTIONAL view of a foundry cupola is shown in Fig. 105. It consists of a tall, narrow cylinder of firebrick, lined on the inside with a daubed-on refractory, and supported on the outside by a steel " shell ". The bottom of the cylinder consists of two half-doors that can be dropped to allow the residue to drop out at the end of a " blow ".

The method of working the furnace is as follows. Any minor repairs to the refractory lining are done, using the fettling door. The bottom doors are closed, and a well-compacted sand bed is laid down. A slope is required on this bed so that molten metal in the furnace bottom will run towards the tapping hole. The tapping hole is made by ramming sand around an iron rod of suitable size, which is then withdrawn. Paper and wood are laid in the bottom and a layer of free burning coke put on. This is followed by the coke bed. This is a layer of selected furnace coke, strong, firm pieces of fairly large size being required. The coke bed is built up well above the tuyeres, which are the holes through which air is forced. The fire is lighted, and the natural draught of air through the fettling hole is relied upon to ignite the coke. When the coke is well alight the fettling hole is built up with a good thickness of sand and the steel door clamped in position. A plug of sand and clay called a " bod " is placed on the end of a thin iron rod or " bod stick ", and the tapping hole is " bodded up ".

Alternate layers of coke and iron with a little limestone are now added. The iron consists of a mixture of scrap and pig iron in weighted amounts, the pig iron being selected to give the required silicon, manganese and phosphorus contents to the final castings. The ratio of iron to coke is roughly 8 : 1 over a period of several hours. Naturally, in a short " blow " the weight of coke in the coke bed will upset this ratio.

The limestone is required to act as a flux for the coke-ash and the sand adhering to the pig iron. Excessive limestone has a bad effect on the furnace lining ; approximately 14 lb. of limestone per 1 cwt. of coke is the correct amount under average conditions.

When the cupola has been filled up to the charging door, the blast is turned on. The air for the blast is supplied by a motor-driven fan at a pressure of about $\frac{1}{2}$ lb. per square inch ; it enters through the tuyeres, and the coke bed soon glows white hot. Within ten minutes the first molten metal trickles through the coke bed and collects on the sand bed.

The " bod " is taken out and the metal is collected in suitable ladles.   As
the level of the charge sinks below the charging door, further iron and coke

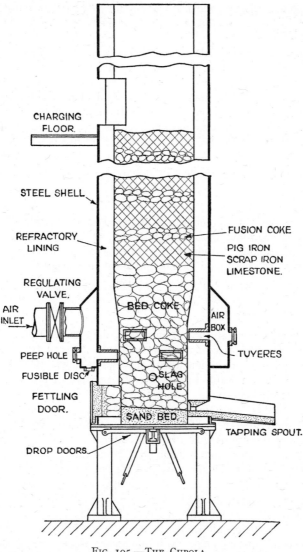

FIG. 105.—THE CUPOLA.

are added.   When the cupola is at full heat the ratio of iron to coke may
be raised to 10 : 1.

When a reasonable amount of slag has been fluxed out by the limestone,
the furnace may be " bodded up " whilst the metal collects in the furnace

bottom. The slag floats on top of the metal and as the level of the metal rises, the slag is blown out of the slag hole by the air blast.

The total weight of metal melted will depend upon the length of the " blow " and the size of cupola. The melting rate may vary from 15 cwt. to 10 tons per hour, according to size. The length of blow varies between two and six hours.

After the necessary weight of metal has been obtained, any excess is cast into pigs on the shop floor and the blast is shut off. The furnace bottom is dropped and the slag and remaining coke raked out as far as possible. The cupola is then allowed to cool off ready for inspection. The whole process can then be repeated. In many foundries the cupola is repaired and fixed during the morning, and is then lit. Soon after lunch the " blow " is started and continues until late afternoon. The cupola can then be allowed to cool off overnight. In working this system two cupolas are a great help. One may then be taken out of service when necessary.

Sand Mills

The facing sand for the foundry is prepared in a sand mill. New sand, old sand, coal dust and any necessary " binders " are put in the mill and subjected to rubbing and churning actions so as to thoroughly mix the ingredients. The sand may then be put through a disintegrator, where it is whirled round to break up any small " cakes ".

Mechanical Ramming

It was pointed out at the beginning of Chapter XIII that the rapid production of moulds is a very important point. The machines which are now to be described are designed with this end in view. Before going into details it will be advisable to consider the purpose of ramming and the mechanics of the operation.

Moulding sands have angular grains. As stated in the last chapter, they are bonded together with a thin layer of damp clay which clings to the surface of the grains. If a body of sand is poured into a mould the grains will have a random arrangement. Hand ramming consolidates the sand by forcing the grains into interlocking positions, *i.e.*, the grains have a wedging action. It is not only the grains which are struck that are driven into the interstices, the blows of the rammer will be transmitted by the grains to other grains within the body of the sand, just as a single billiard ball can transmit its momentum to a whole group. However, the momentum of each single grain diminishes as the energy of the blow spreads out into the sand. Consequently, the moulder puts down a thin layer of sand, applies the rammer to consolidate the sand, and then repeats the process.

There are several other methods of ramming the sand. The principal ones are as follows.

1. **Slinging the Sand.** The sand is thrown into the mould at high speed by machine. Each grain of sand then possesses the necessary momentum to produce the packing or ramming action. Slinging is probably the most accurate method of machine ramming. It can be used for both large and small moulds. When correctly adjusted, sand slinging will produce more even ramming than any hand-ramming operation.

2. **Squeezing the Sand.** Squeezing is only suitable for shallow moulds, as the energy of the " push " cannot be transmitted very far into the sand. There are two distinct systems of squeezing. The sand may be squeezed into a moulding box which already contains the pattern, or, alternatively, the pattern may be forced into a moulding box which already contains a body of sand. The latter method is more satisfactory if the mould is fairly deep, but it is not quite so simple in operation as the former method. The squeeze may be applied manually by means of a screw-jack, but in modern practice pneumatic or electric power is used.

3. **Jolting the Sand.** In this system, the moulding box, with a pattern in place, is placed on the table of a machine, and the box is filled with sand. The table is then given a series of rapid blows which impart energy to the sand. The grains of sand are thus given the necessary momentum to enable them to pack together. The sand which surrounds the pattern near the bottom of the box will receive energy from the sand above. In consequence, the densest packing of sand will be round the pattern ; this is the correct arrangement. Therefore, jolt ramming can be employed with deep moulds, but is limited by the size of table of the jolt machine and the necessity for drawing the pattern and lifting the rammed box.

Details of the three systems will now be given.

Sand Slingers

The sand slinger is a machine for ramming the sand to the correct density. There are few moulding shops where the sand slinger cannot be used to advantage : it is quite wrong to consider the slinger as suitable only for mechanised foundries.

The principle of the machine is illustrated by Fig. 106, which shows the slinger head. The sand is brought to the head by a conveyor belt and enters the impeller head through a port in the rear. The stream of sand flowing from the belt is directed across the path of the tip or bucket carried on the rotating impeller head. The tip thus cuts off a definite charge of sand every revolution, compresses it against the liner by centrifugal force and discharges it vertically downwards at high velocity into the mould below. The peripheral speed of the impeller, the form of the tip and the path of the sand stream are all designed to deliver exact " wads " of sand at the correct velocity.

There are three types of sand slinger, each designed to suit particular foundry conditions. The general shop which has a wide variety of work, some of it made in the floor, may be best served by a portable machine as shown in Fig. 107. The sand is shovelled by hand into the hopper, where it is delivered to an automatic riddle. From the riddle, another shute delivers the clean sand to the conveyor belt which takes it to the sand slinger head. The operator moves the head to and fro over the area to be rammed. The operation is repeated continuously, gradually building up the mould, course by course, just as in hand ramming, but at a much greater speed. With large moulds, the ramming time with a sand slinger is about one-sixth the time required for hand ramming.

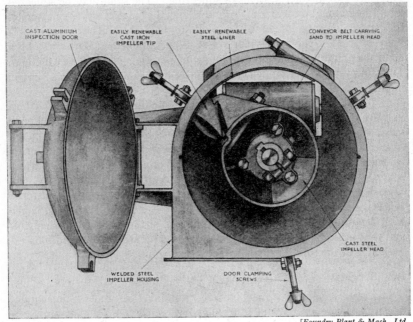

[*Foundry Plant & Mach., Ltd.*

FIG. 106.—SAND SLINGER HEAD.

In shops where the boxes are portable, either by crane or conveyor belt, the stationary sand slinger has advantages. The machine is then part of the fixed equipment and the work is conveyed to the slinging station. If the shop has mechanical sand conveyors, the sand is brought automatically to the hopper of the sand slinger, thus cutting out the need for hand shovelling.

In the heavy foundry the mobile type of sand slinger is used. The machine runs on rails along one side, or down the centre of the moulding shop. The moulds are built alongside the track. When a mould is ready for ramming, the sand slinger is moved along the track to the appropriate position and ramming proceeds. These machines have a very long arm and can cover a large area of shop floor.

[*Foundry Plant & Mach., Ltd.*

FIG. 107.—PORTABLE SAND SLINGER.

Machine Moulding

The plate pattern has already been described in the previous chapter. The modern view is that any casting worth putting on a plate is best moulded on a machine. Fig. 108 shows a plate pattern in position in a box ready for ramming. In a shallow box the sand can be squeezed on to the pattern. It will be necessary to have the correct quantity of sand

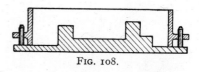

FIG. 108.

in the box so that it will be squeezed to the correct density. Accordingly, a sand frame is placed over the box and sand is poured into the box and frame (see Fig. 109). A pressure plate with a squeeze board attached is placed over the sand frame. The pattern and box are forced upwards by a pneumatic cylinder until the sand has been consolidated into the box. The sand frame is made to the correct depth to ensure that the ramming will be of the requisite firmness. The squeeze board has a thickness equal to the depth of the sand frame.

Fig. 110 shows a plate pattern in position on a squeeze-type machine. The pattern is mounted on the machine table and is registered by the two large dowels. The next operation is to place the box in position, upside down on top of the plate. The box has two lugs with holes which engage the dowels, but the box rests on the four pillars at the corners of the pattern. The sand frame is put on and the box and frame are filled with

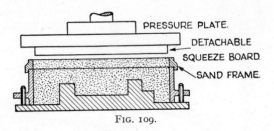

FIG. 109.

sand. The pressure plate and squeeze board are attached to a head which is swivelled to one side to give easy access to the box. This head is now swung round over the box. It will be noted that the head abuts against a lug on the machine frame. The table of the machine is lifted by air

[Foundry Equipment, Ltd.
FIG. 110.

pressure and the squeeze board is forced into the sand frame, thus consolidating the mould. It will be noted that the pressure plate can be adjusted to the correct height by a screw.

The pneumatic cylinder now lowers the table and pattern, but the four pillars shown in Fig. 110 support the box, and thus the pattern is drawn. To assist in the drawing operation, the downward stroke of the piston of the pneumatic cylinder is accompanied by a small, but rapid, vibration. When the pattern has been drawn, the mould is lifted off the machine and turned over.

In addition to the pneumatically operated machines there are others which are operated by electricity. In these a solenoid takes the place of the pneumatic cylinder. Very briefly, the solenoid has an iron core attached to the underside of the machine table and a coil attached to the machine frame. When electric current is passed through the coil, the iron core and the table are lifted up. An electrical vibratory device can be fitted. Electrically operated squeeze machines are shown in Fig. 119.

With deeper moulds the method outlined above is not satisfactory, as the tightest packing of the sand is immediately under the squeeze board, that is, at the bottom of the box. The tightest packing should be at the joint face, that is, at the surface of the plate. Accordingly, **double squeezing** may be used. This is shown in Fig. 111. Two presser boards

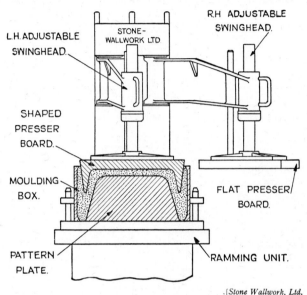

.[Stone Wallwork, Ltd.

FIG. 111.—DOUBLE SQUEEZING.

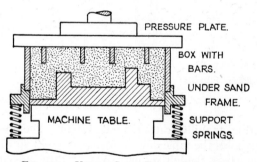

FIG. 112.—UNDER SAND FRAME RAMMING.

are used, one to consolidate the sand round the pattern, and the other to finish off the mould bottom. Alternatively, the **under sand frame** method may be used. This is shown, diagrammatically, in Fig. 112. The frame is supported on springs, and the pattern plate is placed inside the frame. The box, which can have bars if necessary, is placed on the frame and filled with sand. The pressure plate is then swung into position and the table lifts. The pattern plate is thus **forced into the sand**, and the tightest packing is immediately under the plate and round the pattern. At the same time the sand will be forced up between the box bars.

For deep moulds, the **jolt** principle may be employed. The table which carries the pattern and box may be given a series of jolts which consolidate the sand. Generally, a combined squeezing and jolting action is used.

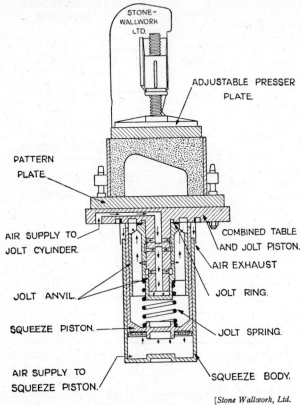

[*Stone Wallwork, Ltd.*]

FIG. 113.—JOLT RAMMING.

The diagram (Fig. 113) illustrates the jolt system. The pressure plate on top of the box holds the table down; the compressed air forces the anvil down and compresses the jolt spring. When the air pressure is suddenly released as the air ports coincide, the anvil is thrown at the table by spring action to give the jolt.

Roll-over Machines

Many deep moulds have large " cods "; these are large sand projections which are liable to break off if the mould is turned over carelessly. In these cases a **roll-over**-type machine is used. Most roll-over machines operate on the combined squeeze–jolt principle. Fig. 114 shows the roll-over machine with the necessary pneumatic controls. The method of operation is as follows.

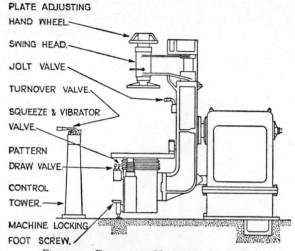

PLATE ADJUSTING
HAND WHEEL.

SWING HEAD.

JOLT VALVE.

TURNOVER VALVE.

SQUEEZE & VIBRATOR
VALVE.

PATTERN
DRAW VALVE.

CONTROL
TOWER.

MACHINE LOCKING
FOOT SCREW.

FIG. 114.—ROLL-OVER MOULDING MACHINE.

The head is swung away whilst the box is positioned and filled with sand. The pressure plate is screwed down to position and the jolt–squeeze action rams up the mould. With the pressure still on, the machine

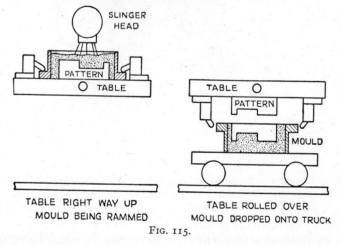

SLINGER
HEAD

PATTERN

TABLE

TABLE

PATTERN

MOULD

TABLE RIGHT WAY UP
MOULD BEING RAMMED

TABLE ROLLED OVER
MOULD DROPPED ONTO TRUCK

FIG. 115.

is rolled through 180°, thus bringing the mould right way up. The pressure is released and the machine table rises, leaving the mould on the pressure plate, which is now at the bottom.

Large moulds of shallow depth are made on special roll-over machines. The pattern is fixed to the table; and a box is placed over the pattern.

The box is pneumatically clamped to the table. When the ramming is complete, the table, pattern and box roll over as a unit. A truck on a short rail-track is run into position below the table. The box and mould are lowered on to the truck, leaving the pattern fixed to the table. The truck is run out, the table is rolled over and is then ready to receive another box (see Fig. 115).

A considerable part of the equipment in machine moulding consists of

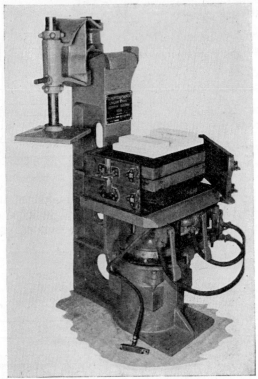

[*Foundry Equipment, Ltd.*
FIG. 116.—SNAP FLASK MOULDING.

moulding boxes, which cannot be used again until the mould has been cast up, the casting knocked out and the box returned to the machine. With mass-production methods a very large number of boxes is required, which represents a large sum of money.

Two methods of reducing this cost have been devised. These are the **snap flask** and the **boxless moulding machine.**

Snap-flask Moulding

The snap-flask method is shown in Fig. 116. The snap flask is a wooden moulding box, it has a hinged corner and a snap fastener at the opposite corner. Specially shaped guide pins are provided to locate the pattern plate and the boxes. The two half-flasks are placed one on each side of the pattern plate, the drag being at the top. The drag is filled with sand, and a bottom board, which fits *inside* the flask, is placed on top. The flask is then turned over, the cope is filled with sand and a top board is added. The mould is then rammed up, either by a squeeze or a squeeze–jolt machine. Both halves are rammed at the same time, the two boards being forced inside their respective boxes. The runner and risers are made from the top board.

[*Foundry Equipment, Ltd.*

FIG. 117.—BOXLESS MOULDING.

After ramming, the top part is lifted off and turned over; the mould is examined and finished as required. The plate pattern is lifted out and the bottom part is finished off. Any cores required are placed in the bottom part and the top part is replaced. The snap fastener is now unlocked, the flask removed, and the mould is left assembled on the bottom board. It is then taken to a conveyor, where the top part is weighted down and the mould goes to the casting station.

Boxless Moulding Machines

The logical development of snap-flask moulding is a machine which has the necessary containers permanently attached. Such a machine is shown in Fig. 117. The machine is shown in the " open " position, ready to receive sand.   The pattern plate with a " top part " is carried on a swinging arm, and the pressure plate is also swung away.   A bottom board and box (not shown) are put in, and the necessary amount of sand is inserted.   The pattern plate is brought to the front, and the head is swung to position, where it is locked under the projection on the main column of the machine.   After the squeezing action an automatic vibrator is set in motion.   At the same time the bottom box descends, thus stripping the pattern.   The pattern can then be swung aside and the mould lifted up on the bottom board.   For small shallow moulds, this " boxless " system is extremely rapid.

Under suitable conditions, and using shallow moulds, several of the machines described in the preceding pages can produce 100 half-moulds per hour.

Mechanised Foundries

More machinery is now the most urgent need of the foundry industry. Technically the average " general " foundry is far behind the other departments in most engineering works.   There are great opportunities

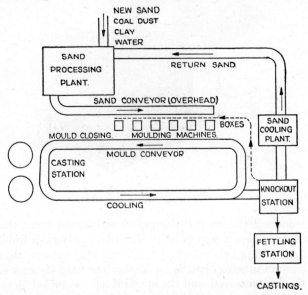

FIG. 118.—LAYOUT OF MECHANISED FOUNDRY.

for the production engineer who has mastered the principles of foundry practice.   He will find that whilst he has been striving to save minutes in the machine shop, hours can be saved by mechanisation in the foundry.

Where reasonable numbers of indentical castings are to be made, it becomes possible to lay out the shop on similar lines to other departments.

Fig. 118 is a diagram illustrating the main points of a mechanised foundry, which will be explained in detail.

In mechanising, the first essential is to get rid of the sand floor. The sand is dirty, it ruins the transport system and it wears everything away. Sand is required to make moulds. It should be brought to the moulding machines as required, the spillage disposed of immediately, and the finished moulds taken away as quickly as possible for casting. When the sand has been knocked out from the cast-up mould, it should be returned for re-processing. In the mechanised foundry there is no separate facing and backing sand ; instead a " standard " sand is prepared.

[British Insul. Callender's Cables, Ltd.

FIG. 119.

Following the mechanised system as laid down in Fig. 118, the old sand from the casting knock-out station drops through grids in the floor. It passes along a conveyor belt, and any new sand required is added. The new sand helps to cool the old sand : if this cooling effect is not sufficient, then a sand-cooling plant can be introduced. The sand is riddled automatically, whilst a magnetic separator removes any iron. It then passes to the sand mill, where coal dust is added, together with binding materials and the necessary quantity of water. After milling, the sand passes through a disintegrator which breaks up any " cakes " and brings the sand into good condition. It then passes along a conveyor to storage hoppers or straight to the moulding machines. Fig. 119 shows the sand hoppers arranged above a row of electrically operated moulding machines. By pulling the lever, the operator can drop the right quantity of sand straight into the moulding box. The rammed boxes then pass on to the conveyor ready for delivery to the casting station. After casting up, the moulds go to the knock-out station. The knock-out station is equipped with fume extractors. When the sand has fallen through the grids at the knock-out station, it has reached the lowest point of the system : it is now returned for re-conditioning.

The moulding machines are usually arranged in a row. In front of them is a conveyor in the form of a loop. The length of the conveyor is designed to suit the particular conditions. If the conveyor is mechanically driven, the speed and length are arranged to allow sufficient time after

[*Stone Wallwork, Ltd.*

FIG. 120.—MECHANISED FOUNDRY.

casting up before the knock-out station is reached. Two types of conveyor are in general use. The flat-topped type shown in Fig. 120 is a series of separate small trucks running on rails which can turn round bends. Some foundries use a roller conveyor, along which the moulds are pushed by hand. Such a roller conveyor may have a gradual slope so that gravity assists in the conveying. In this case " humpers " may be provided : these are power-driven rollers for raising the moulds where required.

Fig. 120 is a good example of the clean conditions obtainable with a planned layout. The floor grids should be noted. Surplus sand is swept away down the grids : under the floor a hopper catches all sand from the grids and deposits it on a belt conveyor, which returns it to the sand-preparation plant.

In some installations the machine operators leave the half-moulds open when passing them to the conveyor ; in fact, top and bottom half-moulds may be made on separate machines. The half-moulds then proceed to the closing station, where any necessary cores are inserted. The cores are brought from the core shop by a separate conveyor.

The moulds now go to the casting station, which is adjacent to the cupolas. Here they are cast up and allowed to cool off before going to the knock-out station.

To assist the workers at the knock-out station, mechanical pushers may be used to push the cast-up mould on to the knock-out grid.

The empty boxes must be returned as quickly as possible to the moulding machines. This may be done by a pendulum conveyor, which consists of a series of hooks carried on an overhead track, the empty boxes being hung on the hooks. A pendulum conveyor is shown (top left) in Fig. 120. These conveyors can be taken round fairly sharp corners, and may rise up to clear obstructions. Alternatively, a gravity roller conveyor may be used, the boxes then proceeding by their own weight to the machine. The roller conveyor can have " humper " rollers where required. A roller conveyor is shown in Fig. 119. The boxes are brought back along the wall side, out of the way of the workers.

The mechanisation of the core shop is important. It is useless to speed up mould production unless core production can keep pace. In addition to the mechanical transport of sand to the worker, core-making machines can be provided. These are similar in principle to the moulding machines, but the sand is, of course, rammed into the core box instead of the mould. A steel belt conveyor may be used to carry cores through the drying ovens. Until they have been dried out, the cores are fragile, and accordingly they are mounted on suitable metal cradles. From the ovens, the cores and cradles may be taken to the mould-closing station by pendulum conveyor. The same conveyor will return the empty cradles.

The Cleaning of Castings

When the casting has been removed from the mould, the runners and risers are knocked off or cut away, any " fins ", due to the mould joints, are trimmed up by chipping or grinding and the surface of the casting is cleaned of sand. Much of this cleaning can be done by **shot blasting**. The shot is in the form of chilled-iron pellets, which may be round, or may be crushed to angular particles with many cutting facets. The tough, evenly graded shot is thrown in a high-velocity stream at the surface to be cleaned. The sand and grit together with the shot are cleared away, and the shot is then recovered from the debris.

The process produces considerable amounts of dust, and must be done in an enclosed space. For large castings, a blast room is provided ; a typical example is shown in Fig. 121. This is of pressed-steel construction and has a floor-level turntable with a door across the diameter. Dirty castings are placed on one half of the table, which is then rotated half a turn to take the castings inside the room.   These castings are shot blasted whilst the other half of the table is unloaded of clean castings and reloaded with dirty ones.   The operator carries a shot gun which is fixed to a flexible pipe through which the shot proceeds to the gun.   He wears a respirator helmet with a front window to give clear vision.   A rubber cape protects his neck and shoulders.   He is also equipped with elbow-length gloves, knee-length rubber boots and a long rubber apron.

The roof of the chamber is provided with air-inlet ports, which do not allow escape of the shot.   The dusty air is continually exhausted through

[*Spencer & Halstead, Ltd.*

FIG. 121.—SHOT BLAST ROOM.

the floor, which is perforated.   The air passes through a dust arrestor and then through the suction fan.   The spent shot, scale and sand also pass through the floor perforations and are taken by an elevator to the separating plant, where the shot is separated out and is then available for further use.   Smaller castings may be cleaned in hand cabinets.   The operator directs the shot gun from outside the cabinet, observing the progress of the work through a window in the side of the cabinet.

The common method of projecting the shot at high speed from the muzzle of the gun is by entrainment in a stream of compressed air.   Fig. 122 shows how this is accomplished.   The large hopper is charged with shot through the mushroom-shaped inlet valve.   The air cock is then opened, putting the hopper under pressure.   The compressed air proceeding along the horizontal pipe enters the Venturi tube, where it falls in pressure but gains velocity : at the same time, shot is drawn from the bottom of the hopper, the volume of the shot being determined by the position of the shot-control valve. The stream of air and shot then proceeds along the pipe. At the shot-blast nozzle there is a further loss of pressure and gain in velocity.

Fig. 123 shows a rotary-table blast-cleaning machine which does not require an air supply. The work can be placed directly on the main

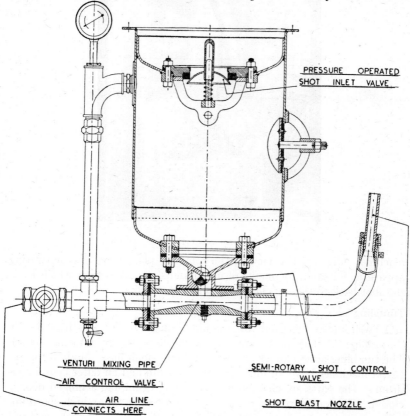

PRESSURE OPERATED
SHOT INLET VALVE

VENTURI MIXING PIPE

AIR CONTROL VALVE

AIR LINE
CONNECTS HERE

SEMI-ROTARY SHOT CONTROL
VALVE

SHOT BLAST NOZZLE

[*Spencer & Halstead, Ltd.*]

FIG. 122.—SHOT BLAST MECHANISM.

turntable, which carries it through the leather curtain on the left and thus into the blast chamber. The main turntable is sometimes equipped with small auxiliary-tables which themselves rotate, thus presenting all sides of the work to the stream of shot.

The shot is projected on to the work by high-speed impellers. The shot and debris then fall through holes in the table on to a lower table. From the lower table, the shot and debris which are removed by scrapers, pass to separating apparatus, so that the shot is recovered. Meanwhile, the cleaned castings emerge through the curtain on the right-hand side of the

[Spencer & Halstead Ltd.

FIG. 123.—AIRLESS SHOT BLASTING PLANT.

machine. Fig. 123 is a view of the complete plant which has separating apparatus for sand, fragments of metal and shot. A system which leads the shot back to the impellers is also incorporated.

Tumbling

A well-known method of cleaning small robust castings is by "tumbling". The parts are placed inside a slowly rotating barrel. The tumbling action knocks off the sand and small fins. Modern rotary-barrel machines have an inner perforated-drum and an outer containing-drum. The parts are charged into the inner drum and a hinged door is closed. The barrel rotates at 2 r.p.m. At the same time a high-speed impeller projects a stream of shot over the castings. The spent shot, sand and dust fall through the holes in the inner drum and are collected and passed through a separator. A few minutes tumbling and blasting is sufficient to clean a full charge of small castings, which normally weigh about 5 cwt.

Hydraulic Cleaning of Castings

In this process a high-speed jet of water (200 ft. per second) in which sand is entrained is played upon the castings to be cleaned. The scouring effect washes away the surface sand and quickly " eats out " the cores, leaving the core-irons and risers to be removed afterwards. One advantage of the process is that no dust is formed. The system is most suitable for foundries producing heavy castings on a large scale.

CHAPTER XVI

PRESSURE DIE CASTING

THE production of castings by forcing molten metal under pressure into steel dies is a very important branch of the foundry industry. The size of casting produced is usually small by general foundry standards : castings with dimensions larger than about 12 in. are comparatively rare.

On the other hand, millions of small articles are die cast every year. Certain metals, notably cast iron and steel, are not suitable for die casting owing to their high melting temperatures and the danger of the casting sticking to the die surfaces.

The economic limitation of the process is the need for large numbers of identical parts, as the manufacture of the dies is rather expensive. The smallest number of parts that will justify setting up a machine is dependent upon the complexity of the dies required. For simple parts, a rough figure is 2,000 castings, but for larger components, the figure may well be 15,000. A fully-automatic machine may be capable of producing 2,000 parts per hour, but the simpler and cheaper semi-automatic machines may be limited to 150 per hour.

The Merits of Die Castings

A good pressure die casting is homogeneous and has a clean, smooth surface much superior to that of a sand casting. In dimensional accuracy it is equal to a good deal of the work done in a general machine shop, so that much of the machining inevitable on a sand casting can be eliminated. Die castings can be made with a much thinner section than sand castings, so that in suitable cases the weight of the component can be reduced considerably. Composite pressure die castings can be made, *i.e.*, a component can be fixed in a die and another component is then cast round it. A simple example is the casting of a screwed stud in place.

Suitable Metals

The most suitable metals for die castings are alloys of zinc, copper and aluminium ; and alloys of magnesium and aluminium ; in each case suitable compositions have been worked out for particular purposes.

The Die-casting Principle

The elementary principles of pressure die casting are :
    1. The forcing of the metal at a suitable temperature and pressure into the die, so that the die cavity is completely filled.
    2. The opening of the die and the ejection of the casting.

The temperature required depends upon the metal being cast and also upon the pressure used. The higher the pressure, the lower may be the temperature of injection. The metal entering the die cavity solidifies first on the walls, and thus restricts the passage available for further metal; however, this further metal, if it has sufficient pressure energy, will continue to force its way through, much of the pressure energy being transformed into heat energy by the frictional resistance. Final solidification of the mass will be delayed by the heat energy developed by the friction. It will be realised that the correct pressure will be determined by the shape of the die cavity; long thin passages require a greater pressure so that the heat energy developed will hold the metal in the molten state for a sufficient length of time.

It is important that the casting should be ejected from the die at the right moment. Obviously, the casting must be sufficiently solid to retain its shape, but in cooling it will shrink and certain surfaces of the die will resist the shrinking process, thus setting up internal stresses in the component. Ejector pins are fitted to the die, and as the die is opened by the machine, the ejector pins force the casting out of the die cavity.

The die is usually in two portions. A fixed platen has the " sprue " or opening for the entry of the metal and one portion of the die, whilst a moving platen carries the remaining portion of the die, which is equipped with the ejector pins already mentioned.

The designing of dies is a highly skilled process. In service, the die will start cold and will require warming up initially, but afterwards the hot metal will heat up the die. The high temperature at which the die operates may cause it to warp, particularly where there is a considerable thickness of metal. Consequently, the casting cavity or cavities must be distributed as evenly as possible. It is frequently necessary to provide channels for water cooling. Arrangements must also be made for the escape of air. These air vents must be narrow so that large " flashes " will not be left on the casting, but the vents must not be stopped by the first rush of metal entering the die.

Component Design

Components to be die cast must be designed with careful regard to the problems of die design. Sudden changes of section should be avoided if possible. If a heavy boss is unavoidable it must be placed close to the sprue. The casting must have some taper so that it can be ejected from the die. It should always be borne in mind that dies in general are cut out by rotary cutters, consequently, the use of standard radii will help the die sinker. Narrow recesses in the casting mean narrow projections on the die, which will be difficult to machine and fragile in use.

Die-casting Machines

There are many different types of die-casting machine, but they fall into three general categories which are illustrated. Fig. 124 is a diagram of a direct-air-operated " Gooseneck " machine, and Fig. 125 is a general view of the same machine. A vessel which is immersed in a bath of molten

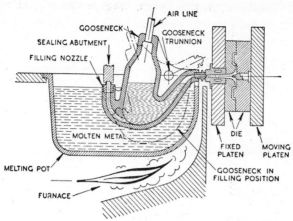

[Birmingham Al. Casting Co.

FIG. 124.—" GOOSENECK " DIE CASTING.

metal can be tilted so that the outlet nozzle can be made to enter the sprue of the fixed platen. Air pressure up to 600 lb. per square inch inside the vessel then forces metal at high velocity into the die cavity. It is

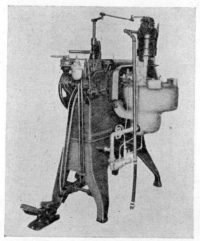

[Wm. Coulthard, Ltd.

FIG. 125.—" GOOSENECK " DIE
CASTING MACHINE.

necessary to have the metal in a very fluid condition for satisfactory operation. This type of machine is not so widely used today as formerly. It is not suitable for certain alloys—notably aluminium, which has a strong

affinity for iron and tends to " pick up " this metal from the machine.
Castings made by the process show a tendency to porosity.

   The Cold Chamber apparatus shown, diagrammatically, in Fig. 126 is

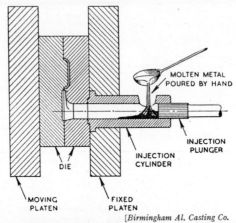

MOLTEN METAL
POURED BY HAND

INJECTION
PLUNGER

INJECTION
CYLINDER

DIE

MOVING
PLATEN

FIXED
PLATEN

[*Birmingham Al. Casting Co.*

FIG. 126.—COLD CHAMBER DIE CASTING.

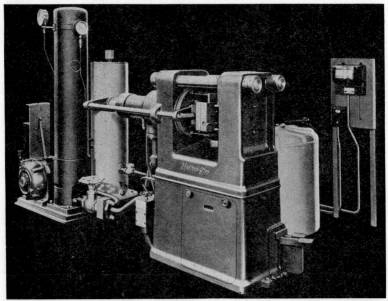

[*Wm. Coulthard, Ltd.*

FIG. 127.—COLD CHAMBER DIE CASTING PLANT.

now much favoured.   It is the most suitable machine for aluminium alloys.
The cold chamber is a cylinder into which a plunger is fitted.   The plunger
is operated by a hydraulic press.   Molten metal, sufficient for a single

" shot ", is poured into the cylinder through the aperture at the top and is then forced into the die by the plunger. Pressures up to 10,000 lb. per square inch may be used. In the diagram the metal is being poured by hand, but automatic machines are equipped with mechanical means for ladling the correct charge for each " shot ". The metal is melted in a separate pot, which can be made of graphite or other suitable refractory material. Thus there is little risk of metal " pick up " as with the Goose-neck machine. The pressure that can be applied is only limited by the power of the press. The dies used in the cold-chamber process must be extremely well jointed and of substantial design to resist the pressures employed, which occasionally reach 10,000 lb. per square inch. The

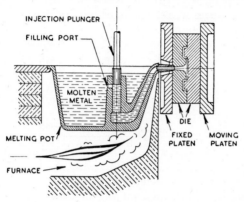

[*Birmingham Al. Casting Co.*

FIG. 128.—HOT CHAMBER DIE CASTING.

machine itself must be strongly constructed. Fig. 127 shows a complete cold-chamber installation illustrating this point. The actual die-casting machine is shown at the front ; the strong frame and the two large bolts at the top should be noted. On the left is the hydraulic system for feeding the hydraulic press. The electrically heated melting furnace is at the rear.

The Hot Chamber system is used for alloys of zinc, lead, tin and similar low-melting-point alloys. Of these metals, zinc alloys are the most popular. The most suitable casting pressure is about 1500 lb. per square inch, with a casting temperature of about 400° C. Under these conditions, since zinc has no affinity for iron, the hot-chamber process is very suitable. From the diagram (Fig. 128) it will be seen that the injection cylinder is immersed in the molten metal. The plunger forces a " shot " into the die on each down stroke. The plunger stroke and the die opening and closing movements are synchronised, thus giving a very high rate of production.

CHAPTER XVII

PLANE SURFACES

Sir Joseph Whitworth pointed out that the plane surface was the basis of most of the precision work in engineering, and the industry owes him a great debt for the original work he did about the year 1840 in instituting a proper system for making accurate plane surfaces. Most machine tools have a series of plane surfaces disposed at certain fixed angles to each other, and these surfaces are the datum planes from which the shape of the machined article is determined. Engineering measurement is largely based on **end standards of length**, which for the moment may be described as measures depending on the distance apart of two parallel plane surfaces.

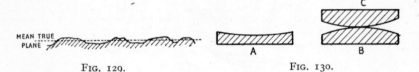

FIG. 129.   FIG. 130.

The engineer's **surface plate** is made in many sizes, the most useful being those of rectangular shape and varying in size from 4 in. × 4 in. to 6 ft. × 4 ft. The small plates have two handles, whilst the large plates are mounted on stands, and are usually called surface tables.

The accuracy of the flat surface is denoted by the maximum deviation from the " mean true plane " ; this term is illustrated in Fig. 129. British Standard Specification No. 817, 1938, states the maximum deviation for various sizes of plate and for several grades of accuracy. For example, in the best quality of plate (Grade A) the greatest permissible deviation is 0·0005 in. on a plate 6 ft. × 4 ft. Another important point is the number and distribution of the " high spots ". These must be numerous and evenly spaced.

Plane surfaces may be originated as follows. Three plates, A, B and C, of equal size are made in good close-grained cast iron ; they are rough machined, and are then allowed to " age " for some months to allow any internal strains to work out. After ageing, some warping will probably have occurred. This is removed by planing up on a good planing machine, only light cuts being used. The three plates are now " bedded up " by hand scraping, the following order being used throughout : A is bedded to B, then A to C and finally B to C.

The principle involved in this procedure is illustrated by Fig. 130. B and C may both be convex, but on being brought together this defect will be shown up and partially corrected. Each in turn will now show up the concavity of A.

After a number of repetitions, the surfaces will become flat within the desired limits.

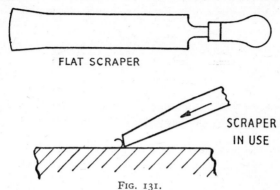

FLAT SCRAPER

SCRAPER
IN USE

FIG. 131.

The process of " bedding " may now be described briefly. One of the surfaces is very thinly coated with red lead and oil or prussian blue marking compound. Two surfaces are now rubbed together; the coated surface will be rubbed clean at its high spots, whilst the clean plate will be marked at the high spots. Both plates are now scraped with a flat scraper at the high spots, and the rubbing is repeated. The high spots will

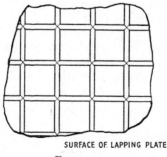

SURFACE OF LAPPING PLATE

FIG. 132.

thus be gradually distributed over the whole of both plates until the two surfaces correspond very closely.

The ordinary flat scraper is shown in Fig. 131. Flat scrapers are often made from 14-in. flat files; these are ground up to remove the serrations, and are then forged to shape at the end and hardened and tempered. The cutting edge is ground slightly convex to a large radius, so that the corners do not dig in to the work. A scraper requires frequent honing on an oilstone, as a sharp cutting edge is essential.

Surface plates are also finished by grinding on a precision grinding machine or by hand lapping on a lapping plate.

Lapping plates are usually made from soft cast iron. They should be as flat as possible, but not necessarily as flat as the surface plate. Usually a series of V grooves is machined across the lapping face, as shown in Fig. 132. The pitch of the grooves is about ⅜ in. The surface of the plate is smeared with fine abrasive dust mixed with oil, and the surface plate

FIG. 133.

is rubbed on the lap. Providing the high spots on the lap are well distributed, the surface produced will be much more accurate than that of the lap.

Hardened steel **toolmaker's flats** are ground and lapped to an accuracy of 0·00002 in. over the whole surface. They are usually circular and about 8 in. diameter.

Straight-edges

The straight-edge may be regarded as a long, narrow surface plate; three straight-edges may be originated in the same manner as three ordinary surface plates. Straight-edges up to 5 ft. long may be of plain, rectangular section. The longer the straight-edge the greater must be the depth, to prevent "sagging" when in use. Straight-edges longer than 5 ft. are usually made in cast iron and of "bow-back" design, as shown in Fig. 133. Straight-edges are used principally to check flat surfaces, to align a number of articles, or to rule accurate straight lines. Where a surface is to be checked, contact may be determined in several ways. When convenient, the most searching test is to have a source of white light behind the straight-edge; a gap of 0·0001 in. can be readily discerned in this way. Other methods used include the smearing of the straight edge with prussian blue or the introduction of thin slips of paper or metal between the two surfaces. The slips should be held equally tightly by the weight of the straight-edge.

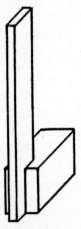

FIG. 134.

The Try-square

The try-square consists of two straight-edges firmly fixed at right angles to each other; the two edges of each straight-edge must be parallel to each other. Fig. 134 shows a typical try-square, and Fig. 135 shows three applications. In C it is desired to rule a line at right angles to a surface.

Cylindrical squares are also made, and are sometimes used as a master square for checking try-squares. A hollow steel cylinder is ground carefully on the diameter and is lapped up on the ends so that these are at right angles to the axis of the cylinder.

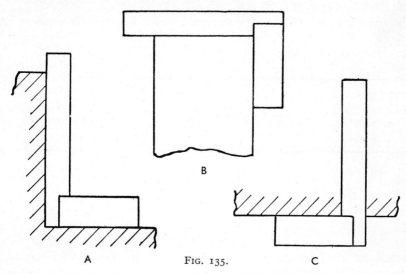

FIG. 135.

The important point about the cylindrical square is that it gives line **contact** with a flat surface.

Generation of Try-squares

Try-squares may be generated in sets of three in a similar manner to the generation of flat surfaces. Fig. 136 illustrates the principle. The base of each square is bedded to the surface plate. Squares *A* and *B* are brought together. In the figure each of these squares is obtuse-angled, so

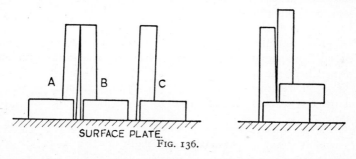

SURFACE PLATE.

FIG. 136.

the upper part of the blades will bed together, and this is the point at which metal is removed. However, each in turn is also bedded with square *C*, which is acute-angled. This will lead to metal being removed from the lower part of each blade. Regular interchange will produce three correct squares. The insides of the squares are then corrected by comparison with the outside of any of the squares (see Fig. 136).

CHAPTER XVIII

ENGINEERING MEASUREMENT

IN medieval times the necessity of having definite standards of length was appreciated and several crude standards were set up. To-day the definition of length has reached a very high standard. The purpose of having accurate standards is to enable different people to make articles of similar size.

Two rods might be loosely stated to be of equal length. Trial by rule might confirm this statement, but the two rods could vary in length to the extent of one millionth of an inch. That such a difference could possibly be important may seem absurd, yet the detection of such small differences is of basic importance in modern engineering practice.

The implications of precision measurement are very wide, and can be only briefly discussed.

The engineer as a scientist is concerned with the exactitude of his methods : the great importance of similarity of observation is now one of the main principles of physics.

From the workshop point of view, the question of interchangeability requires careful consideration in all standard articles. When a part is to be built into a machine it may be necessary for its size to be correct to 0·0001 in. if it is to function correctly. Such parts have to be measured, and the measuring instrument has to be made. In the making of the measuring instrument an accuracy of 0·00001 in. may be needed. Such an accuracy can be obtained only if there is some standard of much greater accuracy, and hence the need for a length standard with an error not exceeding one millionth of an inch.

It can also be demonstrated that if the best results are to be obtained from a given amount of work in the workshop, accurate measuring instruments and gauges are essential. Anyone who has worked in a workshop where the micrometers and other measuring devices are not corrected regularly knows that a great deal of time and energy are wasted, and a careless attitude is generated in the workmen by this unwise procedure.

Standards of Length

The Imperial Standard Yard

This is a bronze bar 38 in. long and 1 in. square section into which two gold plugs 0·10 in. diameter have been inserted. On the surface of each plug a fine line is scribed, and the yard is stated to be the distance from the centre of the line on one plug to the centre of the line on the other plug. The bar and its surroundings must be at a temperature of 62° F. Fig. 137

illustrates the principle of the standard yard. The central vertical lines at each end are the yard-marks; the remaining lines are to assist in finding the very fine marks. It will be noted that the surface of the plugs is on the centre of the bar; this is done to minimise the error due to bending of the bar under its own weight. The bar is supported at what

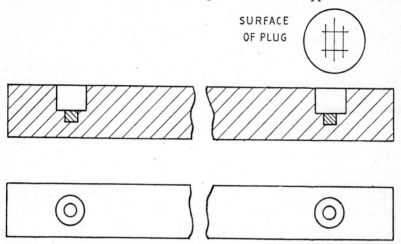

FIG. 137.—THE IMPERIAL STANDARD YARD.

are termed the " Airy Points ", the distance between these points being $\frac{1}{\sqrt{3}}$ of the overall length : with this method of support (see Fig. 138), the surfaces of the gold plugs are horizontal.

From the **Primary Standard** a number of **Secondary Standard** copies were made and distributed to various parts of Britain. Further standards are kept by laboratories and precision-instrument makers. It should be

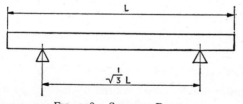

FIG. 138.—SUPPORT POINTS.

clearly understood that there is only one standard yard, and, by law, all other measuring devices are dependent on it. A serious difficulty was revealed in the maintenance of the standard yard. When the secondary standards were re-checked, it was discovered that the metal bars had altered in length—a phenomenon known as **secular change**.

A further method of setting up a standard of length was later suggested. This was to state the length in terms of the wave-length of monochromatic light (light of a single wave-length). The red light of glowing cadmium vapour was chosen, and the Imperial Standard Yard was defined as a certain number of wave-lengths of this light.

A standard of length which is of world-wide importance is the International Standard Metre. This standard was also related to the light standard in a similar manner, and the relationship between the yard and the metre was stated. So far as can be imagined, a light standard is perpetually constant.

The foregoing are termed **line standards**, as the distance between two lines is the basis of measurement. From these line standards the engineer's rule is derived by suitable subdivision.

End standards

With the exception of the rule, most engineering measuring devices depend on end standards of length. An end standard is one in which the basic distance is that between two plane parallel surfaces. A yard end standard consists of a metal bar say $\frac{3}{4}$ in. square section with two parallel plane surface ends.

It will occur to the reader that some difficulty will be encountered when an attempt is made to compare an end standard yard with a line standard yard. It is sufficient to say that at the National Physical Laboratory adequate methods have been devised to make the comparison with an accuracy of the order of one part in ten million.

In engineering practice end standards much shorter than one yard are often required, and accurate subdivision is necessary. If three bars equal in length to each other are placed end to end and together equal one yard, it is obvious that each bar is 1 ft. long. Similarly, twelve bars prepared in the same way would each be 3 in. long. By suitable subdivision and manipulation any desired length standard may be produced. The following are typical examples : six blocks 0·5 in. could be produced from the 3·0-in. bar. A 3·0-in. and a 0·5-in. block could then be placed end to end ; five blocks of equal length which totalled 3·5 in. when piled would each be $\frac{3·5}{5} = 0·7$ in. long. Similarly, five further blocks equal to 3·7 in. would be $\frac{3·7}{5} = 0·74$ in. long, and again $\frac{3·74}{5} = 0·748$ in. long.

Special lapping techniques are required to produce the blocks : in the method devised by the National Physical Laboratory eight blocks of equal thickness are produced at one time.

Slip-gauges

Slip-gauges were invented by the Swedish engineer Johansson about the year 1903, and are often termed Johansson blocks. They are made from alloy steel, and are specially tempered to reduce the possibility of secular change. The shape is rectangular, the size of the plane end surfaces being about $\frac{3}{4}$ in. $\times \frac{3}{8}$ in.

The most useful set of slip-gauges consists of eighty-one pieces arranged as follows.

4 pieces, 1 in., 2 in., 3 in., and 4 in. long.
19 pieces, 0·05 to 0·95 in. in steps of 0·05 in.
49 pieces, 0·101 to 0·149 in. in steps of 0·001 in.
9 pieces, 0·1001 to 0·1009 in. in steps of 0·0001 in.

With such a set many thousands of end-gauges can be built up by placing two or more slip-gauges end to end. If two slip-gauges with slightly greasy surfaces are slid together with a little pressure, they will adhere firmly, and will not fall apart with normal handling. This is termed **wringing** the gauges, and is a rather curious phenomenon, which is not yet thoroughly understood : the adhesive force exceeds that of the atmospheric pressure, and cannot therefore be due to the exclusion of air from the faces in contact. It has been suggested, and is generally accepted, that the adhesive force is largely due to the minute films of grease which lie in the " low spots " of the two surfaces.

This question of wringing is important; according to the accepted theory, there is true metal-to-metal contact at the " high spots " of the surfaces, and consequently there is no increase in real length compared with nominal length when a number of gauges are wrung together.

Experiments have been made to determine what amount of wear takes place due to constant wringing. It was discovered that for all practical purposes the wear is negligible over a long period, provided that the gauges have been properly finished in the course of manufacture.

The accuracy of slip-gauges varies according to the grade, and three grades are manufactured.

1. **Reference.** These have an accuracy of 0·000002 in. per inch length. Such a set often forms the primary standard of length for an engineering works, and this set is used only for comparison with other standards.

2. **Inspection.** This grade has an accuracy of 0·000005 in. per inch length ; it is used in tool-rooms and inspection departments.

3. **Workshop.** The accuracy is 0·00001 in. per inch length.

Care and Use of Slip-gauges

When not in use the gauges are greased and kept in a special box. Before wringing they should be wiped with a clean, soft cloth. Sufficient grease will usually remain to ensure good wringing, but if wringing is difficult, a little paraffin will improve matters. If any gauge refuses to wring, it should be examined carefully for burrs or scratches. The correct method of wringing is to slide the gauges together with a steady pressure ; they should be parted in a similar manner immediately the work has been completed.

Slip-gauges should not be dropped, subjected to heat or damp, or wrung together in the presence of abrasive dust, such as is common near grinding or polishing operations. With refined work it must be remembered that they are correct at one particular temperature : this temperature is marked on the box, and is usually 68° F.

It has been mentioned that a reference set of slip-gauges may be used as a primary length standard. On no account should this set be used for any other purpose than the setting of secondary standards, such as the measuring instruments used in the gauge-checking department. Other and cheaper sets should be used in normal tool-room and shop operations. Even the cheaper sets should not be passed into the shop indiscriminately. The slip-gauge is a handy little tool, and quickly falls into misuse unless

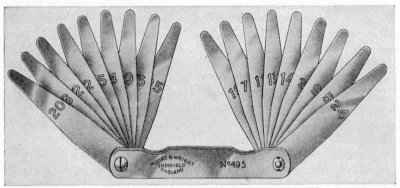

[*Moore and Wright, Ltd.*

FIG. 139.—FEELER GAUGES.

some check is maintained. Thoughtless workmen will even use slip-gauges as packing under machined work unless someone is on the alert to stop such foolish and expensive practices.

The method of assembling slip-gauges to give a particular overall length should be done systematically, as illustrated in the following example.

A length of 3·4657 in. is required.

1. Eliminate the last decimal place . . . . 0·1007 in.
2. Eliminate the third decimal place . . . . 0·1150 in.
3. Eliminate the remaining decimal places . . . 0·2500 in.
4. Complete with suitable whole number . . . 3·0000 in.

Total   3·4657 in.

It should be noted that the third decimal place is eliminated with the 0·115-in. slip ; the 0·125-in. could be used, but step number 3 would have been more difficult.

Feeler Gauges

Sets of thin pieces of steel held together in a holder are termed feeler gauges. A typical set is shown in Fig. 139. A range of thicknesses from

0·0015 in. to 0·025 in. is provided, and therefore combinations may be arranged from 0·0015 in. to about 0·080 in.   These may be used to check narrow gaps.   The accuracy is not equal to that of slip-gauges, and there is a distinct tendency for the thinner feelers to crumple with careless use, but they can be relied on to four places of decimals, and are very handy in the workshop.

The Engineer's Rule

The yard line standard may be subdivided by means of the dividing engine.   This is a machine for scribing a series of fine lines on a steel strip, thus producing the engineer's rule.   The most useful workshop rule is 12 in. long, 1 in. wide and about 0·040 in. thick.   The dimensions should be arranged as follows : one edge with inches divided into $\frac{1}{8}$, $\frac{1}{16}$, $\frac{1}{32}$ and $\frac{1}{64}$ in. ; one edge with inches divided into $\frac{1}{10}$, $\frac{1}{20}$, $\frac{1}{50}$ and $\frac{1}{100}$ in. ; one edge divided into $\frac{1}{12}$ in. ; one edge divided into centimetres, millimetres and half millimetres.   The advantage of the $\frac{1}{12}$ in. marking is debatable,

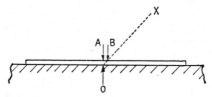

FIG. 140.—PARALLAX ERROR.

but it is sometimes necessary to draw to scale in the workshop, and these marks may then be very useful.

Many workers will not use the finer divisions such as $\frac{1}{64}$ and $\frac{1}{100}$, and instead will try to estimate the mid-point of coarser dividing marks such as $\frac{1}{32}$ in.   The marks on a good rule are about 0·004 in. wide.   The use of these fine, closely spaced marks is tiring to the unaided eye, but in fact this should not be attempted.   Magnifying glasses mounted on stands should always be used for fine work.   Some types have the glass mounted at the correct focus, and may also have internal illumination.

The point is rather important.   In the tool-room there are several methods of setting to very fine limits, but they are either tedious or require expensive apparatus ; setting to 0·010 in. can in many cases be done with a good rule and magnifying glass quicker and cheaper than by any other method.

A source of trouble in fine work with a rule arises from the rule thickness, and is termed **parallax error**.   It is due to incorrect placing of the eye in relation to the mark being used.   Fig. 140 illustrates this point in exaggerated form.   The arrow A indicates the mark on the rule which coincides with point O on the work.   If, however, the rule is viewed from the point X, then B will appear to be the coincident mark.   The remedy is to use a very thin rule, or to bevel the edge of a thicker rule; unfortunately this makes the rule much less robust for general workshop use. Special rules 12 in. long by ½ in. wide and 0·020 in. thick are made for fine measurement.

The field of application of the rule is greatly widened when it is used in conjunction with inside and outside calipers, so that bars and holes can be measured. The possibility of error in deciding the size obtained by the calipers must be guarded against, but for work involving no greater accuracy than $\frac{1}{32}$ in., rule and calipers should be used regularly. With this method, holes and bars up to 12 in. can be measured with apparatus costing a couple of pounds; the cost of a set of inside and outside micrometers to cover the same range will be fifty times that amount. It may be argued that the micrometers will have to be bought anyway, but such expensive instruments should be kept for finer work, in order to preserve them; furthermore, the indiscriminate use of them creates a false

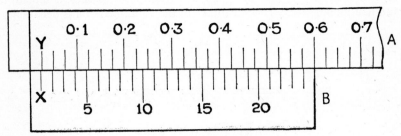

FIG. 141.—VERNIER.

impression in the large workshop, so that many more micrometers are in use (and misuse) than is necessary. The repair and replacement bill for micrometers can be a serious matter in a large workshop.

The Vernier

The vernier attachment allows of much more accurate measurement with a rule, but only an accurately graduated rule is suitable for this attachment, as the working principle of the vernier depends on the coincidence of rule markings. Fig. 141 illustrates the principle of the vernier, which was invented by the French mathematician Pierre Vernier in 1631. A is a rule of any length, graduated in $\frac{1}{40}$-in. divisions. B is a short sliding scale with twenty-five equal divisions; the total length of these twenty-five divisions equals twenty-four of the rule A. The difference in length between a division on A and a division on B will therefore be $\frac{1}{25}$ of $\frac{1}{40}$ in. = 0·001 in. If the two scales are set with the ends level, as shown, then mark X will fall short of mark Y by a distance of 0·001 in., and if the short scale is moved to the right until X and Y are coincident, then this movement must be 0·001 in. Similarly a movement of 0·008 in. would bring the eighth marks together.

Suppose scale *B* is to be moved 0·433 in., the position is shown in Fig. 142. The end of scale *B* is slightly beyond the 0·425 mark.   Counting along scale *B*, it is noted that the eighth mark coincides with a mark on scale *A*, therefore 0·008 in. is added to the 0·425 reading to give 0·433 in.

The Vernier Caliper

This instrument (see Fig. 143) has a fixed jaw attached to the main scale,

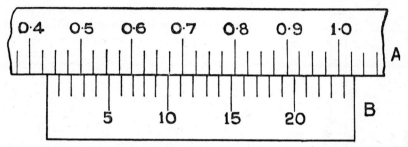

FIG. 142.—VERNIER READING 0·433 IN.

and a movable jaw is fastened to the vernier sliding scale.   The sliding scale has a locking screw to hold it in any desired position.   To assist in the correct setting of the movable jaw another clamp with screw adjust-

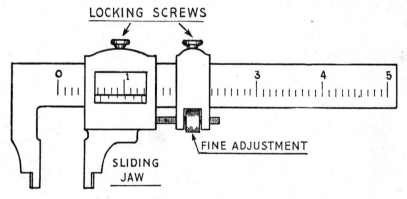

FIG. 143.—VERNIER CALIPER.

ment is fitted.   This latter clamp can be locked, and the movable jaw then be given a fine movement by turning the nut.

As a precision measuring instrument, the vernier has the following advantages :

    1. A large range of sizes can be covered with one caliper.
    2. The only wearing parts are the caliper jaws ; providing these are undamaged, there is no loss of accuracy.

L

The disadvantages are :

    1. Except for small sizes, hexagon or round bars cannot be measured on the diameter, and the " feel " is not so good as the micrometer.

    2. The jaws are comparatively light, and may be sprung out of alignment.

The Vernier Height-gauge

This instrument, which is shown in Fig. 144, is very useful for checking

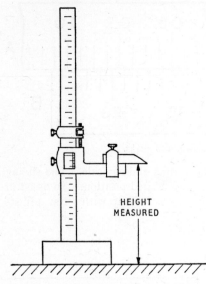

FIG. 144.—VERNIER HEIGHT-GAUGE.

heights from a surface plate. Consider the component shown in Fig. 145. The heights L and M are to be checked. Owing to the hole and the small diameter of the boss and the projecting collar, these dimensions could not be checked with a micrometer or a vernier caliper, but are readily checked with the height-gauge if the component is mounted on the surface plate as shown. The sharp extremity of the gauge finger is also used as a scriber in marking out work.

The Micrometer

The principle of the micrometer is shown in Fig. 146. The movable spindle, B, may be screwed in or out of the tapped hole in the body, A. One end of the spindle has a drum, D, which is evenly graduated round its circumference with twenty-five divisions. A

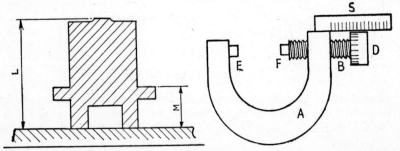

FIG. 145.   FIG. 146.—PRINCIPLE OF THE MICROMETER.

scale, S, is graduated in $\frac{1}{40}$-in. divisions. The spindle B is screwed forty threads per inch.

One complete turn will move $B \frac{1}{40}$ in., and this can be noted on scale S; since there are twenty-five divisions on the drum D, then a movement of one division of the drum equals $\frac{1}{40} \times \frac{1}{25} = 0 \cdot 001$ in. The work to be measured is inserted between the two flat and parallel surfaces, E and F.

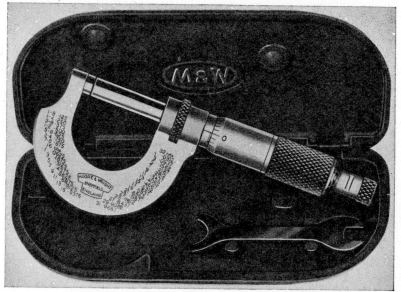

[Moore and Wright, Ltd.

FIG. 147.—0–1 IN. MICROMETER.

A typical workshop micrometer is shown in Fig. 147. The spindle is attached rigidly to the thimble, which has twenty-five divisions. The sleeve is fastened to the frame, and is graduated in $\frac{1}{40}$ in.; for convenience, each $\frac{1}{10}$-in. mark is numbered. Rotation of the thimble will move the

0·059   0·546

FIG. 148.

spindle to or from the anvil. The lock-ring can be tightened to lock the spindle in any position. The micrometer is read as follows. The scale on the sleeve is examined, and the number of divisions uncovered by the thimble is noted, each division representing 0·025 in. To this is added the number of divisions on the thimble that have passed the axial line on the sleeve. Fig. 148 shows two typical readings.

The Vernier Micrometer

To obtain readings of an accuracy of 0·0001 in., the sleeve of the micro-meter may be provided with a vernier scale (see Fig. 149). In an ordinary micrometer the length of a thimble division is 0·050 in., and this represents 0·001 in. anvil movement. The vernier scale has ten divisions equal to nine thimble divisions; thus a vernier division is 0·045 in., and the difference is 0·005 in., which thus represents an anvil movement of 0·0001 in.

Fig. 150 illustrates a reading of 0·4123 in. on a vernier micrometer.

The standard micrometer has a range of 1 in., and a considerable number are required in most workshops. Micrometers are made up to 54 in. between the measuring faces.

A reasonable amount of practice is required before a worker becomes proficient with the micrometer. The principal difficulty is that of acquiring the necessary " feel ". It should be realised that the frame of a micrometer

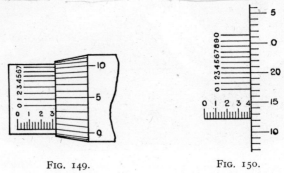

FIG. 149.   FIG. 150.

can be sprung, and therefore only the lightest possible contact of both faces is required. A skilled worker with an acute sense of touch has a lighter " feel " than a novice or heavy-handed worker. The stories that are current in most workshops about the wide variation in the sizes obtained by different workers are merely a proof of the lack of skill in a shop where no systematic training is given. With proper instruction the variation amongst normal workers should not exceed 0·0002 in. with the smaller micrometers; the larger micrometers are rather more difficult to manipulate. It is an excellent practice to set up a few plugs in a workshop and to attach a note giving the exact size. Workers can then be encouraged to try their " feel ", and thus assess their own ability against a known datum. It is perhaps needless to add that such a scheme will work only when the micrometers are reliable.

Many micrometers have a spring-loaded ratchet attached to the end of the spindle; this ratchet is used to rotate the thimble, and will slip if excessive force is used in screwing down the micrometer. Unfortunately, it is usual to set the micrometer, and then try it on the work, and in these circumstances the ratchet is no safeguard against heavy-handed users. Skilled workers usually ignore the ratchet.

Inside Micrometers

The measurement of bores may be done with the inside micrometer. This has a micrometer head, and is extended at the opposite end by a bar (see Fig. 151). Adjustable inside micrometers are often used. These consist of a micrometer head with a socket into which bars of different lengths

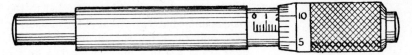

FIG. 151.—INSIDE MICROMETER.

may be fitted. The range of the micrometer is then limited only by the number of bars provided.

It has already been mentioned that the outside micrometer has flat and parallel measuring faces. With the inside micrometer it is necessary to have radiused end faces; the radius used must be less than that of the smallest hole to be measured. The inside micrometer is, of course, much "stiffer" than the outside micrometer, and is thus much more sensitive as regards "feel".

Special Micrometers

There are many devices employing the micrometer head, such as the micrometer depth-gauge, and also many micrometers with special measuring faces. Two special faces are shown in Figs. 152 and 153. Fig. 152

FIG. 152.

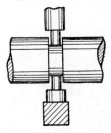

FIG. 153.

illustrates the measuring of the wall thickness of tubing and Fig. 153 is for measuring narrow grooves. Fig. 154 shows a micrometer depth-gauge.

Care of Micrometers

Micrometers, particularly the larger sizes, are expensive, and should be treated with care. The accuracy of a micrometer is often taken for granted, and in the workshop this attitude should be encouraged, otherwise a great deal of time may be wasted; but the maintenance of confidence requires systematic checking and correcting of the micrometers.

Micrometers should be numbered and a log-book maintained. Weekly checking should be a routine matter for some appointed person, but workers should be encouraged to return a micrometer at any time if they doubt its accuracy.

If damage has occurred, the micrometer should either be repaired or returned to the makers immediately. Wear of the measuring faces and the screw-thread are the normal signs of old age in a micrometer, but by far the greatest number of micrometers are damaged by minor accidents in the workshop. It is fatal to reprimand a worker whenever a micrometer is damaged. Everyone will resort to subterfuge to hide the damage after each small accident, and the amount of scrapped work will rise immediately. The remedy lies chiefly in training; but workers who are incorrigibly clumsy should be found work suitable to their talents.

[Moore and Wright, Ltd.
Fig. 154.—Micrometer
Depth-gauge.

Small micrometers can be checked quickly with slip-gauges. For example, a 0—1 in. micrometer should be checked at 0, 0·105, 0·210, 0·315 in., etc., up to 1·0 in. This method gives a check

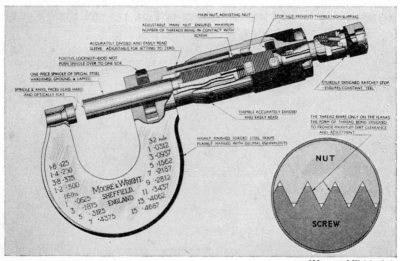

[Moore and Wright, Ltd.
Fig. 155.—Section through Micrometer Head.

in various thimble positions, and the type of error can be determined. The internal construction of a micrometer head is shown in Fig. 155.

[Thomas Mercer, Ltd.

FIG. 156.—INDICATOR DIAL GAUGE.

[Thomas Mercer, Ltd.

FIG. 157.—DIAL GAUGE AS A COMPARATOR.

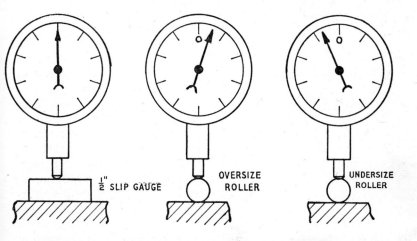

FIG. 158.—USE OF COMPARATOR.

Comparators

In normal workshop practice the rule, the micrometer and slip-gauges may be regarded as **measures**. Each is complete in itself, and is not referred to any other datum : the worker regards the size given as final. There are many other devices, however, which require to be set from a measure. The simplest example is a pair of calipers, but many elaborate comparators are now used. The principle is to set a device from some datum (commonly a set of slip-gauges) and then to measure the components relative to the datum.

For example, a large number of rollers, all nominally 0·500 in. diameter, are to be checked. The comparator is set to 0·500 in. by a slip-gauge, and the rollers are passed through. The comparator will then register the deviation in diameter above or below 0·500 in. for each roller. Unskilled labour may be used once the comparator has been set.

In problems of measurement the student should always decide logically what is the datum of the measuring devices used ; he may then decide what standard of accuracy is to be expected.

The Dial Indicator

This instrument is shown in Fig. 156. The plunger slides in and out of the body, and the motion is recorded by the pointer on the dial. The dial is divided either into divisions of 0·001 in. or 0·0001 in. Usually the dial scale is marked from zero on each half of the circle, and the dial can be rotated relative to the pointer, so that a zero setting can be made for any position of the plunger. The total plunger movement is about 0·4 in. or 0·04 in., according to the division of the dial. The dial-gauge has a lug at the back of the body, so that it can be mounted on a stand or other fixture. Fig. 157 shows a dial-gauge mounted on a stand over a small flat table on which the work to be measured can be placed. One use of this arrangement is illustrated in Fig. 158. This **comparator** principle is of great importance and will be discussed further.

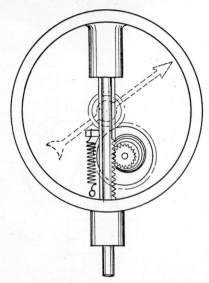

FIG. 159.—DIAL INDICATOR MECHANISM.

A very important feature of this indicator is that the contact pressure of the plunger is maintained by a light spring, and is quite independent of the "feel" of the operator. Fig. 159 shows the internal mechanism of a simple dial-gauge in diagrammatic form. The sliding plunger is supported by two bearings which are integral with the gauge body; two splines on the plunger prevent its rotation. The helical tension spring to the left is the contact spring which provides the pressure on the work. The plunger has a rack which engages with a small pinion. On the pinion shaft, a large gear-wheel is mounted. This meshes with a small pinion mounted on the pointer spindle, thus providing a magnifying movement. The hair spring keeps the gears in contact in one direction at all times, thus eliminating errors due to backlash.

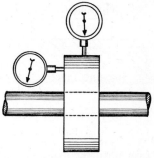

FIG. 160.—CHECKING A COLLAR.

Uses of the Dial Indicator

The dial indicator can be set up as a comparator, as shown in Fig. 158, which illustrates the checking of $\frac{1}{2}$-in.-diameter rollers. To check whether a collar is running truly on a spindle, the indicator is set up as shown in Fig. 160 and the spindle is rotated. It must be noted that this is not a test to see if the collar is a true cylinder with flat ends. If such a test is required, then the dial-gauge movement along the cylinder must be controlled by straight-edges.

Fig. 161 shows a surface being checked for flatness. In this case the indicator must be mounted on a stand with a flat base, and the stand

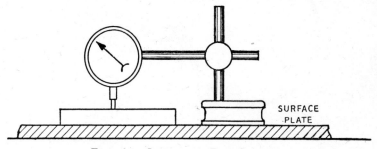

FIG. 161.—CHECKING A FLAT SURFACE.

placed on a good surface plate. The surface under examination can then be explored with the tip of the indicator plunger. The accuracy of the check depends on that of the surface plate used, and in fact the dial-gauge is used to compare the relative flatness of the two surfaces.

Another use of the dial indicator is shown in Fig. 162. This method is used in certain precision-boring machines. It is one way of eliminating the question of " feel ". A component is to have two holes spaced 4·0000 in. apart. It is placed on a boring machine with a sliding table.

The end of the table has a face which is a true plane. A 4·0-in. slip-gauge is placed between the table end and a dial indicator as shown at (I). The dial indicator, which is attached to an immovable part, is set to zero, and the first hole is bored. The slip-gauge is removed, and the table is moved

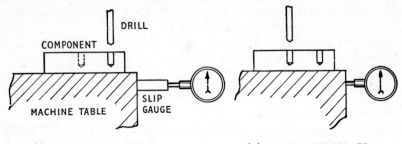

(I) FIRST HOLE DRILLED　　　**(II) SECOND HOLE DRILLED**

FIG. 162.—HOLE SETTING WITH A DIAL INDICATOR.

over until the dial-gauge again reads zero, as shown in (II). The second hole is then bored.

A different type of dial-gauge is shown in Fig. 163. The dial lies face upwards in normal use. The projecting plunger can be inserted in positions where a normal dial-gauge would not be convenient. Fig. 164 shows a

[*E. Capp and Son, Ltd.*

FIG. 163.—" VERDICT " DIAL INDICATOR.

plate with projecting studs. The plate is revolving in a lathe chuck, and it is desired to know if the central stud is revolving truly. The extended plunger of the gauge can be placed on the stud without any danger of the remaining studs fouling the dial-gauge body.

Care of Dial-gauges

These instruments are about the same size as a large pocket watch, and should be treated in a similar manner. They must be kept away from dust and damp and put away in a clean box or a chamois leather bag. Occasional cleaning is required, but they should not be oiled, otherwise dust and fluff may clog the internal gears.

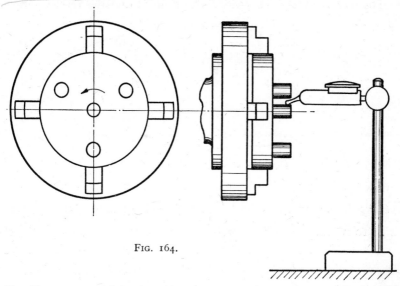

FIG. 164.

The Measurement of Angles

The accurate measurement of the inclination of two surfaces relative to each other is a common engineering problem. The protractor shown

[*Moore and Wright, Ltd.*

FIG. 165.—VERNIER PROTRACTOR.

in Fig. 165 is a useful instrument for this work. The two straight-edges can be set at any angle relative to each other and the angle read off on the circular scale. The usual graduation is in degrees, which may be sub-divided into half degrees. For more accurate work a vernier scale is fitted.

The main scale is then divided into degrees, and the vernier scale is

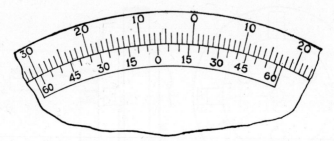

FIG. 166.—VERNIER READING 6° 25′.

divided so that twelve divisions equal 23° on the main scale. Each vernier division thus represents $\frac{23}{12} = 1\frac{11^{\circ}}{12}$, or five minutes of arc less than 2°. To read the vernier, the whole number of degrees is noted, and then

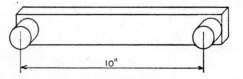

FIG. 167.—A SINE BAR.

the number of divisions is counted up to the point where a line on the vernier scale coincides with a line on the main scale. Each division represents five minutes of arc, and these must be added to the reading. It

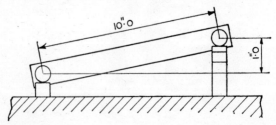

FIG. 168.

is essential, in counting up, to move **away** from the zero mark on the main scale. Fig. 166 shows a reading of 6° 25′.

The Sine Bar

A simple type of sine bar is shown in Fig. 167. A straight-edge has two cylindrical plugs firmly fixed to it at a centre distance of 10·0 in. The plugs are equal in size, and are set at an equal distance from one edge.

Slip-gauges may be set up on a surface plate, and the sine bar is placed with the two plugs resting on top of the slip-gauges, as shown in Fig. 168. Suppose the difference in height is 1·0 in., then the angle of inclination between the surface of the sine bar and the surface of the plate will have the sine 0·10, and is therefore 5° 45′.

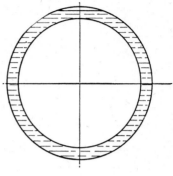

Fig. 169.

The Spirit Level

Fig. 169 shows a circular glass tube of uniform cross-section, which is almost full of liquid. A small bubble of air is left in the tube, and as the tube is rotated, the liquid will remain at the bottom and the air at the top. If the tube is 50 ft. radius and is rotated through 1 minute of arc, then it will move

$$\frac{2 \times \pi \times 50 \times 12}{360 \times 60} = 0·17 \text{ in. approx. at the circumference.}$$

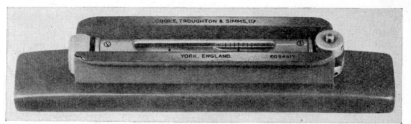

[Cooke, Troughton and Simms, Ltd.

FIG. 170.—BLOCK LEVEL.

If the tube is moved by this amount, then the edge of the bubble will move by the same amount.

A little consideration will bring the conclusion that an increase in tube

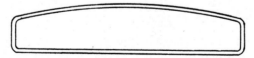

FIG. 171.—VIAL.

radius will give a greater bubble movement for the same angular displacement.

The engineer's **block level**, shown in Fig. 170, has a small portion of such a tube, and this **vial**, as it is termed, has a shape as shown in Fig. 171.

The upper inside surface is carefully ground to a definite radius, and the vial is mounted level in a cast-iron block with a flat base. The outside of the vial has a series of graduations, so that the bubble movement can be accurately determined.

The general formula for determining the sensitivity of a level is illustrated by Fig. 172.

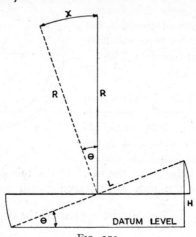

FIG. 172.

Let x = movement of bubble
       R = tube radius in inches
       θ = angle of inclination in seconds of arc

Then
$$x = \frac{2\pi R\theta}{360 \times 60 \times 60} = \frac{2\pi R\theta}{1296000} \quad \cdots \quad (1)$$

Transpose (1) and
$$R = \frac{1296000x}{2\pi\theta} \quad \cdots \cdots \quad (2)$$

If the length of the block $= L$ and it is tilted about its centre through θ seconds of arc, then

$$H = \frac{xL}{R} \text{ for small angles} \quad \cdots \cdots \quad (3)$$

But from (2) substituting for R

$$H = \frac{xL2\pi\theta}{1296000x} = \frac{2\pi\theta L}{1296000} \quad \cdots \cdots \quad (4)$$

Ex.—A level 10 in. long has a bubble movement of $\frac{1}{8}$ in. in an inclination of twenty seconds of arc. State the tube radius, and the packing to be placed under one end for a bubble movement of $\frac{1}{8}$ in.

From (2)
$$R = \frac{1296000}{2\pi \times 20 \times 8} = 1290 \text{ in.} = 107\cdot5 \text{ ft.}$$

From (4)
$$H = \frac{2\pi \times 10 \times 20}{1296000} = 0\cdot00097 \text{ in.}$$

An interesting application of the spirit level is shown diagrammatically in Fig. 173. It is desired to know the height of component A. It is placed on a flat, level surface close to slip-gauges nearly the same height. Two equal rollers are placed exactly 2 in. apart as shown. If the twenty-seconds level of the last example is used and the bubble moves one gradu-

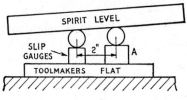

FIG. 173.

ation from the centre position, then the difference in height between the component and the slip-gauges is :

$$0\cdot00097 \times \frac{2}{10} = 0\cdot000194 \text{ in.}$$

If the whole set-up was turned through 180°, then the level would tilt the other way, thus doubling the bubble movement. In the **tilting level comparator** a much more sensitive level is used, and the dial is graduated directly to represent difference in height between two ball-points fixed to the base. The bubble movement is observed through a microscope.

A pile of slip-gauges is placed on the base together with the component to be measured. The level is lowered so that the ball-points rest on the component and the slip-gauges and the reading noted. The base is now rotated half a turn, and a further reading is taken. By this means the height of a component can be measured to one millionth of an inch.

CHAPTER XIX

GAUGES

WHERE a particular dimension has to be repeated many times—as for example in the turning of bars—gauges of standard sizes may replace micrometers. Such gauges will reduce the possibility of error, since no setting is required, as with the micrometer or vernier caliper.

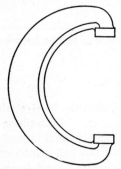

FIG. 174.—SNAP-GAUGE.

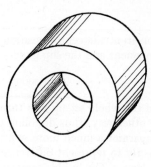

FIG. 175.—RING-GAUGE.

Fig. 174 shows a standard **snap-gauge**. The size must be "felt", as with the micrometer, and if the bar is machined incorrectly, then the gauge will not indicate the size. Such a gauge is a **checking device**, and

FIG. 176.

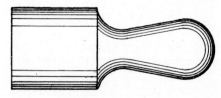

FIG. 177.—PLUG-GAUGE.

not a **measuring instrument**. It must itself be checked periodically against some datum, such as a set of slip-gauges.

The **ring-gauge** (Fig. 175) may be used for checking round bars. It has the disadvantage that it must be threaded over the end of the bar and it may give a "false fit" on oval work (see Fig. 176), but if a ring-gauge of a definite size—say 1 in. bore—is passed along a bar, it is an assurance that the bar is nowhere larger than 1 in. diameter; this could not be ascertained very quickly with a snap-gauge.

The **plug-gauge** (Fig. 177) is the companion to the ring-gauge. It is used for gauging bores; and again, its principal function is to determine that a hole is nowhere less than a given diameter. The **pin-gauge** (Fig. 178) is a plain bar, usually of steel, with conical ends; it is useful for large bores, where a plug-gauge would be clumsy and expensive to make. The **taper plug gauge** (Fig. 179) is used to check conical holes; only the ends

FIG. 178.—PIN-GAUGE.

of the hole being checked can be examined visually, but such a gauge is usually smeared with prussian blue and the " bedding " between the hole and gauge surfaces is examined. It is difficult to measure the actual diameters of a tapered hole, since there are no parallel surfaces; however, if the maximum and minimum diameters of the plug-gauge are known, the lateral position of the gauge in the hole will indicate the hole diameters, as illustrated in the following example.

A plate 2 in. thick has a hole with sides inclined at 10° to the axis. A taper plug gauge 4 in. long—" fits " correctly in the hole and the small end

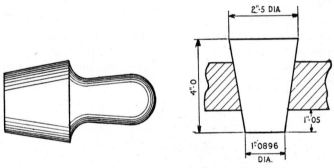

FIG. 179.—TAPER PLUG GAUGE.   FIG. 180.

protrudes 1·050 in. beyond the plate (see Fig. 180). The two ends of the gauge are 2·5 in. and 1·0896 in. diameter. What are the maximum and minimum diameters of the hole?

Tan 10° = 0·1763
Change in diameter per inch length = 0·1763 × 2 = 0·3526 in.
Small diameter of hole = 1·0896 + (0·3526 × 1·05) = 1·4598 in.
Large diameter of hole = 2·5 − (0·3526 × 0·95) = 2·165 in.

Profile Gauges

Gauges made from flat steel plate shaped to the contour of a component are used to check various outlines. Typical examples are the standard sets of internal and external radius-gauges and thread-pitch gauges.

M

Usually the check is made by examining the component and gauge silhouetted before a source of light. Fig. 181 shows a set of radius-gauges and Fig. 182 shows a set of thread-pitch gauges.

Receiver Gauges

A component may have many dimensions, most of which need not be very accurately maintained, but may still have a few dimensions which

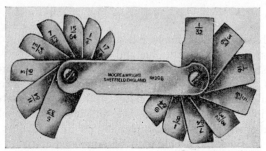

[*Moore and Wright, Ltd.*

FIG. 181.—RADIUS-GAUGES.

must be maintained very closely if the part is to function correctly. An example is shown in Fig. 183. If the component is to work correctly, the three dimensions shown must be very accurate. The 2·5-in. dimension can be checked quite easily with a snap-gauge, but for the two remaining dimensions the receiver gauge shown in Fig. 184 might be employed.

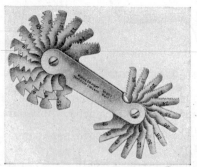

[*Moore and Wright, Ltd.*

FIG. 182.—THREAD-PITCH GAUGES.

Each component is placed on the pin A, which should be a close fit in the hole, and the radiused surface should just touch the end of the peg B at all points when the part is swung round on the pin. If desired, a dial indicator could be substituted for the peg B, so as to register the amount of deviation. Some receiver gauges have a number of dial indicators arranged at various points, so that many dimensions are checked at one time.

Material for Gauges

The most serviceable material for gauges is an oil-hardening alloy steel, and certain special " non-shrink " steels are manufactured. Plain carbon

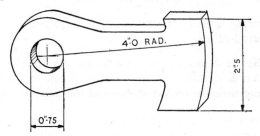

FIG. 183.

steel with about 0·8% carbon is often used, but with this steel there is considerably more danger of warping during quenching. With some gauges this warping may be corrected by grinding after hardening, but this will not counteract the tendency for further warping to occur, possibly over a period of months.

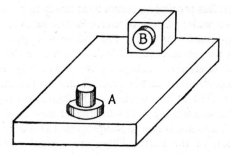

FIG. 184.—RECEIVER GAUGE.

In the workshop, temporary gauges, particularly those of large size, are often made from mild steel which is subsequently case hardened.

Wear of Gauges

A certain amount of wear on the gauging surfaces must take place every time a gauge is in use, and after some time this will interfere with the correct working. It is possible in some cases to regrind the gauge to another size, but a more satisfactory method is to deposit hard chromium on the gauge faces and regrind to the original size. The life of the gauge can thus be prolonged almost indefinitely; furthermore, the chromium surface is much more resistant to wear than is a hardened steel surface.

CHAPTER XX

LIMIT SYSTEMS

WHEN a drawing is being dimensioned, the draughtsman has to bear in mind two considerations.

1. What processes are available for making the part?
2. What deviation from the sizes given can be tolerated without interfering with the correct working of the part?

The first consideration often determines the design of the part, or, more precisely, the processes available in a works determine the product made. For example, the threaded portion of a micrometer spindle is made on special thread-grinding machines, whereas the thread for an ordinary bolt can be made in many ways; consequently the making of micrometers is confined to a few specialist firms.

Tolerance

In general, the less precisely a component needs to be made, the cheaper it will be, since a wider variety of methods will be available and the less skill will be required to make it. For this reason, part drawings should always state the maximum permissible deviation from the given dimension. This is termed **tolerance**. Tolerance is always required to allow for unavoidable imperfections in the product due to the methods of manufacture and the skill of the worker. The blacksmith may be given a tolerance of $\frac{1}{8}$ in. on a forging. The toolmaker may be given 0·0002 in. on a gauge. The difference is due to the processes available for manufacture and the function of the part. There are several systems of marking tolerances on part drawings; the most common is as follows.

Suppose a shaft is to be 2·0 in. diameter and the maximum tolerance is to be 0·002 in. The shaft diameter will be dimensioned: $2''{\cdot}0 \begin{array}{c} + \text{ 0·001} \\ - \text{ 0·001} \end{array}$.

The top limiting size is thus 2·001 in. and the bottom limiting size is 1·999 in. If circumstances permitted, the same tolerance could be used to give a size $2''{\cdot}0 \begin{array}{c} + \text{ 0·002} \\ - \text{ 0·000} \end{array}$, thus altering both limiting sizes. It should be noted that in the second case one of the limiting sizes coincides with the nominal size—i.e., with 2·0 in.—and no part smaller than this is acceptable. When the limiting sizes are arranged in this manner they are said to be **unilateral limits**, as the tolerance is on one side of the nominal size. When the two limits are one on each side of the nominal size, they are said to be **bilateral**. The following further examples of unilateral and bilateral limits will illustrate the point ; all have 0·002 in. tolerance.

Unilateral limits.	Bilateral limits.
$2''\!\cdot\!0{+0\cdot0025 \atop +0\cdot0005}$	$2''\!\cdot\!0\ {+0\cdot0015 \atop -0\cdot0005}$
$2''\!\cdot\!0{+0\cdot004 \atop +0\cdot002}$	$2''\!\cdot\!0\ {+0\cdot0005 \atop -0\cdot0015}$
$2''\!\cdot\!0{-0\cdot000 \atop -0\cdot002}$	$1''\!\cdot\!997{+0\cdot001 \atop -0\cdot001}$
$2''\!\cdot\!0{-0\cdot001 \atop -0\cdot003}$	$2''\!\cdot\!003{+0\cdot001 \atop -0\cdot001}$

From these examples the following points should be noted.

1. In unilateral limits **both** limiting sizes can be over or under the nominal size.

2. In bilateral limits the tolerance does not necessarily extend **equally** on each side of the nominal size.

3. When the dimension required is slightly different from an even dimension, this can be accommodated in unilateral limits in many cases by altering the limit positions, but with bilateral limits the nominal size must be amended.

Allowance

Consider the case of the 2·0-in. shaft already mentioned, and suppose that a bush was to be bored so that the shaft could revolve in it. If seizure is not to occur, there must be clearance between the shaft and the hole to give room for lubricant and for expansion of the shaft if it should heat up. An **allowance** must therefore be made to ensure this clearance. It might be decided that the clearance must not be less than 0·002 in. Now, this could be arranged in many ways, depending on the limits used, but below two ways of doing it are given, one with unilateral limits and one with bilateral limits.

	Hole size.	Shaft size.
Unilateral	$1''\!\cdot\!9995{+0\cdot001 \atop -0\cdot000}$	$2''\!\cdot\!0\ {-0\cdot0025 \atop -0\cdot0035}$
Bilateral	$2''\!\cdot\!0\ {+0\cdot0005 \atop -0\cdot0005}$	$1''\!\cdot\!997{+0\cdot0005 \atop -0\cdot0005}$

Setting out the dimensions in full, we have the following :

Hole Size : 1·9995 in. minimum, 2·0005 in. maximum.
Shaft Size : 1·9965 in. minimum, 1·9975 in. maximum.
The maximum clearance is therefore 2·0005 − 1·9965 = 0·004 in.
The minimum clearance is therefore 1·9995 − 1·9975 = 0·002 in.

It will be noted that the hole size has been kept as close as possible to the nominal size, and the allowance placed on the shaft. This is termed working on a **hole basis**, and is usual ; the opposite method—i.e., placing the allowance on the hole—is termed working on a **shaft basis**, and is not commonly practised. In most workshops there are far more flexible processes for machining and measuring shafts than for holes, consequently the hole basis is much more convenient, as it restricts the variation in hole sizes to very narrow limits.

Types of Fit

The three types of fit are as follows :

1. **Interference fits**, where the shaft is always larger than the hole.
2. **Transition fits**, where the shaft may be slightly larger or slightly smaller than the hole and still be within the limits.
3. **Clearance fits**, where the shaft is always smaller than the hole.

If a pulley, gear-wheel or similar part is to be a tight fit on a shaft, then the limits must be arranged to give an interference fit. For example, if the wheel is dimensioned $2''\cdot 0 \begin{array}{c} + \ 0\cdot000 \\ - \ 0\cdot0005 \end{array}$ in the bore, then the shaft might be dimensioned $2''\cdot 0 \begin{array}{c} + \ 0\cdot001 \\ + \ 0\cdot0005 \end{array}$. An interference fit would be obtained, the maximum interference being 0·0015 in. and the minimum interference 0·0005 in. It will be realised that the force required to press in the shaft will be much greater with the maximum interference ; for this reason the modern tendency is to specify very close limits for both hole and shaft when interference fits are required. The development of accurate grinding machines has been an important factor in this matter.

Many students who have still to obtain practical experience of the matter have great difficulty in appreciating the result of an interference fit ; they feel that it is impossible to place a shaft in a hole if the hole is slightly smaller than the shaft. It is trusted that the following explanation may help them ; if possible, the proof should be verified by personal study. The author freely acknowledges the source of explanation ; it is set out lucidly in " The Strength of Materials " by A. Morley (Messrs. Longmans, Green & Co.) ; the adaptation is crude, but, it is hoped, effective.

Suppose a steel ring 2·0 in. bore 4·0 in. outside diameter and 2·0 in. deep is to be placed on a steel shaft 2·001 in. diameter. The shaft will be compressed slightly and the hole in the ring will be expanded a little. Let us consider the stresses in the ring.

Let f = maximum hoop stress in ring

        A = allowance per inch diameter = 0·0005 in.

        K = ratio : $\dfrac{\text{outer diameter of ring}}{\text{bore of ring}} = 2$

        E = Modulus of elasticity for steel = 13,000 tons

Then $f = EA\ \dfrac{(K^2 + 1)}{(2K^2)}$

(It should be noted that for various values of K, the limits are $f = EA$ and $f = \dfrac{EA}{2}$).

In this case
$$f = 13000 \times 0{\cdot}0005 \times \tfrac{5}{8}$$
$$= 4{\cdot}06 \text{ tons per sq. in.}$$

This is quite a reasonable value for steel.

Now consider the gripping pressure (p)

$$p = EA\,\frac{(K^2 - 1)}{(2K^2)}$$

(Note that when $f = EA$, then $p = 0$, and when $f = \dfrac{EA}{2}$, then $p = \dfrac{EA}{2}$).

$$p = 13000 \times 0{\cdot}0005 \times \tfrac{3}{8}$$
$$= 2{\cdot}44 \text{ tons/sq. in.}$$

The total area of the bore of the ring

$$= 2 \times \pi \times 2$$
$$= 12{\cdot}5 \text{ sq. in.}$$

The total load on the bore $= 12{\cdot}5 \times 2{\cdot}44 = 30{\cdot}5$ tons.

Suppose that the ring is already in position on the shaft and we require to know the load necessary to force it off again. It will be necessary to assume a coefficient of friction between the two surfaces. Let us assume that this will be 0·25.

The total load to move the shaft in the ring will be

$$30{\cdot}5 \times 0{\cdot}25 = 7{\cdot}625 \text{ tons.}$$

Such a load could be applied very easily by a mechanical or a hydraulic press. In placing the shaft inside the ring the press could again be used, in which case, if flake graphite were applied to the shaft and the ring-bore, the load on the press would be considerably less than 7·625 tons, and the two would part again just as easily. An alternative would be to heat up the ring in hot oil to, say, 150° C., when it would slip into place and grip the shaft as it cooled. When the ring was quite cold, the stress and gripping pressure already calculated would apply.

The preceding explanation may also serve to answer the question as to what occurs when a 1-in. plug-gauge is inserted in a 1-in. ring-gauge, and to explode the fallacy that they will instantly seize. If both gauges are exactly equal in size (a highly improbable condition), then the ring cannot be stretched, the allowance is nil, the hoop stress is therefore nil, and so is the gripping pressure. Generally, we may expect the plug-gauge to be a few millionths of an inch **larger** than the ring-gauge, so that a moderate push will send the plug-gauge through the ring-gauge. Careful experiments have demonstrated that this is quite true.

Seizure of a ring-gauge on a plug-gauge does occur sometimes ; it is due to some careless person leaving the two together for a long time in a damp atmosphere. The two smooth surfaces are in very close proximity, and when corrosion occurs the iron oxide is mutual to them both. When an attempt is made to part the gauges, the oxide film " galls " and scores the surfaces, which cannot then be parted without heavy pressure.

In cases where a shaft is to fit a hole with as little " shake " as possible, but no heavy gripping pressure is required, **transition fits** may be employed. If both a hole and a shaft are dimensioned $2''\cdot 0 \begin{array}{l} + \ 0\cdot 000 \\ - \ 0\cdot 0005 \end{array}$, then either an interference or a clearance of 0·0005 in. is possible, although it is unlikely that the two extreme cases will meet, and the majority of assemblies will have very light clearances or interferences.

Clearance fits vary considerably, since much depends on the duty of the parts and the methods of manufacture. A high-speed shaft may have to rotate without danger of seizure, but yet without the slightest unnecessary clearance : many such cases are encountered in machine tools.

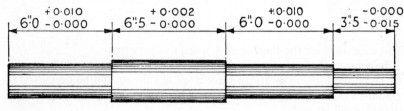

$$6''\cdot 0 \begin{array}{l} + 0\cdot 010 \\ - 0\cdot 000 \end{array} \qquad 6''\cdot 5 \begin{array}{l} + 0\cdot 002 \\ - 0\cdot 000 \end{array} \qquad 6''\cdot 0 \begin{array}{l} + 0\cdot 010 \\ - 0\cdot 000 \end{array} \qquad 3''\cdot 5 \begin{array}{l} - 0\cdot 000 \\ - 0\cdot 015 \end{array}$$

FIG. 185.

In other cases it may be only a question of ensuring adequate clearance— e.g., an ordinary black bolt in a hole in a pipe-flange. The lathe spindle or other machine-tool part will be finished to the closest limits and smoothest possible surface, and similarly with the bearing in which it fits : the bolt will be hot forged in a die and the hole drilled as quickly as possible, with little regard to smoothness or slight variations in diameter.

In the case of clearance fits it is important to understand the difference between a large allowance and a large tolerance. Consider a bush bored $2''\cdot 0 \begin{array}{l} + \ 0\cdot 001 \\ - \ 0\cdot 000 \end{array}$. If the shaft has an allowance of 0·010 in. and a tolerance of 0·001 in., then it could be dimensioned $2''\cdot 0 \begin{array}{l} - \ 0\cdot 010 \\ - \ 0\cdot 011 \end{array}$ and the maximum and minimum clearances would be 0·012 in. and 0·010 in. respectively. By altering the allowance to 0·001 in. and the tolerance to 0·010 in., the dimension could be written $2''\cdot 0 \begin{array}{l} - \ 0\cdot 001 \\ - \ 0\cdot 011 \end{array}$, thus giving a minimum clearance of only 0·001 in. There are certain instances where a large allowance must be accompanied by a small tolerance.

The reader will have noted one point not yet mentioned. In calculations involving limits it is necessary to add the tolerances together, even when the dimensions are subtracted.   For this reason care is required when a part drawing is being dimensioned.   Consider the shaft shown in Fig. 185. The overall length may vary between 21·985 in. and 22·022 in., a tolerance of 0·037 in.   If the job had been dimensioned from one end, the principal difficulty would be in keeping the 6·5-in. dimension within close limits, as is required.   The remedy is to dimension from one end of the 6·5-in.

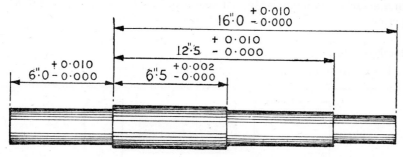

FIG. 186.

dimension as shown in Fig. 186.   The reader should calculate for himself that the tolerance on the 3·5-in. dimension is now 0·020 in. and the same tolerance applies to the overall length.

Surface Finish

Another important point in connection with close fits is that of surface finish.   This question has received much attention in recent years, but there is only space here for a very brief discussion.   When a shaft has been turned the surface may be somewhat as shown in Fig. 187.   On measuring this surface the anvil of the measuring instrument makes contact with the crests of the waves, and this is the size indicated.   In service these crests may quickly wear away, thus altering the fit considerably.

The configuration of these waves is important, since sharp waves will wear more than shallow ones, and large waves will have to wear to a considerable

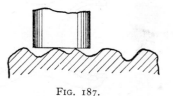

FIG. 187.

extent before a large proportion of the surface makes contact.   Different methods of machining produce different wave-shapes, and two important facts have been discovered.   In the first place, the heavier the cutting pressure, the more the surface layer of metal will be distorted and weakened.   Secondly, the largest waves are produced by blunt cutting tools at low speeds.   Two methods are used to obtain a smooth surface. With normal cutting tools high speeds and light cuts are required, but in most cases the very smooth surfaces are produced by special finishing processes, such as lapping and honing.

The presence of weakened and distorted metal near the surface has been discovered by means of the microscope, but surface waviness can be measured by several different types of instrument. Generally, the method used is to produce a greatly magnified picture of the surface.

When a smooth, undistorted surface is required, this can be ensured by stating the limit of surface waviness that can be tolerated. This is done in a manner rather similar to that shown in Fig. 129—i.e., the maximum permissible deviation from a true plane may be stated.

Limit Gauges

If full advantage is to be obtained from a limit system it is essential to

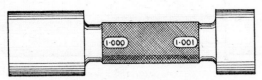

FIG. 188.—LIMIT PLUG-GAUGE.

use limit gauges whenever possible, as the checking of work can be done more positively and more quickly with limit gauges than with adjustable measuring instruments. The limit plug-gauge (Fig. 188) and the limit snap-gauges shown in Fig. 189 are the commonest types.

The plug-gauge has a long " go " end made to the lower limit and a short " not go " end made to the upper limit. This difference in length

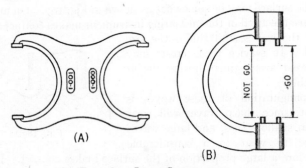

FIG. 189.—LIMIT SNAP-GAUGES.

helps in rapid identification of each end ; furthermore, since the " not go " end should not enter the hole, a long gauging surface is unnecessary.

The double-ended snap-gauge A in Fig. 189 is used for the smaller sizes ; for larger dimensions the double-anvil type B is preferred. The outer anvils are set to the " go " or top dimension, and the inner anvils to the " not go " or bottom dimension. With the double-anvil type a certain amount of adjustment is usually possible, and the gauge can be set for different limits. Furthermore, adjustment can be made for wear.

The question of wear is important in limit gauges, and it is usual to arrange for the workshop gauges to be slightly "inside the limits", so that a small amount of wear is permissible without passing bad work. The inspectors' gauges are made correct size. This arrangement lends itself to the gauge rota system practised in many large works. A new gauge is always made "inside the limits", and is first used in the work-

shop. After a certain amount of wear has occurred it becomes an inspection gauge for a while, but when further wear definitely places it "outside the limits" it is chromium plated on the wearing surfaces, and reground "inside the limits" for further use as a workman's gauge. By this means the workman is not given the full tolerance shown on the drawing, although the amount lost rarely exceeds 10% of the tolerance. In any case, doubtful work will usually be sent forward for inspection, and there it will be checked by gauges which are "on the limits", or possibly even slightly outside them.

The question of "feel" arises quite frequently with limit gauges, and a snap-gauge can easily be sprung in forcing it on to the work. The correct procedure in most cases is to let the weight of the gauge rest on the work; if this is not suffi- cient to cause engagement, the work should be sent back for adjustment.

[*E. H. Jones, Machine Tools, Ltd.*

FIG. 190.—"SIGMA" COMPARATOR.

The comparator principle has already been mentioned, and is illustrated in Fig. 158; where components are being produced to fine limits, com- parators are almost essential. Unskilled labour can be used for rapid, accurate checking, and it is not necessary for the operator to know the actual limiting sizes. The comparator is set by a skilled man, and "limit marks" for the finger are clearly set out. The operator simply throws out any component which does not give a reading between the two marks.

Fig. 190 shows a comparator for precision inspection. The total range of measurement in any one position is ± 0.003 in. The small marks, which are $\frac{1}{10}$ in. apart, each represent 0.0001 in., and thus a difference in height of 0·000025 in. can be detected. The head can be moved on the column to admit work up to 6 in., 9 in., 12 in. or 20 in., according to the particular model used. The large screw at the back locks the head in any desired position. The measuring table can also be moved upwards slightly and locked by the lever in the base.

The two white pointers are limit marks which can be adjusted by the knobs on the front of the head. The small knob on the side of the head is used to make very small adjustments of the measuring scale. The trigger, which can be seen just below the large screw, lifts the plunger clear whilst the work is inserted. The actual indicating finger can be seen at the bottom left-hand corner of the scale.

The whole instrument is quite robust and suitable for workshop inspection purposes. It is " dead beat " in operation—i.e., the finger does not oscillate, thus enabling quick checking to be done.

Even more refined comparators than this are manufactured. Some will detect a difference of 0·000001 in. These are intended for laboratories and metrology departments.

CHAPTER XXI

MARKING OUT AND THE LOCATION OF WORK

WHEN a casting or forging is received for machining it will be larger than the finished size by an amount known as the **machining allowance**; furthermore, holes too small or too intricate for forging or founding may be required. The article is therefore **marked out.** This is done by scribing lines to indicate the position and extent of the necessary machining.

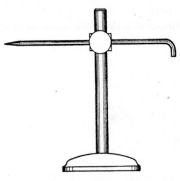

FIG. 191.—SCRIBING BLOCK.

To carry out this work certain datum planes are required. The common datum is the surface plate or " marking-out table " which was described in Chapter XVII. A number of instruments and fixtures are used for marking, measuring or holding the work. The try-square is used to set up machined surfaces at right angles to the surface plate, and also to serve as a guide for a hardened steel scriber with which lines are marked. The scribing block or surface gauge (Fig. 191) is used to scribe lines which will be parallel to the surface plate, and the hooked end of its scriber is

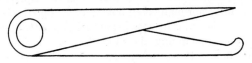

FIG. 192.

used to check relative heights from the surface plate. Scribing compasses of several sizes are required, and also hermaphrodite compasses or " jennies." These latter are shown in Fig. 192. The centre punch (Fig. 193) is used to

FIG. 193.

make the light punch-marks which define important lines and their intersections.

Two common fixtures are the angle plate which holds work at right angles to the surface plate, and the vee-blocks which are used in pairs to hold cylindrical work so that its axis is parallel to the surface plate.

For rough castings and forgings it is usual to chalk the surfaces to give a background for the scribed lines, but for smooth machined work the surfaces are rubbed with prussian blue or with copper sulphate solution. This latter solution leaves a thin coating of copper on the work.   For the finest marking out it is best to clean the work, wipe on a little oil, and polish with a clean rag.   A hard scriber will then make fine smooth lines on most machined surfaces except hard steel.   Non-ferrous metals usually scribe quite readily.   It has been mentioned that lines for machining are ruled ; but another important function of marking out is to try up the casting or forging to see that it is machined to the best advantage.   For this reason the work is laid out from the part drawing, the centre lines being

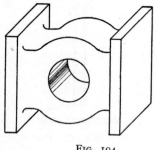

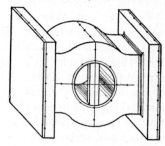

FIG. 194.   FIG. 195.

scribed and centre punched, and the machining lines measured from these centre lines.

Consider the casting shown in Fig. 194.   The two square end faces are to be machined, and the rough cored hole must be bored so that its centre is 5·0 in. from each face and its axis is parallel to the two faces.   There is intended to be $\frac{1}{8}$-in. machining allowance on each face and $\frac{1}{4}$-in. on the diameter of the hole.   If the machinist recklessly machines both faces equally and obtains an overall length of 10·0 in., he may discover later that the rough hole has been cast out of centre, and cannot then be bored to give the 5·0-in. dimensions.   A preliminary marking out would reveal the eccentricity of the hole, which could then be allowed for by distributing the machining to suit.

The method of marking out would be as follows.   Place the casting on one end-face on the surface plate.   With hooked end of the scribing block make sure that the top face is reasonably parallel with the surface plate : some packing or wedging from the plate may be required.   In the centre hole knock in a wooden " false centre " at each side.   With the " jennies " find the centre of the cored hole, and mark it at each side on the false centres.   With the pointed end of the finger of the scribing block, make sure that the centre at each side is the same height from the plate ; if this is not so, then adjust the centres a little, or tilt the casting slightly, or make both adjustments, depending on what will best suit the final machining.

When the final setting has been decided, firmly mark the centre line at each side with the scribing block and centre-punch it. Lower the scribing-

FIG. 196.—MARKING SHAFT CENTRE.

block point 5·0 in. and scribe the machining mark all round the edge of the lower square face and centre-punch it. Raise the scribing-block point 10·0 in., scribe round the edge of the upper square face and centre-punch it. Mark the circle for boring the centre hole. The completely marked-out casting is shown in Fig. 195.

The use of vee-blocks is illustrated in the marking out of a keyway in a shaft. The shaft is placed in vee-blocks which are known to be a pair.

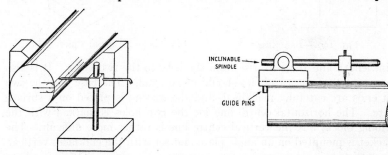

FIG. 197.—MARKING OUT
THE KEYWAY.

FIG. 198.—MARKING OUT END
OF KEYWAY.

The height of the shaft from the plate can be tried at each end by the scribing-block hooked end. If the shaft has no centre marks in the ends these can be made with the jennies, or four lines can be scribed with the scribing block, the shaft being turned through 90° after each line is scribed. The alternative methods are shown in Fig. 196.

From the centre, a centre line is now drawn to the edge and continued along the shaft. Small dividers are set to half the keyway width and two part circles scribed. These part circles are now used to set the scribing block, and the upper and lower edges of the keyway are marked. The shaft is now as shown in Fig. 197. The try-square is used to mark the depth of the keyway. If the shaft is short it may be stood on end so that the inner end of the keyway may be scribed with the scribing block, otherwise a special type of scribing block with guide-pins and an inclinable spindle may be used, as shown in Fig. 198. The base is V-shaped, to rest on the shaft.

It is often advisable to machine some faces of a casting before marking out other important dimensions. The machined faces, which must be chosen carefully and machined with due regard to the final dimensions, are then used as datum faces.

The bracket shown in Fig. 199 has two important dimensions: the

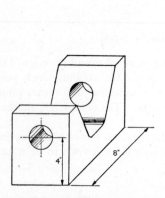

FIG. 199.—BRACKET.

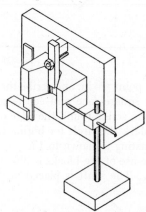

FIG. 200.—MARKING CENTRE LINE.

8 in. length and the 4 in. rise from the base to the two holes. It is also important that the two holes should be co-axial. The base and the two flat ends are carefully machined, and the casting is placed on a surface plate. The horizontal centre line for the two holes is marked with the scribing block, but the vertical centre line is rather more difficult. The bracket is mounted on an angle plate and set with the end faces vertical, this setting being done with a try-square (see Fig. 200). The centre lines can then be drawn with the scribing block.

Accuracy of Marking Out

Ordinary marking out is done with a rule, and the limitations of the rule have already been mentioned. Several other factors tend to lower the accuracy still further: the width of a scribed line may be anything from 0·003 in. to 0·010 in.; the accuracy of punched intersections is often not very good, and cumulative errors arise. Over short lengths on flat surfaces an accuracy of 0·010 in. can be maintained, but with angled surfaces and lengths of a few feet the maximum accuracy may be no better than 0·050 in.

When a high degree of accuracy is required, methods other than plain marking out become essential. Certain of these methods will be described later.

Co-ordinates

Two systems of co-ordinate measurement are used in engineering : **polar co-ordinates** are distances measured along radial lines from a common centre. The three holes shown in Fig. 201 are dimensioned in polar co-ordinates.

It is obvious that the accuracy with which the holes are positioned is dependent on correct setting out of the angles given and of the

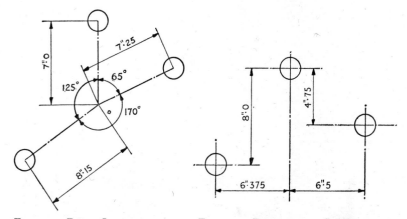

FIG. 201.—POLAR CO-ORDINATES.   FIG. 202.—RECTANGULAR CO-ORDINATES.

distances from the common centre : as the distance from the centre increases, slight angular errors will cause greater displacement of the holes.

The possibility of error is lessened by the use of **rectangular co-ordinates** ; the three holes shown in Fig. 202 are set out by this method. The holes are now dimensioned relative to two centre lines at right angles to each other. In practice it is often possible to use flat-machined surfaces in preference to centre lines, and in such cases the measuring instruments used can be end standards instead of line standards, thus simplifying the measurement. A further advantage is that the linear distances between hole centres can be calculated simply and checked readily.

The Jig-Boring Machine is a machine used for the precise setting out and boring of holes. A heavy column carries a boring head which can be adjusted up and down the column, and is attached to a rigid base (see Fig. 203). The boring-spindle is mounted in special bearings to prevent any deflection, and is placed exactly at right angles to the work-table.

N

FIG. 203.—THE "NEWALL" JIG-BORING MACHINE.

This spindle can be revolved and fed up and down, but no other movement is possible.

An enlarged view of the table is shown in Fig. 204. The table movement is in two horizontal directions exactly at right angles to each other, thus corresponding to rectangular co-ordinates. The movements are controlled by the two large hand-wheels attached to leadscrews, and small precise movements can thus be made. However, the measurement of motion is not dependent on leadscrews.

A large micrometer head is mounted over a vee-edged channel containing

[*Newall Engineering Co., Ltd.*

FIG. 204.—TABLE OF JIG-BORING MACHINE.

rollers. Each roller is accurate to 0·00002 in., and the accuracy of the roller spacing is of the same order. Each roller forms a datum point for setting the micrometer. Thus the table may be moved an exact number of inches relative to the rollers, and the remaining fraction of an inch is measured by the micrometer which reads to 0·0001 in. To eliminate "feel" in the micrometer reading, an indicator dial gauge is fixed to the machine table. The plunger of this gauge is in contact with the microm- eter spindle through a rocking lever. After the work has been correctly positioned in relation to the table, and clamped down, the table and cross- slide are moved until the spindle is accurately located in relation to the two right angular datum surfaces which have been chosen on the work. Then both the micrometer and the dial indicator are set to zero. To move to subsequent positions the micrometer carriage is placed on the required inch roller, the micrometer itself set to the decimal portion of the dimension, and the table moved until the dial indicator again reaches zero. It may also be noted that when a workpiece is being bored, the slightest movement of the table would be detected by the dial-gauge.

These machines are relatively expensive, but they provide a rapid way of setting out holes to an accuracy of 0·0001 in. In large tool-rooms they are indispensable. In addition, where the number of components required is relatively small but accuracy is essential, the jig-boring machine is often used as a production machine, thereby eliminating the need for complicated and costly jigs.

In many small tool-rooms, the setting out of holes to close limits is still carried out by means of toolmaker's buttons. This method is fairly

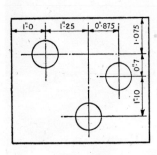

FIG. 205.

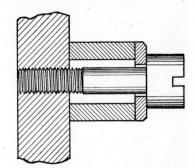

FIG. 206.—TOOLMAKER'S BUTTON.

accurate, but very slow compared with the jig-boring machine ; it is also much more dependent on individual skill.

Suppose three holes each 0·625 in. diameter are to be bored in a plate to the dimensions shown in Fig. 205. The sides A and B of the plate and the top surface will require to be machined flat and truly at right angles to each other. Three ¼-in. tapped holes are marked out, drilled and tapped, using a rule and any drilling machine. The toolmaker's button is a hollow cylinder carefully ground on the circumference and the ends. Three buttons are mounted as shown in Fig. 206, each one being lightly secured by its setscrew. Each button must now be set concentric with the desired position of the 0·625-in. hole. The movements are made by lightly tapping the buttons with a piece of wood—an operation which requires a good sense of touch and considerable patience. The measurement of the actual position is done by various means, according to circumstance ; but the commonest instruments are slip-gauges, vernier height-gauge or micrometer. An example is shown in Fig. 207. Here the button is being set by slip-gauges from a straight-edge at the edge of the work, allowance being made, of course, for half the button diameter. In similar circumstances the tool-fitter might prefer to stand the jig plate on its edge on a surface plate and then use the vernier height-gauge.

When all the buttons have been correctly positioned and the holding screws firmly secured, the plate is ready for machining. If the plate is of reasonable size, it is mounted on a centre lathe and fixed with one button on the lathe centre line—i.e., when the plate revolves in the lathe, the button runs truly. The method of checking has already been illustrated

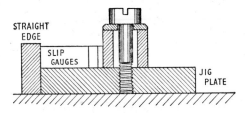

FIG. 207.—SETTING A BUTTON.

in Fig. 164. This is an assurance that the proposed hole is concentric with the lathe centre line. The button is removed and a 0·625-in.-diameter hole is bored. Each button in turn is brought on the lathe centre line, removed, and the corresponding hole drilled.

The reader will remember that the original tapped hole for the button-setting screw was marked out by rule, and will not be concentric with the final hole. Therefore, in boring the hole the following procedure is adopted: the original threaded hole is opened out with a short drill to, say, ½ in. diameter, this drill following the tapped hole to some extent. A small boring tool is now used to open out the hole, and with a number of light cuts the final hole is brought to the desired centre.

A common tool-room problem is the boring of holes spaced out equally round a circle. This may be done on the jig-boring machine if a circular dividing table is available, but the disc-and-button method is also practised.

For example, let us say that eight holes are to be bored very accurately at 45° to each other on a 8·25-in.-diameter pitch circle. Eight buttons each 0·600-in. diameter are available. A mild steel disc 7·650-in. diameter and about ½ in. thick is turned on a lathe.

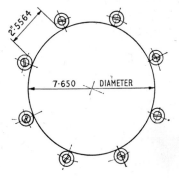

FIG. 208.

This is placed on the work which has already been marked out by rule and compasses and has eight ¼-in. Whitworth tapping holes. The disc and buttons are arranged as shown in Fig. 208. The polar distances of 4·125 in. are thus fixed automatically by keeping the buttons in contact with the disc. The chordal distance of 2·5564 in. is set by slip-gauges. In some cases the centre of the eight holes must be very accurately placed; if so, the disc must have a central hole, and it is then set by slip-gauges or other instrument and secured to the work in the same way as a button.

In cases where the work is too large to be manœuvred on a lathe it may be placed on a vertical milling machine, or even a good radial drilling

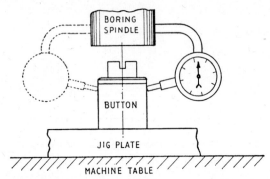

FIG. 209.—CENTERING MACHINE SPINDLE OVER BUTTON.

machine, and each button brought directly under the boring spindle as shown in Fig. 209. The dial-gauge should give the same reading throughout a revolution of the boring spindle.

Jigs

The example just discussed is typical of many simple drill jigs. Bolt- and stud-holes arranged in a circle are a very common feature of engineering components. The continual marking out of these holes is avoided by the

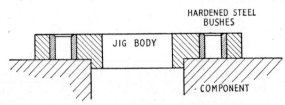

FIG. 210.—DRILL JIG.

use of a jig. This is a flat plate which is arranged to lie on the face of the work and has some device for correct positioning. The jig has holes spaced out accurately, and these are used to guide the drill to the correct position. It is usual to insert very hard steel bushes in the holes, so that the drill will not enlarge them. A section through a simple plate-jig is shown in Fig. 210. It will be noted that this jig has a spigot which fits in a bore in the work, thus ensuring concentricity. If the holes have to be disposed correctly relative to a centre line, then either this centre line must be marked on the work and the jig or, alternatively, a projection on the work must engage a slot in the jig, or vice versa.

The use of jigs is not confined to drilling operations on a flat component; in mass-production work elaborate and costly jigs may be used to control a wide variety of machining operations. These only become economically feasible when large numbers of identical parts are being made.

The advantages of jigs may be summarised as follows :

1. Marking out and other measuring and setting-out methods are eliminated.

2. Unskilled workers may proceed confidently and quickly, knowing that the jig will guide and control the cutting tool.

3. The assembly of parts is facilitated, since all components will be identical, and much " trying " and filing of work is eliminated.

4. Parts will be strictly interchangeable, and if the product is sold over a wide area, the problem of spare parts will be simplified.

Bolt holes often have $\frac{1}{16}$-in. or even $\frac{1}{8}$-in. clearance for the bolt, and the student may doubt the necessity of making precision jigs for such work. It must be remembered that the jig, once made, will be used on many components, and the extra cost of an accurately made jig is spread over a large output. Furthermore, it is surprising how small errors accumulate in a mechanism during assembly. When a clearance is specified, it is better to ensure its observance, rather than to allow careless marking out and machining to encroach upon it.

Location of Work

The Six-point Principle is of great importance in the location of work for machining. This principle states that any body which is not constrained is capable of motion in six directions, and cannot be constrained completely unless contact is made with it at not less than six points.

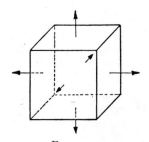

FIG. 211.

In the case of the cube shown in Fig. 211 these motions may be stated as : up or down, left or right, backwards or forwards. If each side of the cube abuts on an immovable face, then movement (except distortion) is impossible. In workshop practice, when work is to be done on a component, all unwanted motion must be prevented. Engineering components are usually irregular in shape, and the unwanted motions may not be at right angles to each other ; but the principle still holds. Movements can be resolved in three planes at right angles to each other.

The size and position of the faces of the component will determine which shall be used as abutting faces to prevent motion. When a number of operations are to be performed, some changes in the abutment faces may have to be made to leave particular faces clear for machining, but such changes should be avoided as far as possible, as they confuse the logical sequence of events and leave loopholes for inaccuracy. Many castings and forgings have a large, flat face machined as a first operation. This face is used as a datum, and all subsequent operations are related to it.

The continual resetting of a component for various machining operations is a common source of error, as the previously machined faces have to be set in relation to the new operation. This difficulty has led to the development of machines which perform a number of operations; when the component has to be machined at a new point it is not released, but instead a portion of the machine tool is moved to the appropriate position. This entails very accurate workmanship in the machine tool, since the movable portions must be located exactly in each position, but it is much simpler to do this once when making the machine tool than to do it each time a fresh component is worked upon.

Clamping Work

Whilst the six-point principle is followed closely in jig practice, it is not always convenient in the workshop, where components of various shapes and sizes follow each other. It is only necessary to watch the work passing through a radial drilling machine to realise the inconvenience of attempting to work strictly to the six-point principle.

Instead of a series of solid abutments, friction is often relied upon to prevent motion, and the component is gripped firmly in some fixture such as a lathe chuck. Where gripping pressure is relied upon, the following information is required :

1. The direction and intensity of the cutting forces.
2. The frictional resistance set up by the gripping pressure.
3. The maximum permissible gripping force relative to the component and the clamping device—i.e., the rigidity of the component and the strength of the clamps. In regard to this point it may be noted that one of the commonest troubles in precision machining is that the clamps distort the work, which is carefully machined, but goes slightly out of shape when the clamps are released. For this reason, much work has to be scraped or lapped up by hand after machining. The modern tendency is to finish a component by a process which has a low cutting force—e.g., grinding, honing, super-finishing—and which thus allows the work to be gripped very lightly.

During the nineteenth century it was considered axiomatic that the slide-ways of machine tools must be scraped up by hand, even after the most careful machining, since the machine clamps would cause distortion :

of recent years the practice of grinding machine slide-ways has become common, but this work is usually performed without any clamping of the castings, thus avoiding distortion.   One great advantage of the ground slide-way is that it can be hardened to give better wearing properties.   As a matter of interest, it may be mentioned that there is fierce difference of opinion as to the relative merits of ground and hand-scraped slide-ways ; like most technical arguments where experts are dogmatically and diametrically opposed to each other, the truth probably lies half-way between the two extremes.   It can be said with certainty that both ground and hand-scraped slide-ways are in successful use.

CHAPTER XXII

METAL-CUTTING TOOLS

FIG. 212 is a cross-section of a simple metal-cutting tool. The surface XY is termed the tool breast or cutting face. Angle A is sometimes called the **breast angle,** B is called the **wedge angle** and C the **clearance angle.** The three angles together total 90°. The chip of metal slides along the tool

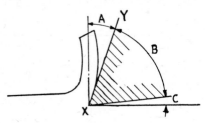

FIG. 212.

breast and is curled away from it; this action causes considerable wear of the tool. The cleavage of metal is initiated at the point X, and the sharpness of this edge is of great importance. Reducing the angle B will increase the sharpness, but will reduce the strength of the wedge. Vari-

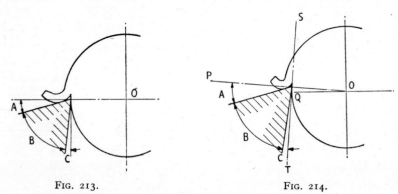

FIG. 213.   FIG. 214.

ations in the angle B are made by altering angle A, the clearance angle C is not varied to any great extent.

Fig. 213 illustrates the cutting of a bar rotating about its centre O. The top edge of the tool is shown on the horizontal centre line of the work. This does not always apply in practice, the top edge is frequently placed slightly above the centre line. This latter position is illustrated in Fig. 214

in an exaggerated form. The angles A, B, C, are now related to the tangent ST to the point of contact and a radial line OP passing through this point. The effect of raising the tool will be to reduce the angle C and increase the angle A. The clearance angle must be sufficient to prevent rubbing of the front of the tool on the work. If the maximum value for angle POQ is, say, $3°$, then the clearance angle C could be made $6°$.

The discussion up to this point has assumed that the cutting edge is wider than the work—a condition rarely encountered in practice. When the work is wider than the tool, then the total cut must be divided into a number of passes, this being done by means of a **feed motion**. Fig. 215 shows a planing tool. The cutting motion is at right angles to the paper— i.e., in the direction of the reader. The cutting edge, which is curved at the tip, extends from J to L, but only the portion JK is engaged; the length JK is determined by the **depth of cut** D. The feed motion is given to the tool just before the commencement of each cutting stroke. Thus

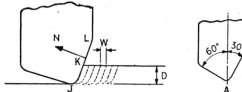

FIG. 215.   FIG. 216.—TOOL-NOSE PLAN ANGLES.

the metal is removed in parallel strips, the distance W being the width of cut or **feed per stroke**.

The principal cutting edge is not, therefore, at the nose, but to one side of it, this side being determined by the direction of feed. The breast, wedge and tool angles are related to a cross-sectional plane at right angles to the cutting edge, and this plane is indicated by the arrow N. It will be noted that the plan angles on each side of the tool nose are not equal, the angle on the cutting side relative to the tool axis being much the greater. Generally, the angle of the cutting edge to the tool axis is not greater than $30°$, whilst the angle on the trailing side usually exceeds $60°$. For this reason, the tools are " handed ", and if the feed motion is in the opposite direction, an opposite handed tool is required. The tool shown in Fig. 215 is termed a **right-hand tool**.

Three plan angles are shown in Fig. 216. The tool at C is often termed a **knife-tool**, and it should be noted that the breast, wedge and clearance angles of this tool are measured at right angles to the tool axis. Knife tools usually have a very small tip or nose radius.

In the case of the lathe-tool, the work rotates and the feed is applied continuously. Consequently, the metal is removed in the form of a helix. The feed may be stated in one of two ways, either as a distance per revolution or the number of revolutions per inch of feed. In Fig. 217 W is the feed per revolution and D is the depth of cut. As before, the angles A, B and C are measured on the plane at right angles to the cutting edge. Since the tool is moving forward steadily, the clearance angle C (see Fig. 212) must be sufficient to clear the helical shape of the cut surface, and must therefore be increased with a large feed. For a bar 2 in. diameter, being machined with a feed of 0·1 in. per revolution, the tangent of the helix angle will be $\dfrac{0·1}{2\pi} = 0·0159$, and the minimum clearance angle will be 1°. In practice a clearance angle of 4—6° is commonly employed.

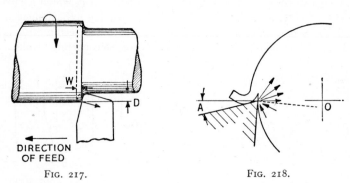

FIG. 217.   FIG. 218.

A considerable amount of research work has been done on metal cutting tools, the principal information sought being as follows.

    1. Maximum speed of metal removal.
    2. Maximum " life " of a tool between re-grinds.
    3. Minimum power consumption per unit of metal removed.
    4. Best surface finish obtainable.

All these objectives cannot necessarily be pursued at one time. For example, it is generally recognised that if metal is to be removed at the greatest possible speed, the tool will require frequent re-grinding. A decision in practice will involve investigating the total cost caused by re-grinding the particular tool. The most economical life for a tool-cutting edge may thus be as low as thirty minutes, or as high as 300 minutes actual cutting time.

The behaviour of the chip of metal parted from the work and the state of the parent metal close to the cut have been thoroughly investigated. The stresses set up in the work are shown in Fig. 218. The dotted line indicates the plane at which the stresses change from tensile to compressive. The angle made by this plane varies with the angle A of the tool.

The chip of metal is subjected to a very great compressive stress, and, as shown in Fig. 219, it is deflected sharply at the plane Q—P by the top face or breast of the tool. Owing to this stress, the chip is thickened and shortened about this plane. With brittle materials, the chips shear off at this plane (the discontinuous chip). With ductile materials, the chips flow along the tool breast in a deformed state (the continuous chip).

The Built-up Edge

It has been noted that in rough turning ductile materials a small quantity of material adheres to the tip of the tool, as shown in Fig. 220. This built-up edge, which is sometimes firmly welded to the tip of the tool, is constantly built up and broken down by the heavy sliding pressure

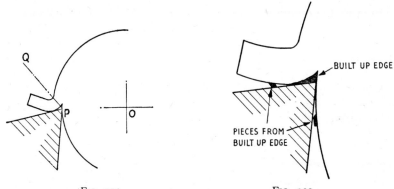

FIG. 219.   FIG. 220.

of the chip on the tool breast, pieces breaking away as shown. Under these conditions the loose pieces prevent the work from having a good surface finish. This fact may not be of great importance in rough turning, but in finishing operations it is essential to prevent the formation of a built-up edge.

The built-up edge is usually present when the machining is done at moderate speeds with a coarse feed; it is encouraged by the use of small breast angles and a dull cutting edge, and is associated with high friction between the chip and the tool breast. In finish-machining operations the best results are obtained by adherence to the following methods:

1. High cutting speeds.
2. Fine feeds.
3. Maximum breast angle.
4. Sharp cutting edges.
5. Minimum friction between chip and tool breast.

The use of the hard carbides of tungsten and titanium in the so-called " tipped tools " permits high cutting speeds to be used and prolongs the life of the cutting edge. Furthermore, the friction between the chip and the tool is low, providing a suitable grade of carbide is chosen. The inclusion of lead or manganese sulphide in the metal to be cut also reduces the friction between chip and tool. These inclusions are used in the free-cutting bars for capstan and automatic lathe work.

Suitable cutting fluids have a pronounced effect on metal cutting. They are used for three principal reasons.

1. To take away the heat generated by cutting, and thus prevent heating up and softening of the tool.

2. To reduce the friction between the tool and work.

3. To wash away the chips or swarf from the vicinity of the tool edge.

In order to perform the first of these functions, the fluid should have a high specific heat, and a water-base fluid is indicated. Such water-base solutions are prepared by adding certain soaps to water to form the familiar milky liquid. The second function is best done by an oil-base solution, usually with the addition of sulphur in some form. In this case the specific heat of the cutting fluid will be lower, but there will be much less possibility of the chip adhering to the tool breast. The material to be cut, and the type of machining to be done, will decide which of these two types is better in any particular case.

The water-base solutions are cheaper, but whichever is chosen, the following properties are important.

1. The fluid must not be injurious to the operator, and should not be offensive by smelling unpleasantly or marking clothing.

2. It must "keep" well, and must not make a chemical attack on the work, the machine tool, or the container in which it is kept.

The following are brief notes on the different engineering materials and the cutting fluids employed on them. Cast iron is turned, bored, milled and planed in the dry condition, as the graphite which it contains acts as a lubricant and breaks up the chips. Tapping and reaming of cast iron require a mineral oil. Mild steel is machined generally with a water-base solution, except that in some cases an oil-base solution is preferred for finish turning to give a better surface. Machine tapping and reaming, and deep boring operations, are best done with oil. Hand tapping is done with lard oil. Alloy steels, particularly the harder grades, usually require oil-base fluids for all normal machining work and lard oil for hand tapping and reaming ; rape oil is used for machine broaching. Brasses and bronzes require water-base solutions. Aluminium may be machined dry. If a water-base solution is used, care must be taken in selecting a suitable fluid, as aluminium is readily attacked by alkaline solutions.

Most metals are ground with water in which a little carbonate of soda has been dissolved.

In all cases a good flow of coolant is advisable, providing that it does not spoil the operator's view of the work. Occasional drops of water falling on a heated tool can easily cause it to crack. This is particularly important with the carbide-tipped tools (see later), and unless really good coolant flow can be arranged, dry cutting is best with these tools.

Materials for Cutting Tools

Plain high-carbon steel is still in use for some cutting tools, such as hand-taps, chisels and scrapers, whilst special tools which will be used only

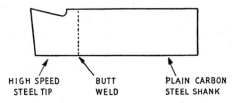

HIGH SPEED STEEL TIP   BUTT WELD   PLAIN CARBON STEEL SHANK

FIG. 221.—BUTT WELDED TOOL.

occasionally may be made in this material—e.g., "form tools" which can be made quickly and cheaply in plain high carbon steel and are easily heat treated.

[Taylor and Jones, Ltd.

FIG. 222.—TOOL-BIT IN HOLDER.

High-speed steel has been described in Chapter VI. It has ousted plain carbon steel for all general machine-shop tools. In order to reduce the cost, a high-speed steel " head " may be butt welded on to a plain medium-carbon steel shank as shown in Fig. 221. Another method of economising on expensive high-speed steels is to provide a **tool-bit holder**, as shown in Fig. 222. The holder is split, and contains internal springs which force the two halves slightly apart. There is a rectangular slot into which short pieces or " tool-bits " are placed. When the holder is clamped into the machine-tool post the tool-bit is firmly gripped in position, but a slight release of the clamp will allow the holder to spring apart, thus releasing the tool-bit for re-sharpening. Adaptors of L section are provided so that various rectangular tool-bits can be used.

Fig. 223 shows a typical " tipped tool ". The material of the tip is mainly a mixture of tungsten carbide, titanium carbide and cobalt. The first two materials are present in the form of extremely hard particles embedded in a cobalt matrix. This composite substance is expensive and brittle, and small tips are made by a " sintering " or baking process which causes the cobalt to form the matrix round the carbide particles.

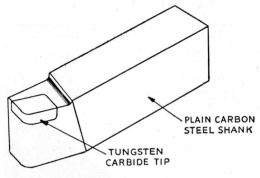

PLAIN CARBON STEEL SHANK

TUNGSTEN CARBIDE TIP

FIG. 223.—TIPPED TOOL.

They are then brazed on to the ends of plain carbon steel shanks which have a carefully shaped recess to receive the tip. Various grades are provided to suit different types of metal cutting. Originally only simple lathe tools were sold, but now many complicated tools, such as milling cutters and reamers, may have " tipped " cutting edges. Just as the high-speed steels superseded the plain high-carbon steels, so the carbide-tipped tools are now gradually replacing high-speed tools, as still higher cutting speeds are introduced. The metallic carbides are not heat treated in any way, and their hardness, even when heated to redness, is still higher than that of high-speed steel. They are rough ground on special silicon carbide wheels, but can be finish ground only on diamond-impregnated grinding wheels. The carbide-tipped tool definitely requires more care in use than the H.S.S. tool, and workers should be instructed accordingly.

The following table gives some indication of the relative cutting speeds for the three types of cutting tools when used in the centre lathe on three common engineering materials.

Type of tool.	Grey cast iron.	Mild steel.	Soft tool steel.
Plain high-carbon steel	20— 40	20— 40	10— 20
High-speed steel	60—120	40—120	20— 40
Carbide-tipped tool	200—350	300—600	50—100

Tool Angles

Fig. 224 shows the conventional method of illustrating the cutting angles of standard single-point tools. This method is the most convenient, as grinding is done on a machine equipped with a tilting table, as shown

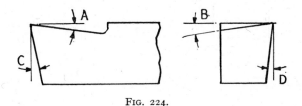

FIG. 224.

in Fig. 225. In this figure the edge of the wheel is used, but in many cases the flat side of a special " cup " wheel may be used. Various names are given to the four angles; those used in the following table are probably

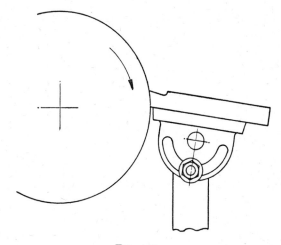

FIG. 225.

the most common. In recent years there has been some controversy amongst eminent engineers as to the most suitable names. This is unfortunate, as the real problem is to induce everyone to use the same names.

Material cut	Top rake.	Side rake.	Front clearance.	Side clearance.
	A	B	C	D
Mild steel	20°	20°	10°	6°
Medium-carbon steel . .	10°	12°	10°	6°
Tool steel (unhardened) .	6°	8°	6°	6°
Brass	0°	0°	6°	6°
Cast iron	10°	12°	10°	6°
Aluminium . . .	40°	15°	6°	6°

o

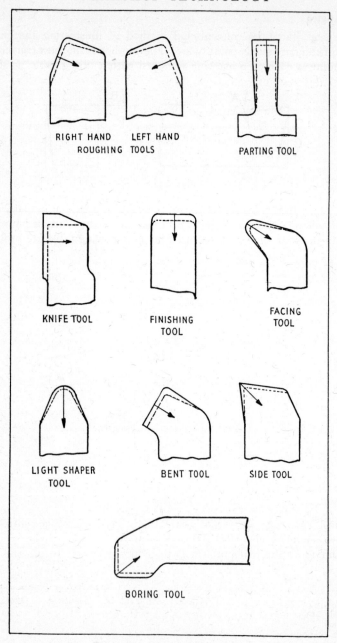

RIGHT HAND   LEFT HAND
ROUGHING TOOLS

PARTING TOOL

KNIFE TOOL

FINISHING
TOOL

FACING
TOOL

LIGHT SHAPER
TOOL

BENT TOOL

SIDE TOOL

BORING TOOL

FIG. 226.—TOOL-NOSE SHAPES.

Tool-nose Shapes

The shape of the tool nose is varied to suit the work, and a selection of shapes is shown in Fig. 226. The direction of maximum rake is shown by the arrow. The clearance is shown by dotted lines.

The right-hand or left-hand roughing tool is selected, according to the direction of feed. The knife-tool is useful for bar turning, as the main cutting force is in a direction parallel to the axis of the work, and there is thus less chance of deflecting slender work. The finishing tool is intended only for light cuts, otherwise it is quickly blunted. The parting-off tool for cutting a narrow groove in bar material is tapered in section—that is, side clearance is provided on both sides—to clear the work. The facing tool is for work on flat surfaces in the lathe—e.g., flanges. The round-nose shaper tool can be used for right-hand or left-hand feeds; it has top rake, but no side rake, and is very useful for many small surfacing jobs that are

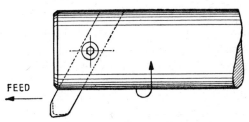

FEED

FIG. 227.—BORING BAR.

typical of much of the work on a shaping machine. The bent tool is preferred by some turners, since by varying the angle at which it is set to the work a preferred setting can be obtained. The side tool is used for facing, and is fed inwards along its own longitudinal axis. It has the reputation of penetrating any hard skin on the metal; it is also used for turning a square shoulder on a bar by being fed outwards along its axis. It is a rather weak tool, and should be used only for its own special purpose. The boring tool is useful for small bores, but if the hole is deep compared with its diameter, difficulty is experienced, since the overhang required will set up tool vibration which will produce " chatter marks " on the work.

Boring Bars

For holes of reasonably large diameter the boring bar with a separate tool is more rigid than the boring tool. If the front end of the bar can be supported or " piloted ", a better finish is obtained, and there is less danger of producing tapered holes due to deflection of the bar. A boring bar is shown in Fig. 227 and a piloted bar in Fig. 228.

Forming Tools

The tools previously mentioned are used to produce flat surfaces or circular sections by their motion relative to the work-piece—for example, a cylinder is produced in a lathe by rotating the work and moving the tool in a straight line parallel to the axis of rotation of the work; a cone requires the tool to traverse a straight line inclined to the work axis, and curved profiles are made by traversing the tool over a curved path. Such processes are termed **generation**, and the work is termed a **generated shape**.

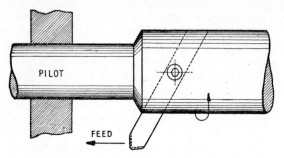

FIG. 228.—PILOTED BORING BAR.

Generation consists therefore of producing a shape by causing the tool and the work to move in certain paths relative to each other; the shape of the tool is not reproduced, and in many cases is quite immaterial. However, many shapes can be produced more easily by making a tool to a particular profile and using the tool to reproduce its profile **in reverse** on the work-piece. This is called **forming**, and the tool is termed a **form tool**. Fig. 229

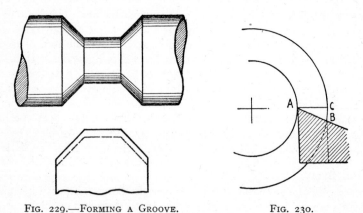

FIG. 229.—FORMING A GROOVE.   FIG. 230.

shows a groove in a bar and the shape of tool required to produce it. In this case the tool is fed straight into the work, and the feed motion must be stopped at a certain point if the correct form is to be obtained.

In most cases the breast of a form tool has no top rake, but is kept flat. Consideration of Fig. 230 will show that top rake would alter the form produced on the work. The tool breast extends from A to B, but the form produced extends from A to C. This is obviously a shorter distance. If top rake is used a " correction " must be calculated. The flat tool breast must be placed exactly on the centre line of the work.

Form Relief

A form tool requires front clearance, like other tools, and the front face of the tool must therefore have the profile inclined at the clearance angle. This is known as form relief. The tool is sharpened on the tool breast only, as shown in Fig. 231.

There are various methods of producing the form-relieved profile, but the following is commonly employed. A flat plate-gauge is made by hand filing to the reverse of the **tool nose**. From this gauge a mild-steel crushing roller is made in the centre lathe : the diameter of this roller is not im-

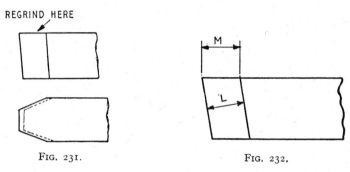

REGRIND HERE

FIG. 231.   FIG. 232.

portant, but the profile is carefully made to fit the gauge exactly. The crushing roller is now used to make a reversed profile on a grinding wheel. To do this, the wheel is roughed out by diamond dressing and then revolved slowly, in contact with the crushing roller, which revolves in unison with it and is gradually forced into the wheel surface.

The form tool is machined fairly closely to the shape and then hardened, and is mounted in a vice on the grinding-machine table. The tool is inclined at the desired relief or clearance angle, and the front face is ground to shape by the wheel. The process is shown in Fig. 233.

If a number of form tools of identical pattern are required, the grinding wheel is shaped by the mild-steel crushing roller, and is then used to grind a hardened steel roller, which will serve to re-crush the wheel many times.

It was emphasised that the original flat gauge is made to the shape of the tool nose. Note that the profile depth is represented by the distance L in Fig. 232. This distance is measured at right angles to the front of the tool. The form depth produced on the work is, of course, represented by the distance M. Widths will not be affected. In making the flat gauge the distance L must be calculated from the distance M, the relationship being $L = M \cos \theta$, where $\theta = $ clearance angle.

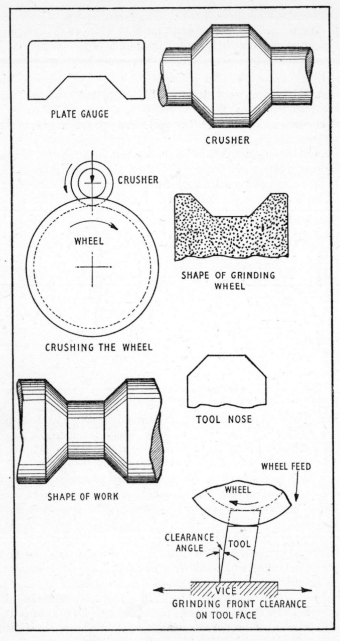

PLATE GAUGE

CRUSHER

CRUSHER

WHEEL

CRUSHING THE WHEEL

SHAPE OF GRINDING
WHEEL

TOOL NOSE

SHAPE OF WORK

WHEEL FEED

WHEEL

CLEARANCE
ANGLE   TOOL

VICE

GRINDING FRONT CLEARANCE
ON TOOL FACE

FIG. 233.—MAKING A FORM TOOL.

Storage and Distribution of Tools

The machine-shop tool-store should always have an adequate stock of sharpened tools of all the standard shapes. Any special tools should be prepared in the tool-room, before the job for which they are required is put on the machines. This preparation is automatic in a well-organised workshop, in other shops it is done haphazardly, with considerable waste of time and temper.

The grinding of all tools must be done in the tool-room by a specially trained worker ; any other course is fatal to fast and accurate production. Two conditions are essential if this method is to succeed :

1. There must be no off-hand grinding machines in the shop, and the management must be adamant against the specious arguments for their introduction.

2. There must always be a sharpened tool ready to be exchanged for the blunted tool sent back by the machine operator. The tool-grinder must have an efficient deputy. If both the tool-grinder and the deputy are absent, the tool-room foreman must grind the tools himself. A minor but important point in tool exchange is to suppress firmly the self-appointed critics in the tool-room who pass remarks about damaged tools. If a particular worker is using too many tools, the shop foreman should investigate quietly and tactfully, and try to improve the position by logical discussion.

[*T. S. Harrison and Sons, Ltd.*

FIG. 234.—TOOL-GRINDING MACHINE.

Tool Grinding

The grinding of single-point tools is usually divided into two operations. The first operation is to grind the forged tool to the shape required, including the particular angles required, as previously mentioned. This work is done with a fairly coarse grinding wheel to obtain a fast rate of metal removal. A typical wheel would be a $30H$. It is then necessary to obtain a keen cutting edge. This is done with a finer wheel—say a $60J$. A tool-grinding machine is illustrated in Fig. 234. The central motor has a spindle at each end. One spindle carries the roughing wheel, and the finishing wheel is fixed to the other spindle.

Immediately the cutting edge is dulled the tool should be withdrawn from service and re-ground. If a tool is kept in use after the edge is dull, the cutting force will rise rapidly, the work surface will be rough, and, due to overheating, the cutting edge may crumble away entirely. If the tool is allowed to reach this state, a good deal of grinding will be required to restore the correct shape, and a large amount of valuable material will have to be ground away. On the other hand, if the tool is re-ground at the right time the sharpening operation can be done quickly, and with little loss of material.

The working face of the grinding wheel should not be allowed to develop a wavy surface, as this will prevent the correct shaping of tools. A diamond in a special holder is passed across the wheel face to true it up immediately any hollow places develop. A good operator will not use the centre of the wheel face all the time, but will try to use as much of the width as possible, thus avoiding rapid wear of the wheel at one place.

Tool grinding is usually done dry. Driblets of water falling on a hot tool are liable to cause fine surface cracks, particularly near the cutting edge, which is likely to be the hottest place during grinding operations. Surface cracks near the cutting edge will cause rapid crumbling when the tool is put to work. Dry grinding sets up considerable heat, and consequently special grinding wheels are required. These have cool cutting qualities. In all cases the grinding must be done with a light pressure, and if the tool shows signs of " blueing ", grinding should be stopped for a short time.

Wet grinding of tools is sometimes practised, but a deluge of water is required; consequently the progress of the work cannot be watched by the operator.

Safety precautions are very important in grinding. The tool-rest should fit as closely as possible to the wheel surface, to prevent any possibility of the work becoming wedged between the wheel and the rest. This wedging action is highly dangerous, and may cause a serious injury to the operator's hands or may lead to a burst wheel. In dry grinding a dust-removal system is essential, and a transparent shield over the front of the wheel is a safeguard against sparks which may fly out and burn the operator or his clothing.

CHAPTER XXIII

THE LATHE

A SIMPLE lathe is a machine for revolving a piece of material at a suitable speed, and then, by use of suitable cutting tools, articles of circular cross-section are cut from the material. The size of lathes varies very greatly, but all are elaborations of the simple lathe. Fig. 235 illustrates a typical sliding, surfacing and screw-cutting lathe such as is commonly used in the engineering workshop.

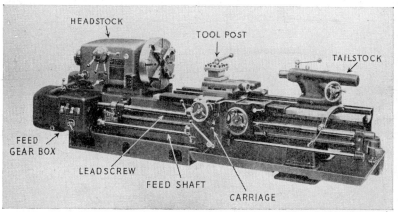

[*Dean, Smith and Grace, Ltd.*

FIG. 235.—A CENTRE LATHE.

The dimensions which decide the size of work done in a particular lathe are :

1. The maximum distance between the headstock and tailstock centres. This is usually termed the **length between centres.**
2. The largest diameter of work that will revolve without fouling the bed. This is termed **swing-over bed.**
3. The largest diameter of work that will revolve without fouling the tool carriage—usually referred to as the **swing-over carriage.**

Another dimension which becomes important with certain classes of bar work is the diameter of the hole through the lathe spindle.

The base of the lathe is the bed. This is usually an iron casting of substantial design carefully machined and then ground or hand scraped with the utmost care. The alignment of the various parts of the lathe depends on the accuracy of the bed. Furthermore, this accuracy must be maintained when the stresses set up by working conditions are applied. A box form of casting is usually employed. A typical cross-section is shown in Fig. 236. Suitable holes are cast in the horizontal ribs to allow the swarf to fall through for easy removal. The top surface of the bed

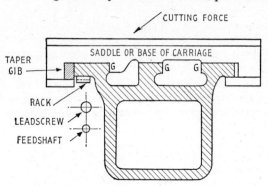

FIG. 236.—SECTION THROUGH LATHE BED.

takes the weight of the headstock, the tailstock and the carriage, but the guiding surfaces for the carriage and the tailstock are the narrow surfaces marked G in Fig. 236. These must be true, straight edges if accurate work is to be produced; they must be carefully protected from damage. Generally, the " shears " or sliding surfaces are " chilled " when the bed

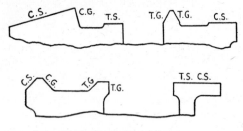

C.G.   CARRIAGE GUIDE SURFACE
C.S.   CARRIAGE SUPPORT SURFACE
T.G.   TAILSTOCK GUIDE SURFACE
T.S.   TAILSTOCK SUPPORT SURFACE

FIG. 237.—LATHE SHEARS.

is cast, in order to obtain a close-grained, hard-wearing surface after machining. Fig. 236 is by no means the only arrangement of shears. Two other arrangements are shown in Fig. 237, and the bed section shown in Fig. 243 may also be noted. With this latter type, the carriage is guided by a vertical face and the tailstock by a single vee, the back surfaces are for support only.

The **headstock** is securely bolted to one end of the lathe bed, with its centre line parallel to the bed guideways in horizontal and vertical planes. The lathe driving motor may be built into the headstock, or, alternatively, a constant-speed pulley may be used to take the power input. In this latter case it is best to have the driving motor on the floor close to the lathe, or, alternatively, to attach it to the end of the lathe bed with its pulley in line with the lathe pulley.

Within the headstock casting a gearbox is arranged so that the **lathe spindle** may be revolved at various speeds, according to the nature of the

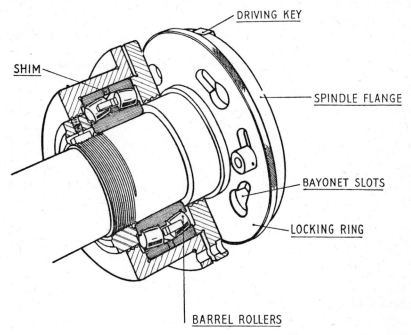

[John Lang and Sons, Ltd.

FIG. 238.—LATHE SPINDLE WITH PRE-LOADED BEARING.

work. The design of the lathe spindle and its bearings is of the utmost importance, as the thrust of the cutting tool will tend to deflect the spindle. The spindle, which is made of high-tensile steel, suitably hardened and tempered, is mounted on two large bearings placed at opposite ends of the headstock casting. These bearings have the minimum running clearance, and may be phosphor-bronze bushes accurately finished in the bore by honing, or may be heavy ball or roller bearings. In either case, one bearing is arranged to take the thrust of cutting and prevent the spindle from moving endways; the other bearing usually allows the spindle to expand longitudinally when heated.

The use of **pre-loaded** bearings should be noted. A lathe spindle may run in a certain position when unloaded, but the application of a cutting tool to the work is liable to move it over if there is any " play " in the bearings. In the pre-loaded roller bearing there is no " play " ; instead the rollers are always pressed against the inner track with a fixed force or pre-load.

Fig. 238 shows a patented design of front bearing for a lathe spindle. The double row of barrel rollers runs on a solid double inner track and a split double outer track. The two halves of the outer track are separated by a shim, the thickness of which is carefully set. Thus, when the bearing is assembled, the two outer tracks are pressed together and the required pre-load pressure is placed on the rollers.

It may also be noted that, due to the shape of the rollers and tracks, the bearing has self-aligning properties and will take end thrust in both directions.

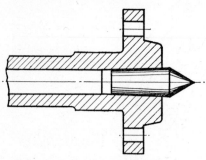

The overhang of the spindle nose is kept to a minimum to guard against bending. Fig. 239 shows a typical spindle nose. The spindle is hollow, to allow long bars to be passed through. The live centre revolves with the spindle ; when it is not required, it may be removed from its taper

FIG. 239.—SPINDLE NOSE.

socket. The various face plates and chucks are all made to be secured to the flange by bolts or studs and positioned by the taper spigot. The flange in Fig. 238 is a quick release type. The chucks have four studs which can pass through the flange and locking ring with the nuts in place. When the chuck has been pushed in place, the locking ring is rotated slightly to bring the narrow end of the slots under the nuts, which are then tightened by about half a turn. This design has the tapered spigot already mentioned and also a fitted driving key which takes all driving strain off the studs.

At the bottom of the headstock a further small gearbox is provided. This transmits the power for driving the feed-shaft and the leadscrew. These two are devices for moving the lathe carriage. The feed-shaft is used for most turning operations, but when the carriage motion must be synchronised with the rotation of the lathe spindle, the leadscrew is used. This matter will be discussed more fully under screw-cutting operations.

A typical all-geared headstock is shown in Fig. 240. The motor is placed at the rear, and drives a constant-speed pulley. Two gear levers are used to obtain the twelve different spindle speeds, which range from 8 to 400 r.p.m. The upper spindle gear-lever has three positions, the right and left positions provide two ranges of speeds—high and low. When the lever is in the central " neutral " position the lathe spindle is free and may be turned by hand. The lower gate-change lever has six positions, each giving a different speed; thus the two levers between them provide the twelve speeds. The **feed-shaft** is connected to the feed gearbox by a **slipping clutch**; this clutch is a valuable safety device which will operate if the feed-shaft is overloaded due to the carriage jamming.

The feed gearbox is connected by a train of gears to the spindle gearbox. Seven changes of feed are provided by the feed-change lever at the bottom left. The two horizontal feed-change levers each doubles the number, and the vertical lever at the left again doubles the number, thus providing fifty-six feed changes. The circular guard on the extreme left covers part

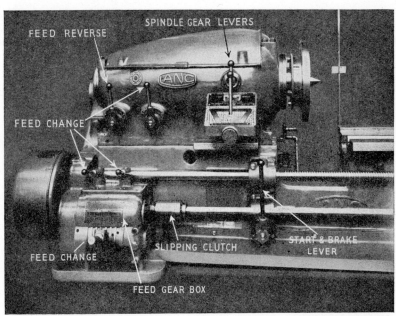

[*John Lang and Sons, Ltd.*

FIG. 240.—ALL-GEARED HEADSTOCK.

of the screw-cutting gear-train. If further variations of screw-cutting rate should be required, this gear-train can be modified quickly. The maximum screw-cutting rate that can be arranged is 7-in. travel for one revolution of the lathe spindle. The feed reverse lever reverses the direction of travel of the carriage.

The start-and-stop lever operates multi-plate friction clutches, and has three positions giving—" start reverse ", " stop " and " start forward " to the spindle.

The **tailstock** is used to carry the dead centre which supports the outer end of the work. The tailstock can be moved along the bed to suit various lengths of work. It can be locked in any position. It is guided by a pair of shears. Generally one pair of shears is used to locate both headstock and tailstock in one vertical plane; a separate parallel shear is used to guide the cutting tool. Some types of tailstock are mounted on a saddle which slides on the bed; it is then possible to set the tailstock in any position by means of the screws. With this arrangement a device is

FIG. 241.—TAILSTOCK DETAILS.

required for quickly re-setting the tailstock on the lathe centre line. A movable poppet inside the tailstock barrel can be advanced or retracted by means of the hand-wheel. The poppet has a taper socket in which a dead centre is mounted. This centre can be removed and a drill, reamer or other tool substituted for it. A tailstock is shown in Fig. 241 lifted from its saddle. The surface W is square with the lathe axis, and is kept hard up to the faces XX by tightening the screw Y. The side adjustment of the tailstock body is made by means of the two screws B, which are kept securely tightened after setting to position. The screw Y is loosened before and tightened after each adjustment. The poppet D is locked in position by the lever C.

The **carriage** slides along the lathe bed and is guided by the front shear. The width of the carriage at the front shear is of great importance. The bearing surface on the shear should be as long as possible, so that there will be no tendency to tilt when heavy cuts are being taken—a phenomenon known as **cross wind**. The principal reasons for providing a separate shear for guiding the carriage are that the guiding surface of the carriage may then pass part way up the side of the headstock when the tool is close up to the spindle nose ; also, the guideway may be arranged directly over the bed-rack, the leadscrew and the feed-shaft, thus minimising the twisting couple when the carriage is being power driven in a sliding cut. The carriage is kept up to the guideway by means of a sliding piece or taper gib (see Fig. 236). This gib has a screw arrangement, so that it can be adjusted to allow the carriage to slide but not to have " shake ".

The movement of the carriage is controlled by the **apron gears**. Along the front of the bed a steel rack is fixed firmly, and for normal turning work the carriage is moved by means of a pinion in the apron which gears with the rack. The hand-wheel is used to move the carriage manually. When the power feed is engaged, the pinion is driven by the feed-shaft through the apron gears. These gears are also arranged to give power feed to the surfacing movement of the slide rest.

The carriage and apron of a lathe are shown in Fig. 242 A. The large hand-wheel gives manual traverse to the carriage. Just behind this wheel can be seen the knob for disengaging the hand traverse when automatic feed is engaged. The smaller hand-wheel gives manual traverse to the cross-slide. To engage either longitudinal or cross traverse, one of the two buttons (bottom centre) is pressed. Neither can be engaged when screw cutting.

Referring to Fig. 242 B, the two small worms which are driven by the feed-shaft provide the drive for the automatic feed through worm-wheels. These convey the drive to the pinions. The left hand of these two pinions engages with the gear on the extreme left. The spindle of this gear passes through the rear of the apron casing and carries the rack pinion on it. The large hand-wheel shaft passes through the hole (top left) to give a geared reduction for manual traverse. The right hand of the two pinions engages with the large gear in the centre, which provides the drive to the cross-slide screw.

The cam in Fig. 242 B is operated when the lever on right (see Fig. 242 A) is used to engage the leadscrew nut. The latch mechanism attached to the cam then prevents the engagement of the worms in the feed-drive.

The rate of feed of the carriage is varied by the feed gearbox in the head-

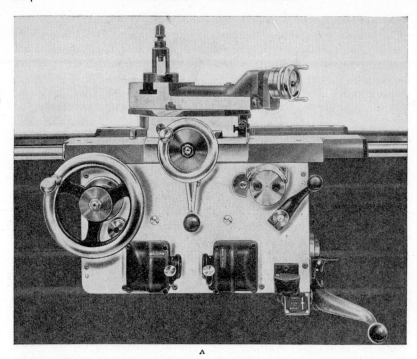

A

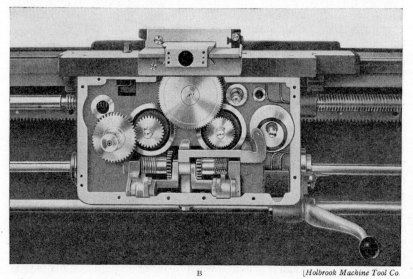

B

Holbrook Machine Tool Co.

FIG. 242.—LATHE CARRIAGE AND APRON.

stock. It may cover a range from 0·002 to 0·1 in. per spindle revolution, these figures depending on the size and duty of the lathe. The actual feed per revolution is dependent on a number of factors, such as the accuracy of the apron gears and the bed-rack, the angle of twist due to torque in the feed-shaft. For normal cutting slight variations are unimportant, but in the machining of screw-threads a more positive means of driving the carriage is required. It is for this purpose that a leadscrew is fitted. The leadscrew is made from a medium-carbon steel, and has a surface-hardened Acme thread. On small lathes the pitch of the thread is $\frac{1}{4}$ in.; on large lathes a $\frac{1}{2}$-in. or 1-in. pitch leadscrew is usual. The diameter of the screw is between $1\frac{1}{4}$ and 2 in., this large diameter making for a stiff screw and a large thread surface. The leadscrew is driven by the same gearbox as the feed-shaft, but it engages the carriage by means of two half-nuts which are

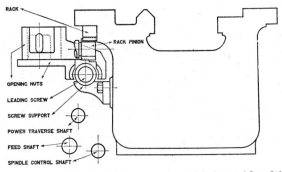

[*John Lang and Sons, Ltd.*]

FIG. 243.—CARRIAGE OPERATING GEAR.

opened and closed by a lever on the apron. These are clearly shown in Fig. 243 on each side of the leading screw. The screw support should also be noted, this is clear of all projections when the carriage is moved. The accuracy of leadscrews has received much attention from reputable makers, and leadscrews with a guaranteed accuracy of 0·0002 in. per foot length are fitted to high-class lathes. It is the elimination of the apron gears and feed-shaft together with the accurate thread which allow screw cutting to fine limits. During screw cutting a heavy longitudinal thrust is developed in the leadscrew. This is counteracted by the fitting of special thrust bearings. A patented type of thrust bearing is shown in Fig. 244. All normal machining should be done with the feed-shaft, to keep leadscrew wear to a minimum, and in fact, it is best to disconnect the leadscrew gears when not screw cutting, the leadscrew is then stationary and free from wear.

The **cross slide** of the carriage carries the **slide-rest**, which is moved by means of a short leadscrew. The cross slide must be set exactly at right angles to the main shears, as this slide is the guideway used when producing

P

a flat cylinder end—an operation usually termed **surfacing**. In the **compound slide-rest**, which is shown in Fig. 242 A, a further short slide is carried ; this can be swivelled to any desired angle, and is used for turning short tapers and for certain other operations. Both the cross slide and the top slide of the compound rest have large hand-wheels with micrometer dials graduated in o·oor-in. intervals. These are used in the precise setting of depths of cut in finishing work. The main cross slide also may have power feed, taken from the apron gears. When the cross slide is in use the carriage can be locked on the bed to prevent any longitudinal movement.

The following interlocks are arranged. When the leadscrew nut is engaged, no power feed can be operated, and vice versa ; when the carriage is locked for surfacing purposes, neither the longitudinal feed nor the leadscrew can be engaged ; when the cross feed is engaged, no longitudinal feed can be used, and vice versa.

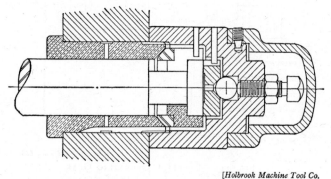

[*Holbrook Machine Tool Co.*

FIG. 244.—LEADSCREW THRUST BEARING.

On top of the rest the **tool-post** is placed. This is the fixture for holding the tool or tools. Many lathes have a slotted pillar to take one tool at a time (see Fig. 242 A), but some are fitted with a rotating tool-post. This latter type will take four tools, each of which can be brought to the work in turn by a single-lever movement which rotates and then locks the tool-post. This is termed a **turret** tool-post. The turret tool-post is shown in Fig. 235. It may be noted that it was the invention of the slide-rest by Henry Maudsley (1771–1831) that opened up the great potentialities of the centre lathe.

Types of Lathe Work

A common type of lathe work is turning **between centres**. The work is drilled at each end by means of a centre drill, as shown in Fig. 245. The cylindrical portion at the bottom ensures that the lathe centre only engages the cone-shaped part, and clears at the point. It will be realised that a bar properly held between centres cannot move in any

way except to rotate about its own axis, consequently the conical surfaces
are the datum faces from which all diameters are produced.   For this
reason the centre holes should be drilled very carefully, and for precision
work, such as gauges, the centres should be machine ground or lapped out
with a conical lap and fine grinding paste.   The conical surfaces are very
small, and are not easy to lubricate.   If the work is heavy, adequate

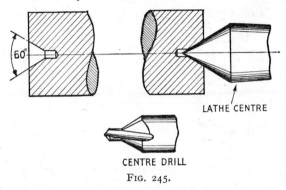

LATHE CENTRE

CENTRE DRILL

FIG. 245.

support must be given to prevent wearing of the surface at the tailstock
end (the headstock centre revolves with the work).   The tailstock centre
must be adjusted with care : too heavy pressure prevents lubrication, and
too light a pressure will allow the work to " jump " when the cut is
applied.   The revolving centre shown in Fig. 246 is a useful fitting for
high-speed work.   The taper roller-bearing is pre-loaded by the screwed
nut, the ball thrust-bearing takes the end thrust, and the small roller-

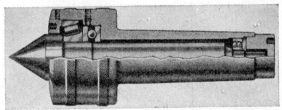

[*John Lang and Sons, Ltd.*

FIG. 246.—REVOLVING CENTRE.

bearing at the back supports the revolving spindle.   The taper shank fits
the tailstock socket.

The chief advantage of working between centres is that the work can be
removed from the machine and replaced and will still revolve about the
same axis.   Similarly, if a part is turned in a lathe and subsequently
ground in a cylindrical grinder, the same datum faces are used throughout.
The student may be puzzled to decide whether the six-point principle is
applicable to centred work.   It may be pointed out that a circle is
determined if three points on its circumference are located.

In order to drive the work, a carrier " dog " is fastened to one end, and the finger of the dog is driven by a catchplate mounted on the spindle nose (see Fig. 247). One serious disadvantage of this method of driving is that the work cannot be machined where the dog fits, and at some stage of the machining process the shaft has to be turned end for end in the lathe.

It is not possible, of course, to turn irregular-shaped pieces between

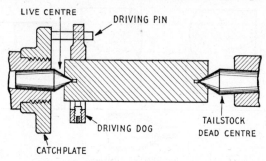

FIG. 247.—WORKING BETWEEN CENTRES.

centres, nor is it possible to bore a hole through the work. However, the use of centred **mandrels** opens up a wide field of application for work between centres.

A mandrel is a piece of round bar which has been centred at each end and has then been machined and ground to run truly on the centres. It has a taper of about 0·008 in. per foot length, so that work with a central hole can be pressed on to a suitable part of the mandrel.

If the mandrel is only to be used once, mild steel will be a cheap and

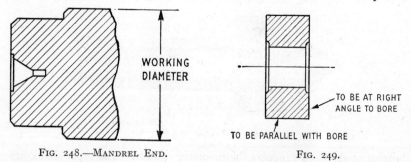

FIG. 248.—MANDREL END.   FIG. 249.

suitable material; but most shops have a set of standard mandrels made from medium-carbon steel. These are hardened and tempered, and ground up to a good finish; the centres may be lapped or ground out after hardening. In order to protect the centres of permanent mandrels, a recess is usually arranged, and the end of the mandrel is made smaller in diameter, so that burrs on the end will not prevent the mounting of work. A mandrel end is shown in Fig. 248.

Fig. 249 illustrates a simple but typical application of mandrel turning.

It is important that the hole in the component should be concentric with the outside diameter and square with the flat faces. The part may be turned up roughly in a chuck and the hole drilled as near central as possible. The hole is finished bored or reamered, and the part is mounted on a suitable mandrel. The circumference and the flat faces of the work are then lightly skimmed up to the final size.

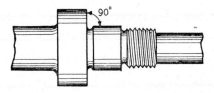

FIG. 250.—COLLARED MANDREL.

Mandrels are made with various fittings, and a mandrel with a collar and screw-thread is shown in Fig. 250.

Chucks

Round, square and hexagon bar of short length is often machined in a suitable chuck. The three-jaw **self-centring chuck** has a **scroll** mechanism

[*F. Pratt and Co., Ltd.*

FIG. 251.—THREE-JAW CHUCK.

[*F. Pratt and Co., Ltd.*

FIG. 252.—FOUR-JAW CHUCK.

so that the jaws move in or out at the same time when the chuck key is turned. If the work is symmetrical to the jaws it is automatically centred by the chuck, and no adjustment is necessary. Where the stock is bright, drawn bar the three-jaw chuck provides a very quick method of gripping it. The majority of work in capstan lathes is done in this type of chuck, shown in Fig. 251.

The four-jaw **independent chuck** has the jaws carried in slots. Each jaw can be adjusted separately by its own screw. Forgings or castings of slightly irregular shape can be gripped by suitable setting of each jaw. The four-jaw independent chuck is shown in Fig. 252. Chucks may be used for long work instead of the dog-and-catchplate method, and work is gripped by the chuck at one end, and the other end rotates on the tailstock centre, as shown in Fig. 253. With this method the work is more

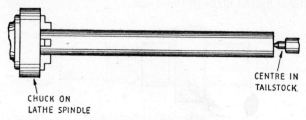

CENTRE IN
TAILSTOCK

CHUCK ON
LATHE SPINDLE

FIG. 253.

rigidly supported, but the location principle of two centres is destroyed.

Two methods of holding work by " false pieces " often occur in chuck work. A short piece of bar may be gripped firmly in a chuck and turned to a suitable diameter : thin section rings which are difficult to grip, owing to their fragility, may be pressed gently on to the bar and lightly machined on their ends or outer circumference. If the bore of such rings requires machining, then a " stack " may be bored out suitably and the rings gently

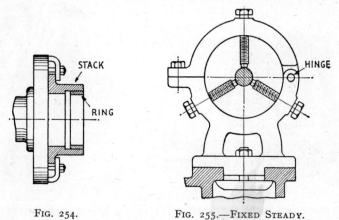

STACK

RING

HINGE

FIG. 254. FIG. 255.—FIXED STEADY.

pressed inside the stack (see Fig. 254). With either of these methods the " false piece " must not be disturbed until all the rings have been completed, as the original machining of the piece provides the datum.

Face-plates

These are plates adapted for mounting on the spindle nose. A number of slots is provided so that irregular-shaped castings or forgings can be clamped to the face-plate by bolts and straps. Brackets or angle plates can be mounted to aid in holding the work. The face-plate may be likened to a revolving surface plate, the surface being at right angles to the lathe axis. Providing the surface is in good condition, it forms an excellent datum for accurate setting of the work.

Steady Rests

These are used for long work where there is a danger that the cutting force of the tool may deflect the work seriously. The **fixed steady** (Fig. 255) is fastened to the lathe bed at a convenient point, the three fingers supporting the work. Unless bright round bar is being used, it is necessary first to machine a short length of bar on which to set the bearing pads of

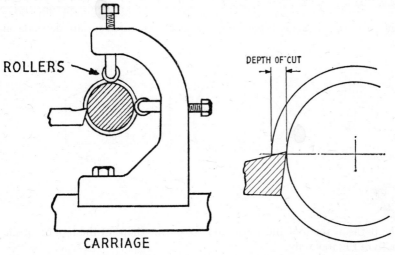

ROLLERS

DEPTH OF CUT

CARRIAGE

FIG. 256.—TRAVELLING STEADY.   FIG. 257.

the steady fingers. The **travelling steady** is arranged to bolt to the carriage, and it thus supports the work immediately behind the tool throughout the traverse. Steadies must be set carefully, so that they are not marking the work but are tight enough to prevent " whipping ". The travelling steady is set on the diameter of the turned work, as it follows the tool (see Fig. 256).

Setting of Tools

This important operation is often done in a negligent manner, and much unsatisfactory work can be traced to this cause. Fig. 257 shows a turning tool set in position for plain bar turning. It is advisable to set the cutting edge on the centre line of the job, but the top rake prevents this if the cut is reasonably deep; consequently it is usual to set the tool point slightly above the centre, and thus none of the cutting edge is below the centre. This precaution is taken to ensure that the tool does not "dig in".

In taper turning it is essential to set the cutting edge on the centre line, otherwise a truly conical shape cannot be generated. The point is illustrated in Fig. 258 in exaggerated form. At the large end of the work the low setting of the tool will cause it to turn a slightly larger diameter, but at the small end of the work the effect will be much more pronounced. The deviation depends on the cosines of the angles a and b. Now, the relationship between the sides of a right-angle triangle is dependent on the squares of the lengths of the sides, and consequently the cosine of an angle does not vary according to a straight-line law. Therefore the shape generated does not have a straight side. In fact, if the tool is set below the centre line, a concave surface is produced. Incidentally, this illustrates the point that in generation the shape of the generated surface depends on

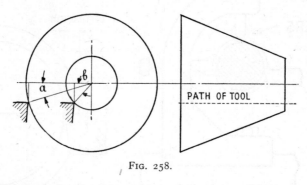

FIG. 258.

the paths of the tool and work, and not on the shape of the tool or on the path of the tool only.

The commonest cause of "chattered" work is excessive overhang of the cutting tool. The tool vibrates as a pendulum, and alternately is forced down, and then springs back due to its elasticity. The minimum possible overhang from the tool-post should be used, and the top slide of a compound rest should not be wound out to the limit, but instead should be kept well over the cross slide.

Finally, when the tool is set the turner should check up to make sure that in making the cut no part of the set-up will foul the tool.

Speeds, Feeds and Depths of Cut

The theoretical considerations have been briefly reviewed in Chapter XXII, but a number of factors must be considered in the turning of any job. The following points have decisive influence.

1. **The Type of Work.** When a rigid article, such as a large-diameter plain bar, is being rough turned, there is little danger of deflection, and surface finish is unimportant, consequently deep cuts at the maximum

speed and feed are employed. The only limits are the rigidity and power input of the lathe and the desired life of the tool edge.

On the other hand, slender work is usually turned with light cuts, but the rate of metal removal may be improved by the use of very high cutting speeds. With some components of a fragile nature the permissible gripping pressure is very low, and consequently light cuts and low speeds may be essential.

2. **Type of Material** being machined and type of material used for the tool. These two factors have already been discussed in Chapter XXII.

3. **Surface Finish Required.** There is a general tendency to use light cuts and high speeds with fine feeds to obtain a good surface finish. Not only is the surface smooth in these circumstances, but also the metal immediately under the surface is less disturbed.

4. **Type of Operation.** Some operations require to be done at low speeds to suit the operator or the type of tool. Screw cutting, tapping and reaming are examples of this. Form tools are expensive, and are expected to have a fairly long life ; when they are in use, feed and speed may be reduced to preserve them. For single-point tools the period between re-grinds may be as low as one hour's cutting time, but certain operations are exceptions to this. In the precision boring of large cylinders, for example, any appreciable tool wear in the finishing cut would lead to a tapered bore, and removing the tool for re-grinding part way through a traverse would be fatal. Such considerations reduce the depth of cut and rate of feed, and in the case of steel cutting tools (as opposed to carbide-tipped tools) the cutting speed also. Another example is in the complicated set-ups in automatic lathes or capstan and turret lathes. It is better to try to arrange a reasonably long run before stopping to re-grind tools. The setter will often reduce the speed or feed of a particular operation if he finds that the tool is blunting much more quickly than any other. He prefers to send all the wearing tools for regrinding at one time, rather than have continued short stoppages.

5. **Use of a Cutting Fluid.** This generally allows a considerable increase in the cutting speed.

6. **Type of Lathe.** A certain minimum amount of work must be done to remove a cubic inch of metal in a lathe ; therefore the maximum power input to the lathe must be considered. The rigidity of the lathe is also an important factor ; it is well known that many old lathes are quite unsuitable for modern carbide-cutting tools, as they were designed before such tools were envisaged. They lack the necessary rigidity, power input and high-speed range.

With a good selection of carbide-tipped tools of various grades and a range of shapes metal may be removed at a remarkable speed in a modern lathe. There is little point in giving a long list of various speeds, feeds and cutting depths for all the different materials, but the following are a few typical examples of modern practice.

Material.	Speed, ft./min.	Depth of cut, ins.	Feed, ins./rev.
Cast iron (130 Brinell no.) . .	200	¼	0·015
Mild steel	350	⅛	0·010
60/40 brass	500	⅜	0·010
Aluminium	700	¼	0·015

Lathe Operations

It is outside the scope of this book to describe how various components are machined, but certain operations call for special mention.

Ending Up

When a piece of bar has been sawn off and centred, a very common operation is that of machining to correct length. This involves working close up to the dead centre. A half centre will enable better work to be done,

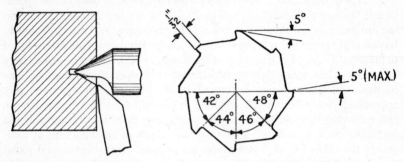

FIG. 259.—ENDING UP.   FIG. 260.—SECTION OF REAMER.

and a tool with a sharp nose angle is required. The operation is shown in Fig. 259.

Drilling, Reaming and Boring

For holes of moderate size, drilling is usually employed; if a smooth finish is required, the hole is drilled slightly under size, and is then reamed. A section through a reamer is shown in Fig. 260. A portion of the reamer immediately behind the cutting edge is ground to give " front clearance " of 5°. This surface is called the " land ", and the 5° angle is termed " primary clearance ". Behind the land, the tool is cut away more sharply to leave room for chips of metal. This is termed " secondary clearance ". The " top rake " never exceeds 5°, and is often zero—i.e., the tool breast is radial. The odd distribution of the cutting edges round the circumference lessens the possibility of " chatter " marks in the hole, due to harmonic vibration. The flutes of the reamer are usually spirally disposed, being given a left-hand inclination. This is equivalent to giving a negative " side-rake " to the cutting edge, and prevents the reamer screwing into the work.

Reamers are operated at a slow speed, and the amount of metal removed is usually 0·008 to 0·003 in. only. Generally, the work is held in a chuck or on a face-plate ; the drill, and later the reamer, are held in the tailstock socket and fed forward by the tailstock hand-wheel. For long work a fixed steady is used to support the work close up to the drill. Further notes on reamers and reaming will be found in Chapter XXVI.

Flat plates and some types of bracket can be drilled more readily if they are fastened to the slide rest or held up against the tailstock. The drill is then put in the lathe spindle socket, and feed is applied to the work by means of the carriage or tailstock hand-wheel. Fig. 261 shows a " drilling pad " fixed in a lathe tailstock.

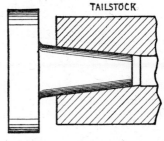

FIG. 261.—DRILL PAD.

One disadvantage of drilling and reaming is the tendency of drills to " wander " away from the desired centre line ; the reamer will automatically follow the same path. This may be counteracted to some extent by first drilling a small " pilot " hole and then following with a larger drill ; but for accurate work a boring tool or boring bar is more satisfactory. If two or more concentric bores have to be produced, a piloted boring bar or counter-bore should always be used. (Counterbores are described in Chapter XXVI.)

Taper Turning and Boring

Setting Over the Tailstock

This is limited to turning between centres, and is suitable only for slight tapers. A typical example is the turning of mandrels. The tailstock is

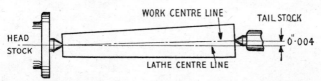

FIG. 262.—TAPER TURNING BY SETTING OVER THE TAILSTOCK.

thrown out of line with the headstock, and is locked in the new position. The set-up is shown in Fig. 262, and the tailstock adjustment is shown in Fig. 241. Consider a bar 1 ft. in length and 0·008 in. smaller in diameter at one end than the other. If the lathe tailstock is 0·004 in. farther away from the front shear than the headstock, the work will be machined 0·008 in. larger in diameter at the tailstock end. This is due to the fact that the cutting tool traverses a path parallel to the front shear. Several points must be noted. The amount of taper is determined by the movement of the tailstock from the central position. If bars of different lengths are to be turned to the same taper, the set-over must be calculated each time—in fact if the bars are all of one length, they must all be centred to the same depth if the tapers are to be identical. The tailstock centre cannot align

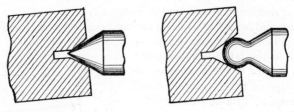

Fig. 263.

itself properly with the centre hole in the bar ; this is shown in exaggerated form in Fig. 263. Sometimes centres with ball ends are used to overcome this difficulty, but they are somewhat fragile.

[Holbrook Machine Tool Co., Ltd.

Fig. 264.—Taper Turning Attachment.

The Taper Turning Attachment

This is shown in Fig. 264. Under ordinary turning conditions the infeed of the tool is determined by the cross slide-screw, but when using the taper turning attachment the slide-rest is freed from this screw and its movement is controlled by the slide on the attachment. The attachment can be pre-set to the required angle and locked in position, thus allowing an exact taper to be reproduced on any number of components; furthermore, internal and external tapers which must match each other can be produced if the attachment is left undisturbed.

Setting the Compound Slide-rest

This method is used for turning short tapers. The top slide can be swivelled to any angle, the setting being made by the graduated base, which is usually marked in degrees. With this method the automatic feed cannot be used, and the tool is fed by hand. Only short tapers can be turned, as the top slide movement is limited; but, within the limitations stated, this is the quickest and simplest method of taper turning.

Another method is occasionally used for taper turning in which the lathe is specially geared. A separate set of gears is provided which enables the carriage to be moved on the bed and the cross slide fed in or out at the same time. By changing the gears the relative amounts of these motions may be changed, thus altering the tapered path of the tool. With this method a taper can be machined for the full length of the bed.

Screw Cutting

With the introduction of capstan lathes equipped with self-opening die-heads, and more recently with the advent of the thread-milling and thread-rolling machines, screw cutting in the lathe has become less common, but is still an important operation. The pitch accuracy of the thread produced depends on the truth of the leadscrew, but the accuracy of the form depends on the skill of the operator, and the use of a correct chasing tool for finishing the thread.

To obtain a particular thread it is necessary to rotate the work and at the same time to traverse the cutting tool parallel to the axis of the work. The speed of the traverse must bear a constant relationship to the speed of rotation of the work. If the lathe spindle and the leadscrew are positively connected by gear-wheels, this condition will apply. Consider a lathe fitted with a leadscrew which has four threads per inch (4 T.P.I.) : if the work and the leadscrew are geared 1 : 1, then the work will also have 4 T.P.I. If the leadscrew rotates once whilst the work revolves four times, then the movement of the cutting tool will be $\frac{1}{16}$ in. per revolution of the work, and the thread produced will be 16 T.P.I.

What is required, therefore, is a positive-geared connection between work and leadscrew, with facilities for changing the gear ratio. In the more expensive lathes this is provided by a gearbox, but on many lathes it is necessary to set up a train of gears to connect the lathe spindle and the leadscrew. **Change-wheels** are supplied in sets, a full set consisting of wheels from twenty teeth to 120 teeth in steps of five.

Returning to the case of the work with 16 T.P.I., a gear-wheel of twenty teeth is placed on the lathe spindle and one of eighty teeth on the leadscrew.   So that the direction of rotation will not be reversed, and to couple wheels of different diameters, an " idler " wheel is placed in the train (see Fig. 265 A).   The number of teeth on the idler wheel is unimportant, as it revolves freely on a stud.   This is termed a **simple** gear-train and the number of teeth in the two wheels is calculated as follows :

$$\frac{\text{T.P.I. of leadscrew}}{\text{T.P.I. of work}} = \frac{4}{16} = \frac{20}{80}$$

Next we may consider a leadscrew of 2 T.P.I. and work of 17 T.P.I.   The ratio is $\frac{2}{17}$, and with a simple gear-train wheels of twenty and 170 teeth would be required.   The ratio can be broken down, however, as follows : $\frac{1}{2} \times \frac{2}{8\cdot5}$; the wheels required would be $\frac{30}{60} \times \frac{20}{85}$.   This would be arranged

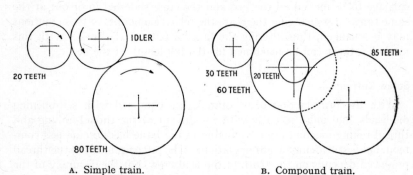

A. Simple train.   B. Compound train.
FIG. 265.—GEAR-TRAINS.

as shown in Fig. 265 B, and is termed a **compound train.**   The sixty- and twenty-tooth wheels are keyed together and revolve on a stud ; the thirty-tooth wheel engages the lathe spindle, and the eighty-five-tooth wheel engages the leadscrew.

The work to be screwed is turned to the top diameter of the thread, and a " landing groove " is machined, as shown in Fig. 266.   This groove gives the necessary clearance for withdrawing the tool at the end of the thread. Fig. 266 also shows the thread profile gauge which is used to check the shape of the tool nose and to ensure that the axis of the tool is at right angles to the axis of the work.

If the tool was fed straight into the work it would cut at both sides, and the two converging chips would crowd together, causing tearing of the work surface, and probably breaking the tool.   To prevent this the cross slide is used for disengaging the tool, but the cut is put on by the top slide. The method is illustrated in Fig. 267.   The tool is left slightly loose in the post, and the cross-slide hand-wheel is brought to zero.   The tool nose is now made to just touch the work, and the tool is firmly secured in the tool-post. Therefore, with the cross-slide hand-wheel at zero, the tip of the tool will always be at the top diameter of the thread. The carriage is now wound to the right, so that the tool just clears the free end of the work. The lathe is started, and the leadscrew nut is engaged, the tool moves to the left and makes a fine spiral mark on the work. When the landing groove is reached, the leadscrew nut is disengaged and the cross slide wound out to clear the tool from the work. The carriage is returned to the starting point, and the cross slide reset to zero. A small cut is now put on by the top-slide hand-wheel, and the process is repeated. By this

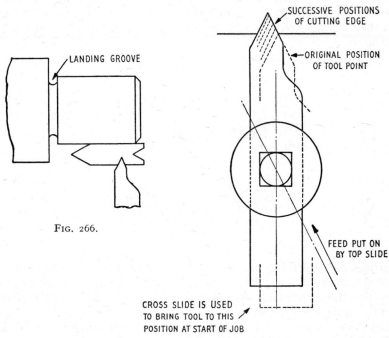

FIG. 266.

FIG. 267.—FEED FOR SCREW CUTTING.

method one side only of the tool will be cutting (see Fig. 267). Twelve or more cuts may be applied before the thread attains full depth.

When the lever is pressed to engage the leadscrew nut, the screw will usually have to turn slightly before the nut slips into place. If the T.P.I. on the work is a multiple of the T.P.I. on the leadscrew, this does not matter; but in all other cases the nut may not engage at the right point for following the partially cut thread. For example, if the work has 6 T.P.I. and the leadscrew has 4 T.P.I., then the work will turn one and a half turns for each turn of the leadscrew. Thus, the nut which may engage on each revolution of the leadscrew may be engaged when the work is turned half a turn, and the next cut will be half a pitch in error compared with previous cuts; the result will be a spoiled thread (see Fig. 268). Actually, the correct engagement occurs once in each two turns of the leadscrew, as this represents three turns of the work.

There are several methods of preventing this occurrence. With short threads and small work the lathe can be revolved backwards by hand with the tool retracted a little. Another method is to calculate how often the work and leadscrew coincide in making complete revolutions. The lathe chuck or catchplate is then marked, and so is the leadscrew, and an abutment is placed on the lathe bed, so that the carriage can be returned each time to the same spot. The carriage is returned to the abutment, and the lathe is revolved until the marks on the leadscrew and the catchplate are in their original positions; the nut is then engaged and the next cut is taken.

On most modern lathes a chasing dial is fitted. This is a dial on the

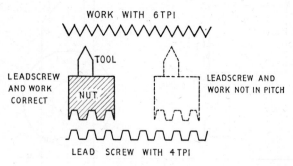

WORK WITH 6 TPI

TOOL

LEADSCREW
AND WORK
CORRECT

NUT

LEADSCREW AND
WORK NOT IN PITCH

LEAD SCREW WITH 4 TPI

FIG. 268.

carriage top, which is connected by a short shaft to a worm-wheel which engages the leadscrew. The dial has eight or sixteen marks, according to whether the worm-wheel has eight or sixteen teeth. There is a fixed mark on the carriage. Thus, when the dial moves one graduation, this indicates that the leadscrew has turned once. In the case of the work with 6 T.P.I. the leadscrew nut could be engaged at every other mark (say the even numbers), as this means every other turn of the leadscrew, and thus every third turn of the work. Again, for 23 T.P.I. the work revolves five and three-quarter times for one revolution of the leadscrew, and the nut may only be engaged at every fourth mark—that is at every fourth revolution of the leadscrew and every twenty-third revolution of the work.

It is interesting to note that some lathes have a 1-in. pitch leadscrew. In this case all whole numbers of threads can be cut without referring to the thread dial, but fractional threads such as $5\frac{1}{2}$ T.P.I. require the use of the thread dial.

Fig. 269 shows the profile of the Whitworth thread, which has a rounded root and crest. This shape cannot be produced by a single-point tool, consequently the thread is completed by a chasing tool. A chasing tool is shown in Fig. 270, and it will be realised that it is a particular type of form tool. It may be applied to the work by hand, and steadied by a guide-bar placed in the tool-post. The thread is picked up by the chaser, which is then pressed firmly into the thread. When the leading edge reaches the landing groove the tool is quickly withdrawn. This chasing operation is

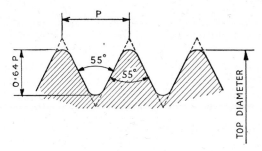

FIG. 269.—WHITWORTH THREAD FORM.

continued until a screw-thread gauge will screw firmly on to the work. Alternatively the chaser may be mounted in the tool-post and the thread completed with the aid of the leadscrew.

Internal threaded work is produced in a similar manner, a landing recess being formed if the hole to be threaded is " blind ". Hand chasing is not

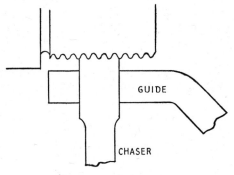

FIG. 270.—THREAD CHASING.

possible, and the chaser is set up in the tool-post : it must be set very carefully into the thread, and the leadscrew nut is then engaged.

Grinding in the Lathe

In small workshops a portable grinding head is sometimes set up on the lathe tool-post in order to finish a bore or diameter. The method is not to be recommended, and should be used only if no other process is possible. The abrasive dust released by the wheel finds its way on to the lathe shears and the leadscrew, and is held there by the oil which is present on these surfaces. If grinding has to be done in the lathe, the sliding surfaces should afterwards be cleaned with paraffin, dried and re-oiled.

Nowadays only the very smallest workshops can afford to be without a grinding machine.

Lathe Alignments

If a lathe is to generate a true cylinder with square ends, the work must revolve about a straight-line axis, and the tool must traverse either of two straight lines as required; one line must be parallel to the work axis, and the other must be at right angles to it. With a new lathe these conditions should apply within 0·0002 in. per foot length when a cut is being made. Over a period of time certain defects appear due to wear, and it should be added that very few lathes escape damage due to careless workmanship. One essential point must be grasped before considering the checking of machine tools or the work produced by them. It has been mentioned previously (see Chapters XVII to XXI) that a satisfactory datum is required before accurate measurements of any sort can be made. In checking machine tools this must always be kept in mind, otherwise the work becomes meaningless. Suppose a bar has been machined between centres in the lathe. The accuracy of the bar considered as a cylinder will depend on the lathe. It might be suspected that the bar is varying in diameter along its length, and this could be determined by a suitable micrometer. It would be quite useless to mount an indicator dial-gauge in the tool-post, and traverse this along the length of the work, since the inaccuracy in the work may be due to the fact that the tool is not traversing a straight path —i.e., the shear of the lathe is not a straight edge, the dial-gauge would merely traverse the same path as the tool. If, however, the dial-gauge is guided by a known straight edge, then the datum has been provided, and the shape of the work is then being compared to the shape of the straight edge. Another method is to mount a known true cylinder in the lathe; the dial-gauge may then be guided by the lathe shear, which will be compared to a straight line on the surface of the cylinder. There are many possible lathe defects, and only the more common ones can be mentioned here.

Headstock Defects

The headstock centre line must be parallel with the bed in both horizontal and vertical planes, otherwise the lathe will not face work at right angles nor turn a parallel cylinder. It will be realised that since the facing tool only cuts to the centre, faced surfaces will either be concave or convex, according to the inclination of the headstock, the defect can therefore be detected by placing a straight-edge on faced work and the micrometer on cylindrical work. A horizontal inclination of the headstock will be much more serious than a vertical inclination; either defect can be measured by the set-up shown in Fig. 271.

The taper hole in the spindle nose may be damaged, usually by burrs being formed at the mouth of the hole. If a round bar is ground up parallel and one end is tapered to suit the spindle nose, this can be inserted and tried with an indicator dial-gauge through one revolution (see Fig. 272). One result of a damaged hole in the spindle nose is that the live centre used with work between centres revolves eccentrically—i.e., the point describes

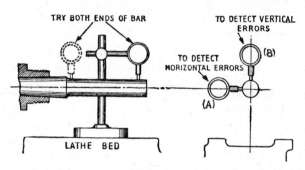

FIG. 271.

a small orbit (see Fig. 273). In consequence, the work centre also moves in the same way, and components turned between centres may show a particular diameter to be eccentric if it is near the headstock end of the work. This defect is rather puzzling to anyone encountering it for the first time. It can be detected with an indicator dial-gauge as shown. The socket should be trimmed up if possible, but if this cannot be done, the live centre should be ground to a true cone with a tool-post grinder, whilst the

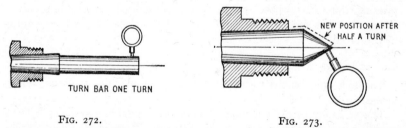

FIG. 272.   FIG. 273.

lathe spindle revolves slowly. After doing this, the centre must not be removed from the socket.

It is interesting to note that the work on a cylindrical grinder is arranged to revolve between two dead centres, thus eliminating the possibility of the live centre revolving in an orbit. This is done by driving the catch-plate round a stationary centre.

A much more serious defect is the permanent bending of the end of the lathe spindle. Fortunately this is rare, and can occur only as the result of a serious accident or the grossest misuse. There is no remedy save fitting a new spindle.

Wear in the spindle bearings causes taper work, usually accompanied by chatter marks. There may be means of taking up the wear; if not, new bearings should be fitted. Chucks and face-plates may not fit the spindle nose squarely, particularly when the threads become worn. The result is taper bores and diameters, and end faces which are not flat. This out-of-squareness is generally due to burrs on the mating faces, or to dirt being trapped. In either case the remedy is obvious.

Misalignment of the Tailstock

This may occur unwittingly as the result of turning a slow taper and omitting to re-align the tailstock. The tailstock may be fitted with a taper dowel pin to register the central position.

Wear of the Guideways

This occurs inevitably in all lathes. Generally, the wear is more pronounced at the headstock end, as much of the work will be short, and the carriage is frequently traversing this part of the bed. If a parallel ground bar with a tapered end is placed in the spindle nose and an indicator dial-gauge is mounted on the tool-post, irregularities of the front shear will be shown up. The horizontal check is most important (position A in Fig. 271), but the vertical position B should also be checked. The result of this wear will be that the work will reveal the same defects as the front shear. The remedy is to plane up the shear and either to bed it to a straight-edge or to grind it up parallel with the lathe centre line.

Chattered and uneven work is often caused by play in the guideways. This play should be taken up by means of the taper gibs or fitting slips, provided for this purpose (see Fig. 236). Besides the main longitudinal slides, the cross slide should also be corrected, otherwise flat faces cannot be produced.

Care of Lathes

The following remarks apply to most other machine tools as well as lathes.

The accuracy of the machine depends on the guiding surfaces. These must be protected from damage at all times. There is a tendency today to fit shields or covers for the guideways, as shown in Fig. 235. This is an excellent idea. Spare tools should be kept in racks, never on the machine bed, where they may be bumped on the bed, or may even become jammed between moving parts. It is for such eventualities that the slipping clutch is fitted (see Fig. 240). The machine should be oiled regularly and all swarf should be removed as soon as possible.

Periodically, the machine should be taken out of service, checked and corrected. This is work for a skilled machine-tool fitter who knows what to examine and how to rectify any defects. The machine should never be taxed beyond its capacity; this entails systematic distribution of the work in the machine-shop and clear instructions to the operators. The most important point is the proper training of young workers, and the fostering of an intelligent pride in the work done and in the machine which helps to do it.

Safety in the Machine-shop

As most apprentices spend at least some portion of their time on the centre lathe, the following points on safety in the machine-shop might be appropriate at the end of this chapter.

Shop safety is largely a matter for the foreman and his deputies, but senior workmen should be encouraged to help in this very important matter. Unsuitable clothing should be discouraged—loose flapping coats or sleeves which are wide or overlong cause accidents. The careless worker should be shown logically to what end his conduct will lead. The foolhardy should be treated with ignominy. Horseplay in the machine-shop is tempting fate. It must be stopped immediately it commences, and any workman who stops it must be backed up uncompromisingly by the management.

Guards and other safety devices must be kept in repair, and never removed by the ordinary worker. Electric wiring deteriorates in time. Whenever the insulation becomes frayed or the wire kinked it should be renewed. The modern practice of using low-voltage lighting on machine tools is an excellent idea. Tools such as spanners, wrenches and tommy-bars should fit snugly ; if they do not do so, they should be renovated or scrapped.

Factory inspectors are people with special knowledge of industrial hazards. Frank discussion places their wisdom at the service of the management ; irritation over their activities is illogical and usually futile.

CHAPTER XXIV

THE VERTICAL BORING MILL : THE PLANING MACHINE

In the machining of heavy work in the centre lathe difficulty is experienced in preventing sagging of the work and deflection of the lathe spindle. In the case of heavy shafts these tendencies can be minimised by the use of steady rests, but when large castings or forgings are being turned on a face-plate the difficulty of preventing bending of the overhung part of the lathe spindle becomes acute. The setting of such parts on the face-plate so that they revolve concentrically is very difficult, and in fact rather dangerous. The component has to be held in the crane throughout the setting, and the slight adjustments which must be made after a trial setting become tedious, as the part is hanging from chains or wires which hamper the work and obstruct the clamping tackle.

The vertical boring mill may be regarded as a lathe with a horizontal face-plate or rotating table. The work may be lowered on to the table and then manœuvred into the correct position in safety, since it will rest in any position : even with very heavy parts, movement is fairly easy with screw-jacks or similar devices. Another operation which is highly suitable for the vertical boring mill is the machining of a large number of small components to one thickness ; they are arranged round the circumference of the table and all machined at one time.

The vertical boring mill is made in very large sizes, and a typical example is shown in Fig. 274. The rotating table is supported on the underside by a circular track carried on a very substantial base. Heavy parts merely increase the load on this track, and therefore do not produce a bending moment, as would occur at the neck of the spindle of a conventional lathe.

A substantial bridge is arranged over the table. It is supported by two massive side columns, on which it can be raised or lowered to suit the height of the work. Two tool-boxes, each with its own slide, are mounted on the bridge. These slides can be swivelled to enable taper turning or boring work to be done. The worm and quadrant for swivelling the slide are shown in Fig. 275. Facing work is done by traversing the tool-boxes along the bridge.

In the heavy engineering industry the vertical boring mill has largely superseded the centre lathe, except of course in the machining of long shafts. It is a very common " first-operation " machine, being used to machine up some large face which then serves as a datum for other machining operations. Square or circular components are suitable for the vertical boring mill ; long components are best machined on the planer. This will be described next, and the similarity between the two machines will be obvious. The notes on foundations and alignments of planing machines may also be taken as generally applicable to boring mills.

Planing Machines

A large planing machine is shown in Fig. 276. The bed is a very rigid

FIG. 274.—LARGE VERTICAL BORING MILL.

iron casting, on the top of which are two slides. The reciprocating table has two slides on the under-side which rest on the bed-slides. The flat top of the table has tee-slots for clamping bolts. The bed is approximately twice as long as the table, so that the table is fully supported throughout its stroke. Two tool-boxes are carried on a cross slide or " rail ", which can be moved up and down on two strong columns attached to the bed. The size of a planer is indicated by the length of the stroke and the maximum height and width which will pass the rail and its supports.

The under-side of the table carries a rack which engages with a helical pinion. This pinion is driven by a motor situated at the side of the bed. Since the table, together with the part being machined, must be accelerated quickly to the maximum speed at the start of the stroke and retarded

[*Craven Bros. (Manchester), Ltd.*

FIG. 275.—TOOL-BOX AND SLIDE WITH QUADRANT.

equally quickly at the end of the stroke, considerable variation occurs in the power input to the pinion. Furthermore, the return stroke of the table should be made as quickly as possible, whilst the speed of the forward or cutting stroke must be varied according to the material being machined.

To meet these unusual demands, a special electrical lay-out is required, and the following is a very brief outline of the system used. A standard

A.C. or D.C. motor is used to drive a D.C. generator which supplies current to the table driving-motor. The voltage of the generator field is variable, and the field can be reversed. By varying the generator field, the speed and power output of the table motor can be varied over a wide range. The maximum power is required when the table is being accelerated at the start of the stroke, and heavy continuous power input is required when a heavy cut is being taken. High speed but lower power are required in making the return stroke. At the end of the short acceleration periods the field strength is automatically adjusted to the stroke conditions. One

[*Craven Bros. (Manchester), Ltd.*

FIG. 276.—LARGE PLANING MACHINE.

of the principal difficulties with the old belt-driven planer was that of retarding the table at the end of the stroke. When a heavy casting or forging was on the table, the momentum acquired was considerable, and was difficult to dissipate. In the case of the modern planer the electric drive forms its own brake, the generator field is reversed, and the surplus energy due to retardation is passed back through the generator set to the electrical supply lines.

It is often necessary to plane two or more small surfaces spaced well apart, as shown in Fig. 277. The table can be moved quickly to bring each face to the cutting tool, and then abruptly slowed down to the correct cutting speed. The variation in speed and torque of the motor is controlled from the table; the edge of the table is arranged to carry movable tappets which throw over suitable switches; these in turn alter the generator field by relay systems. Thus, a pair of tappets is set to reverse the table at each end of the stroke, and further tappets may be set to cause changes in the speed of the cutting stroke at appropriate points. A tappet can be seen fixed in the tee-slot under the right-hand side of the table in Fig. 276.

The tool-feed is put on before the commencement of each cutting stroke, during the over-run period. It is done by moving the tool-box along the rail, a separate motor being provided for this function. The leadscrews for the tool-boxes are shown inside the rail in Fig. 276. This motor starts up automatically when the tool clears the work, just before the reversal of the table. The tool-boxes are mounted on short slides, which normally are vertical to the table; after a cut has been made across the width of the work the tool-boxes are returned and a new cut is put on by lowering the tool-box in the slide. For machining the sides of the work two further tool-boxes may be mounted on the side columns of the planer. In this case the feed motion is parallel to the side columns (i.e., vertical to the

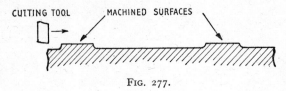

CUTTING TOOL   MACHINED SURFACES

FIG. 277.

table), and the cut adjustment is horizontal to the table. These side tool-boxes are clearly shown in Fig. 276.

The rail is raised and lowered to suit the height of the work by a motor, and since the rail must be locked whilst the cut is being taken across the width of the work, a further small motor is fitted to tighten the nuts which secure the rail to the side columns.

During the return stroke of the table the tip of the tool must not be allowed to rub along the surface just cut, and accordingly the tool is lifted clear during the stroke by means of a solenoid. The drum shaped objects just above each tool-box in Fig. 276 are the solenoids. The connecting lever tilts and lifts the tool-boxes.

The tools used are generally similar to lathe tools, but as there is a distinct shock when the tool nose enters the work, the top rake is often a negative angle, although considerable side rake may be used: tools with the usual top rake are liable to snip at the very tip, as this is the first point to contact the work. For similar reasons, it is advisable to use tools of very heavy cross-section in the planing machine.

A further point arising from the cutting arrangements is the necessity of clamping the work so as to resist the sudden heavy load which occurs at the commencement of each cut. If possible, the work should be " backed up" by a definite abutting face or " stop ", as it is termed, so as to resist the shock. Clamping the work is one of the main points in the craft of planing, and the clamping of a "tricky" job is the hall-mark of a good planer operator. The accuracy of planed surfaces is often impaired by unwise clamping : long work, particularly castings and welded structures, is usually slightly distorted, and whilst it may pull down flat to the table

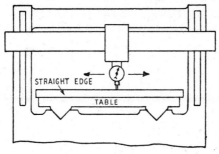

FIG. 278.

when bolted up, and be machined flat whilst fastened down, after the clamps have been released the job will spring back, thus making the machined surfaces either convex or concave. The remedy is to support the part by suitable packings, so that no distortion occurs when the clamping bolts are tightened.

Since the weight of the work and the table press downwards on the bed-slides, and these are mounted on a massive bed-casting, there is little

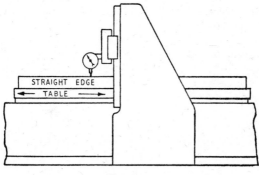

FIG. 279.

danger of deflection of the machine itself, consequently very accurate flat surfaces can be produced by careful work on the planer. When wear does take place, it is usually in the guiding surfaces, and the following description will indicate the principal tests for accuracy.

The planing machine requires a very substantial foundation, and the utmost care should always be taken when the machine is first installed. In any subsequent checking work it is essential to determine that the machine base is still level and has not moved due to subsidence of the foundations.   Careful checking of the table in all positions with a precision spirit level is the first requirement.   If inaccuracies are disclosed, these must be corrected before proceeding to other tests.

Providing the machine is level, a straight-edge may be laid on the table under the cross rail.   A dial-gauge is mounted in the tool-box, which is then traversed across the table, thus checking the accuracy of the tool-feed motion.   The straight-edge is now placed lengthways to the table, which

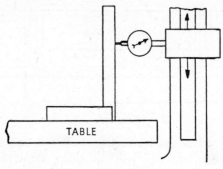

TABLE

FIG. 280.

is moved along the slides, thus moving the straight-edge under the stationary dial-gauge.   If these two motions are correct, the machine will generate a flat surface.

If tool-boxes are fitted on the side columns, these should traverse a path at right angles to the table.   The three tests are illustrated in Figs. 278, 279 and 280 respectively.

CHAPTER XXV

THE SHAPING MACHINE AND THE SLOTTING MACHINE

THE machining of small rectangular components, particularly in moderate quantities, is often carried out on the shaper. This handy little machine occupies a small floor space and is easily set up, much of the work being held in a table-vice. Single-point tools are commonly used. These are

[*Butler Machine Tool Co., Ltd.*

FIG. 281.—26″-STROKE " SUPER " SHAPER.

cheap to buy and are easily re-ground. This is in contrast to the milling machine, which uses expensive cutters. Such cutters must be re-ground on a special grinding machine. In the small workshop and tool-room the shaper is invaluable ; for mass-production work the milling machine is usually preferred.

The relative movements of tool and work are quite different from the planer, as will be seen from Fig. 281, which shows a typical modern shaper.

253

The cutting tool is mounted on the end of a reciprocating ram to obtain the cutting motion, whilst the work-table is moved to give the feed motion. The tool with its box is moved to adjust the depth of cut.

The body casting contains the driving arrangements for the various movements and also carries two slides. The top slide carries the ram, whilst a saddle is mounted on the front slide. This saddle can be raised and lowered by means of a screw-jack, and has a pair of horizontal slides on which the work-table is moved by the feed motion. The outer end of the table is supported by a slide mounted on a bracket, thus improving the rigidity. On some machines the table can be tilted and a circular setting scale is provided. This facilitates the machining of angular faces.

[*Butler Machine Tool Co., Ltd.*

FIG. 282.—SHAPER TOOL-BOX AND SLIDE.

The top slides are of V shape, and the base of the ram has slides to suit (see Fig. 281). The front end of the ram has a short slide carrying the tool-box, the box is moved on the slide by the handle at the top to adjust the cut ; a short vertical feed motion can thus be imparted for machining out a square corner. The tool-box and slide can be swivelled on the ram and set by a circular scale (see Fig. 282). By this means the tool can be fed down a short, angular surface. The tool-box is fixed to a swivel-pin near its top inner surface, thus allowing it to swing forward on the return stroke and clear the work. This motion is termed a **clapper box**, and is illustrated in Fig. 282. The collared end of the swivel-pin can be plainly seen. As in the planing machine, the feed motion is imparted to the tool at the commencement of each cutting stroke, and therefore a little over-run is required.

The quick return on the idle stroke is provided by a mechanical link motion, and Fig. 283 illustrates diagrammatically the principles of a shaper quick-return motion. The crank-pin P revolves about the centre O with uniform angular velocity : it engages with the slotted link FR, which has its fulcrum at F. The pin moves from P to P_1 during the forward or cutting stroke, and from P_1 to P during the return stroke ; thus the cutting stroke will be made at a slower average speed than the return stroke. If the arc P to P_1 represents 210° then the time ratio

$$\frac{\text{cutting stroke}}{\text{return stroke}} = \frac{210}{150} = \frac{7}{5}.$$

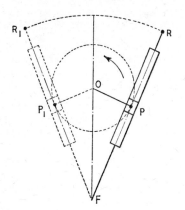

[Butler Machine Tool Co., Ltd.

FIG. 283.

FIG. 284.—STROKE WHEEL.

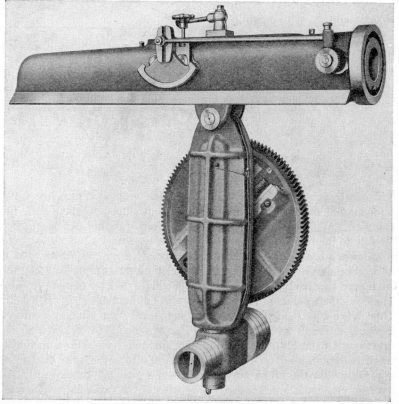

[Butler Machine Tool Co., Ltd.

FIG. 285.—LINK MOTION AND RAM.

The length of stroke $R—R_1$ depends on the radius OP, and in the actual machine, the crank-pin P is mounted in a slot on a revolving disc known as the **stroke wheel** (see Fig. 284); the bevel wheels and screw move the pin relative to the centre of the stroke-wheel. It is also necessary to be able to alter the position of the stroke—for example, a 3-in. stroke might be required at the outer edge of the work-table. To accomplish this the link end R can be moved along the ram and locked in any position. The handle shown on top of the ram in Fig. 281 is the locking handle. The path $R—R_1$ will not be a straight line if the fulcrum F is fixed. In some shapers a short link is used to connect point R to the shaper ram, but in one well-known make of shaper a trunnion takes the place of the fixed fulcrum (see Fig. 285). The lower end of the main link passes through the hole in the horizontal pin, thus allowing the upper end to move in a

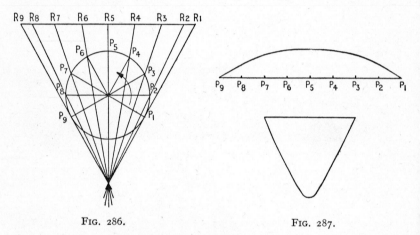

FIG. 286.   FIG. 287.

horizontal path, the shorter distance on the vertical centre line being compensated by the lower end of the link passing farther through the trunnion. With this arrangement the upper end of the link can be attached directly to the ram.

Reference has been made to average speed: Fig. 286 shows what is implied by this remark. The path of the crank-pin is represented by the circle, and the travel of the ram on the cutting stroke by the line $R_1—R_9$. The coincident points of the crank-pin and link end are P_1R_1, P_2R_2, etc. Thus, since $P_1—P_2$, $P_2—P_3$, etc., are equal arcs, the distances covered in equal intervals of time are $R_1—R_2$, $R_2—R_3$. The velocity of the ram at each instant is shown in Fig. 287. This velocity reaches a maximum when the crank-pin is at P_5. On the return stroke the same distance is covered whilst the crank-pin travels from P_9 to P_1, consequently the average velocity is much higher. The areas of the two velocity diagrams are equal, since each represents the same distance, and therefore the average height of the return-stroke diagram is considerably greater.

In giving the particulars of a commercial shaping machine, the makers usually state the maximum and minimum number of cycles per minute and the number of speeds available. The number of cycles is, of course, equal to the number of revolutions per minute of the stroke-wheel.

In shaping-machine calculations the **average cutting speed** is sometimes mentioned. This is the length of the cutting stroke divided by the time required to make one such stroke.

For example : a shaper working on an 18-in. stroke makes thirty cycles per minute. The ratio

$$\frac{\text{cutting time}}{\text{return time}} = \frac{7}{5}.$$

What is the average cutting speed?

Time for one cycle $= \dfrac{1}{30}$ minutes.

Time for one cutting stroke $= \dfrac{7}{12} \times \dfrac{1}{30} = \dfrac{7}{360}$ minutes.

Average cutting speed $= \dfrac{3}{2} \times \dfrac{360}{7} = \dfrac{540}{7} = 77 \cdot 1$ ft. per minute.

The most common work on the shaper is the production of moderate-sized flat surfaces ; for this purpose the work is placed in the vice, or is clamped to the table ; the cut is adjusted by lowering the tool-box on its slide on the end of the ram, and the flat surface is then generated by reciprocating the tool across the work and imparting a horizontal feed motion to the work-table. When two surfaces are to be machined at right angles, the larger surface is placed horizontally and is machined up ; the smaller surface is then machined by feeding the tool downwards in the short slide on the ram end. If this slide is not long enough to feed the tool across the smaller face, then the work must be machined in two operations, being reset at 90° to its original position after the first surface has been machined.

When two faces are disposed at an angle which is not a right angle, then the larger face is machined, and if the second face is narrow, the tool-box slide is turned to the desired angle. If the second face is too wide for this method, then the work must be set at an angle on the table, or a tilting table may be used.

The shaping of a regularly angled component such as a hexagon nut or a part with any number of equally disposed flats or slots is best performed with the component held in an **indexing** fixture or **dividing head**. The principle of a simple dividing head is shown in Fig. 288.

A headstock and tailstock each have a central parallel tongue on their machined base, thus allowing them to be " lined up " by means of one of the table grooves. The tailstock has a movable centre which can be locked in a suitable position. The headstock has a spindle which can be rotated but cannot be moved endways; this spindle can also be locked at any point of its rotation. One end of the spindle has a nose of similar design to the nose of a lathe spindle, thus allowing catchplates or chucks to be mounted. A loose or " live " centre can be inserted in the spindle socket. The other end of the spindle has a key.

Index or dividing plates are provided. These are circular steel discs with a central hole and keyway which are a light press fit on the spindle. Each plate has a ring of circular holes equally spaced out. These holes are at the same radius as a single hole which is drilled into the end face of the dividing head. When any hole in the plate is opposite the hole in the dividing head, a push-fit plunger can be pushed through the plate and into the dividing head, thus fixing the spindle and any work attached to it. Suppose a dividing plate with twelve holes is mounted, then the spindle can be " indexed " the following fractions of one turn : $\frac{1}{12}$, $\frac{1}{6}$, $\frac{1}{4}$, $\frac{1}{3}$, $\frac{1}{2}$, and

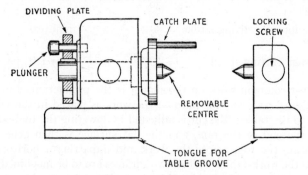

DIVIDING PLATE

CATCH PLATE

LOCKING SCREW

PLUNGER

REMOVABLE CENTRE

TONGUE FOR TABLE GROOVE

FIG. 288.—DIVIDING HEAD.

any work will be indexed the same amount. Thus twelve slots could be machined in a cylindrical job mounted between centres, or six flats could be machined on a nut clamped in a chuck.

The accuracy of the work is dependent on the accuracy of the pitching of the holes in the dividing plate and the absence of " play " in the spindle, the plate and the plunger. The plates can be bored to suit the spindle, and the plunger holes may then be set out and bored by the button method illustrated in Fig. 208. One central disc should be used for all the plates so that the pitch circle diameter will not vary. The hole in the dividing head can then be drilled from one of the plates. It can also have a hardened steel bush driven tightly in as a safeguard against wear. A set of plates as follows will cover a very wide range of work : sixteen holes, fifteen holes, fourteen holes, thirteen holes, twelve holes, eleven holes, ten holes, nine holes.

It may also be noted that a gear-wheel might be fitted in place of the dividing plate, and if this wheel is connected to the feed mechanism, the work can be rotated before each cutting stroke : thus a shape closely approaching a cylinder can be generated, if the rotation is very slow. If a form-tool with a suitable radius is used, the component can then be formed to a true cylinder.

Shaping-machine alignments

The following are certain of the alignment tests which may be applied to the shaping machine. The machine should first be tested for level with

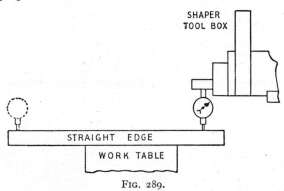

FIG. 289.

a precision spirit level on the main sliding surfaces and the work-table. Fig. 289 shows the test for determining whether the ram movement is parallel to the top of the work-table. In an old machine the work-table will be dented and marked; these defects must be smoothed as far as possible with a suitable file and a straight-edge placed on the table. The ram movement is then tried relative to the straight-edge throughout the

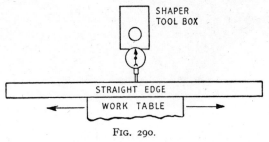

FIG. 290.

full stroke. It is best if the outer end of the straight-edge is found to be slightly high—say up to 0·0005 in. per foot—as the weight of the work will tend to depress the outend of the table. When the ram is in the outer position, as shown dotted in Fig. 289, it is as well to try the vertical " play " between the ram and its slides, since the weight of the ram will cause it to sag during the test; but when cutting, the cutting force will tend to lift the ram in most operations. If the machine-table has sides with tee slots for clamping work, then the ram movement must also be tried to see that it is parallel to these sides.

In surfacing a piece of work, the feed motion is given to the table, and Fig. 290 shows the test for this motion. The straight-edge is placed on the table, which is then moved from end to end of its travel. The shaper tool-box and dial-gauge are kept stationary during this test.

Fig. 292 illustrates the test for the short slide on the end of the ram. The graduated scale must, of course, be set carefully to zero. The same

[*Butler Machine Tool Co., Ltd.*]

FIG. 291.—SLOTTING MACHINE.

test may also be used for the upwards movement of the table which is controlled by the screw-jack operating on the saddle. In making this latter test, the ram-slide will of course be kept stationary.

The Slotting Machine

The slotter illustrated in Fig. 291 may be likened to a vertical shaper, since the reciprocating motion is vertical. The nature of the machine and the type of work performed have led to certain specialised features being included. The quick-return motion for the ram is of a different type to the shaper, it is more compact, but rather more complicated. The length of stroke and stroke position can both be varied as in the shaper, but generally the slotter has a shorter stroke than the shaper.

It would be wrong, however, to consider the slotter as simply a shaper turned on end. In certain classes of work, the slotter would be difficult to replace, and some examples will be given a little later. Furthermore, the slotter is not a light general-utility machine like the shaper, but is sometimes required to remove large amounts of metal. A special range of slotters known as " puncher " slotters are of very rugged construction : equipped with a powerful motor, they can machine out metal at a remarkable speed.

Certain of the advantages of the vertical boring mill may be noted in the slotter. The table is horizontal, and thus the work may be manœuvred

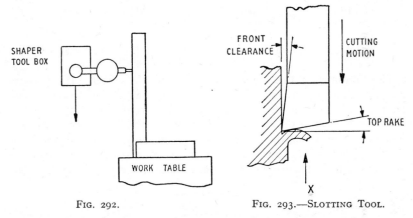

FIG. 292.   FIG. 293.—SLOTTING TOOL.

in comfort. The table is mounted directly over a bed casting and fairly heavy work may be placed on it without serious distortion.

The work-table is usually circular and can be revolved by hand or power feed ; it is graduated round its outer edge, and thus work can be mounted and turned to predetermined angular positions. The circular table is mounted on a pair of slides arranged on a saddle, and this saddle itself moves on another pair of slides on the bed casting. Thus, the work can be revolved, and also moved in two directions at right angles to each other, thus providing both rectangular and polar co-ordinate systems, an unusual feature. The depth of cut is adjusted by one motion, and the feed is put on either with the other straight-line motion or the circular motion. The tool simply reciprocates in one plane, as in the shaping machine.

Slotting tools are unconventional, and a typical tool is shown in Fig. 293, whilst two types of nose shape are shown in Fig. 294. The tool breast is thus on the end of the tool, and the nose shape sketches are inverted plan views from the direction of the arrow X in Fig. 293. These tools are robust and can be inserted into fairly small-diameter holes.   The coupling shown in Fig. 295 is typical of this class of work.

Suppose the coupling is 5 in. through from the face to the back of the boss, and after boring the centre hole, the keyway is to be slotted.   The slotting tool must protrude at least 6 in. beyond the end of the ram, as the ram cannot enter the hole.   With a rectangular nosed tool and manipulating the two straight-feed motions, the work is quickly completed.

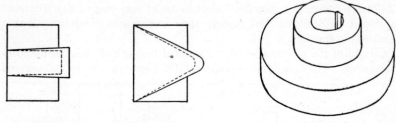

FIG. 294.—TOOL-NOSE SHAPES.   FIG. 295.

The link shown in Fig. 296 is very suitable for the slotter.   If necessary, it could be made from a solid block, a few holes being drilled to make room for the tool, and the centre hole would then be roughed out to shape. Incidentally, this is the class of work for which the " puncher " slotter is designed.   Supposing the link has been roughed out or the hole forged or cast to approximate shape.   It is set on the circular table with the inner edge of the link at a distance of 10 in. from the centre of the table.   The

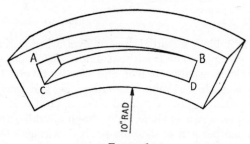

FIG. 296.

surface AB is machined with a round-nosed tool, using the circular power-feed and with the saddle locked in a suitable position.   The tool may then be reversed in the ram, and the surface CD machined.   The two straight sides AC and BD must now be machined to complete the job.   First the table is turned until surface AC is parallel to one of the straight feed motions ; this motion is used to provide the feed whilst the motion at right angles to it is used to adjust the depth of the cut.   The process is then repeated with the surface BD.

Fig. 297 shows a plan view of a splined hole with nine splines.   The circular table can be used as an indexing feature by cutting the first spline with the circular table at zero.   The table is then revolved through 40°, and the process is repeated.

With a little ingenuity, complex profiles consisting of a number of radii and straight lines inclined at various angles to each other may be machined out with accuracy.   Such profiles are required in certain classes of tool-room work, particularly in connection with dies.

A feature which is common to the shaper, the slotter and the planer is the necessity for providing room for tool over-run.   In the examples just quoted the procedure would be to pack up the work clear of the table, but in other cases it is necessary to machine close up to an abutment, as shown in Fig. 298.   This is possible only if a " landing groove " is provided as

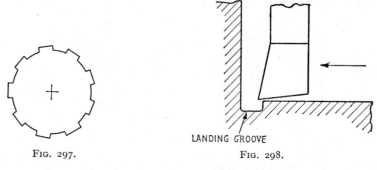

LANDING GROOVE

FIG. 297.   FIG. 298.

shown.   This may be contrasted with milling operations.   When using an end mill, no " landing groove " is needed, but profiles with sharp corners (e.g., a rectangular hole) cannot be machined : on the other hand, in horizontal milling the cutter cannot approach nearer to an abutment than a distance equal to its own radius.

CHAPTER XXVI

DRILLS AND DRILLING MACHINES

THE twist drill is one of the commonest of machine-shop cutting tools. The ordinary twist drill is made from high-speed steel and has two flutes at opposite sides. The flutes may be parallel to, but are more usually spirally inclined to the drill axis. This helix angle determines the " top rake " of the cutting edge and varies from zero for brass to 30° for aluminium; 10° being a common figure. The actual drill diameter is confined

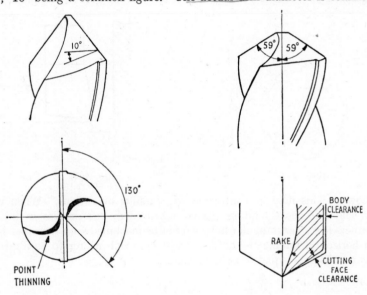

FIG. 299.

to two narrow lands at the cutting edges, thus preventing excessive friction between the drill body and the portion of the hole already drilled. The method of grinding the drill determines the " front clearance ", which is usually 10°. The drill diameter decreases very slightly from the point to the shank to give clearance in deep holes.

Fig. 299 shows the cutting angles referred to, and also certain other important features. The point thinning shown is necessary to assist the drill to penetrate the metal; the central web must be of reasonable thickness to give strength to the drill, and this thickness increases towards the shank, but the point should be kept as thin as is reasonably possible.

Drill grinding can only be done satisfactorily on a drill-grinding machine;

hand grinding should be regarded as an emergency measure only, to be used as the last resort. The factors to be considered in drill grinding may be summarised as follows :

1. The two lips must have equal angles, usually 59° as shown in Fig. 299.

2. The lips must be of equal length and have the same " backing off " or clearance angle.

[Sheffield Twist Drill and Steel Co., Ltd.
FIG. 300.—TWIST DRILLS.

These points are most important if the drill is to cut equally with both edges and is not to " wander " from the desired position nor drill over-size holes.

Certain special drills are obtainable, such as the three- and four-fluted drills used for opening out cored holes in castings. The rough surface of a cored hole tends to " bind " on a two-fluted drill, as the cutting edges are diametrically opposed ; the drill with a larger number of flutes does not suffer from this defect. Other special drills include those having passages for the cutting fluid to travel to the cutting edges ; these are suitable for drilling deep holes. A selection of straight and tapered drills is shown in Fig. 300.

Speeds and Feeds for Twist Drills

These are dependent on a number of conditions, such as apply to other cutting tools—i.e., nature of the material being cut, use of a cutting fluid, life between re-grinds—but, in addition, certain special conditions apply to the twist drill. The cutting edges are usually working at the bottom of a blind hole, consequently it is difficult to get the swarf away from the work. These difficulties increase steadily as the hole is deepened. The cutting speed of a twist drill is usually taken to mean the speed of the outer part of the cutting edges, but the speed decreases proportionately to the centre of the drill, where it is zero ; this is different from the proceedings at the edge of the normal metal-cutting tool, where the cutting speed is reasonably constant.

For these reasons the cutting speed at the outer edge of a drill is rather low compared with most other metal-cutting tools, and the edge of a twist drill is rarely travelling at more than 180 ft. per minute. The following speeds are typical of standard high-speed steel drills for various materials.

> Cast iron 70—100 ft. per minute.
> Mild steel 60—90 ft. per minute.
> 60/40 brass 140—180 ft. per minute.
> Medium-carbon steels 40—60 ft. per minute.

The actual path traversed by the cutting edge of the drill is helical owing to the feed motion, the pitch of the two helices (one for each edge in a standard two-flute drill) being equal to the feed per revolution. It follows, therefore, that the helix angle will be small for the outer edge and will increase rapidly near the drill centre. Thus the feed per revolution should be increased with increasing drill size if a reasonable chip thickness is to be maintained. The following are normal feed rates for various drill sizes and for " hard " and " soft " materials. The following are common soft materials : grey cast iron, mild steel below 0·3% carbon, brass, bronze and aluminium, whilst all alloy steels and plain steels with more than 0·3% carbon are best treated as hard.

Drill diameter, ins.	Hard materials. Feed, ins./rev.	Soft materials. Feed, ins./rev.
$\frac{1}{16}$	0·002	0·002
$\frac{1}{8}$	0·002	0·003
$\frac{1}{4}$	0·003	0·004
$\frac{3}{8}$	0·004	0·006
$\frac{1}{2}$	0·005	0·008
$\frac{3}{4}$	0·007	0·012
1	0·009	0·014

The figures given for feeds and speeds are intended to give the student some general idea of the usual amounts ; in the workshop or in rate setting the charts issued by twist drill makers should be employed.

Reamers

The hole produced by a twist drill has a rather rough surface, and is not usually a very true cylinder. When smooth cylindrical holes are required they are drilled slightly below the finished size with a twist drill, and are then opened out by means of a reamer, which is passed through at a low speed and is usually lubricated with oil.

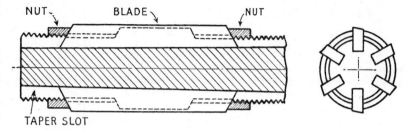

FIG. 301.—PRINCIPLE OF ADJUSTABLE REAMER.

Fixed reamers are used for a particular size of hole, but slight variations in the hole diameter can be made in the workshop by selecting reamers slightly under or over size : this selection is done by trial of the reamer with a suitable ring-gauge. Adjustable reamers are capable of variation over a range of sizes. The adjustment is made in a variety of ways, and may be a few thousandths of an inch, or as much as $\frac{1}{8}$ in., according to

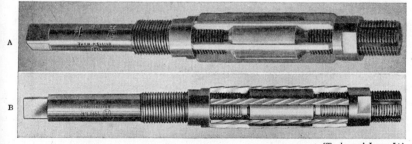

[Taylor and Jones, Ltd.

FIG. 302.—ADJUSTABLE REAMERS.

type. The type shown in Fig. 301 has a fairly wide range of adjustment. The six removable blades are moved along the tapered slots by the two nuts. A movement to the right increases the diameter. Fig. 260 shows a section through a typical fixed reamer which is described in Chapter XXIII. Fig. 302 A shows an adjustable reamer of the type just described. Fig. 302 B shows an improved type. Each of the six blades has a number of cutting edges arranged helically on the blade, providing a very large number of cutting edges. The cutting action is thus distributed over the whole surface of the hole. "Chatter" is eliminated and smooth, even reaming obtained.

The ordinary reamer has the land ground to a small relief angle, but certain reamers have a cylindrical land, all the cutting being done by the end; these are termed "rose reamers". Their cutting action is slower, but they are reputed to produce a straighter hole, as the body of the reamer serves as a guide.

Counterboring

Two-diameter holes such as that shown in Fig. 303 are often required,

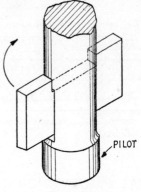

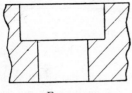

FIG. 303.

FIG. 304.

to take screw and bolt-heads. These may be made by a cutter-bar and loose cutter, as shown in Fig. 304. The lower end of the bar is a close-running fit in the small hole, and is termed a pilot, since it guides the cutter. In the case of holes of standard size, special counterbores, as shown in Fig. 305, are used.

The counterbore or cutter-bar is used for spot facing. This is the light machining of a casting round a bolt-hole to ensure proper seating of the bolt-head or nut.

Drilling Machines

The sensitive drilling machine is the smallest of the fixed types. It is

[Sheffield Twist Drill and Steel Co., Ltd.

FIG. 305.—COUNTERBORE.

frequently arranged for bench mounting. The usual capacity is from $\frac{1}{16}$-in. to $\frac{1}{4}$-in. diameter drills, but certain high-speed machines are suitable for drills from $\frac{1}{64}$ in. to $\frac{1}{16}$ in. diameter. No power feed is provided; the drill-head is counterbalanced and is fed down by a hand lever. This method enables the operator to feel the load on the drill—an important point with small, fragile drills. The speed of rotation is high; a $\frac{1}{8}$-in.-

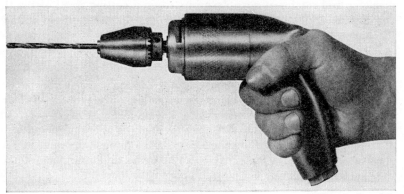

[Dessouter Bros., Ltd.

FIG. 306.—PNEUMATIC DRILL.

[Kerry's G. B., Ltd.

FIG. 307.—SENSITIVE DRILLING MACHINE.

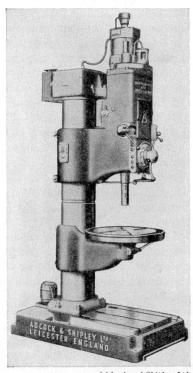

[Adcock and Shipley, Ltd.

FIG. 308.—HEAVY PILLAR DRILL.

diameter drill rotates at 3050 r.p.m. to attain a cutting speed of 100 ft. per minute. Fig. 307 shows a typical high-speed sensitive drilling machine with a range of eight speeds.

The Portable Machine

These machines are extremely useful in the fitting and assembly shops, where many small holes may be required in a large structure which could be moved only at great inconvenience. Some of the smallest electrical and pneumatic machines are outstanding examples of engineering design in miniature. These small machines are pushed through the work by the operator, but larger machines may be set up with a drilling arm and stand. Fig. 306 shows a minute but powerful pneumatic hand drill.

The Pillar Machine

Pillar machines of various capacities are manufactured, the smaller machines having a capacity of $\frac{1}{4}$ to $\frac{3}{4}$ in. diameter ; the $\frac{3}{4}$-in. diameter drill is about the largest size that can be fed by hand, and this is therefore the limit of the sensitive drilling machine. The larger pillar-type machines may have a maximum capacity up to 2 in. diameter, power feed is usually provided. An automatic stop is fitted on most machines ; this can be pre-set, and will disengage the power feed when the drill reaches the correct depth. The table of the machine can be raised and lowered to suit components of various heights. A heavy, pillar-type machine with power movement of head and table is shown in Fig. 308.

Pillar machines may have more than one drill-head, and machines with four heads are quite common. Each head has its own feed arrangements. These multi-spindle machines are useful when components with a number of holes of several different sizes are to be drilled or a hole is to be drilled and counterbored, etc. A different size of drill or a different tool is mounted in each drill-head and the component is brought to each station in turn. This method eliminates the constant changing of drills and other tools, an exasperating procedure which wastes time enormously. Fig. 309 shows a four-spindle pillar-type machine.

The four-spindle drilling machine shown in Fig. 310 has a number of interesting features. The two guide-strips on the table will locate a sliding fixture on which the work is mounted, thus bringing the work to the correct position. The multi-spindle heads will drill, ream or tap a number of holes simultaneously. The multi-spindle heads can be fitted with electric reverse for the withdrawal of taps. The two heads to the right are fitted with automatic cam feed. Once set up, the machine will perform a large number of operations on a component at a remarkable speed. It will be realised, of course, that a large number of identical components must be required to get the full advantage from such a machine.

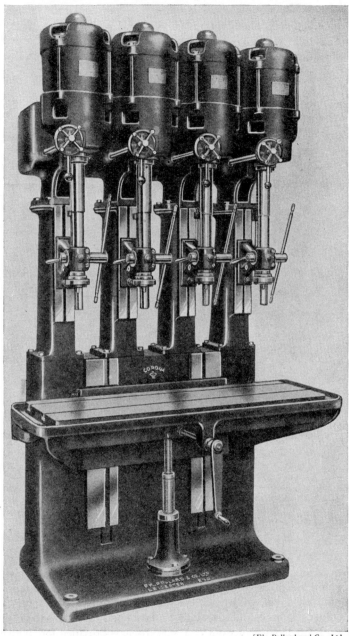

FIG. 309.—FOUR-SPINDLE PILLAR DRILL.

Radial-arm Machines

For large components the pillar-type machine is inconvenient, as the work has to be manœuvred to bring each hole in turn under the drill, then reclamped to the table. The radial machine, a typical example of which is

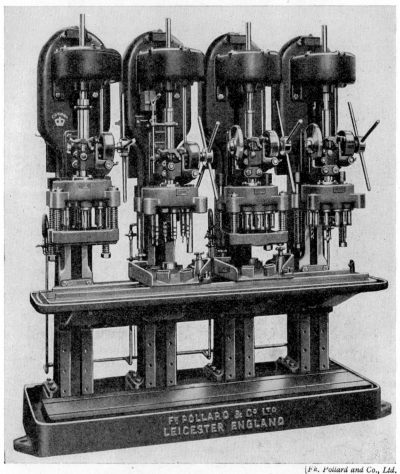

[Fr. Pollard and Co., Ltd.

FIG. 310.—PILLAR DRILL WITH MULTI-SPINDLE HEADS.

shown in Fig. 311, is the most versatile (and also the most expensive) of all the standard drilling machines. A strong and rigid L-shaped arm is mounted on a heavy circular column. The arm can be revolved in a circle over the base, and can also be raised and lowered on the column to suit different heights of work. A loose table is provided for smaller jobs. The drilling head complete with driving motor can be moved on slideways on the arm, thus enabling a hole to be drilled at any position over a considerable area. The arm is raised and lowered by power from a separate motor mounted on top of the column. All the controls are

[*William Asquith, Ltd.*

FIG. 311.—RADIAL-ARM DRILLING MACHINE.

grouped together on the drill-head for the convenience of the operator. The arm is usually swung round by hand, but when the correct drilling position has been attained, a single lever movement locks the drill-head to the arm and the arm to the column.

s

The main controls on the machine shown are as follows. The large hand-wheel moves the drill spindle quickly to position; when the drill

[*William Asquith, Ltd.*

FIG. 312.—RADIAL DRILL WITH TILTING TABLE.

touches the work, a small part of a turn of the same wheel then applies the power-feed. The smaller hand-wheel in front of the large wheel moves the drill-head on the arm. The four-spoke star wheel between the hand-wheels is used to engage and disengage the power-feed when the tool is not touching the work. The levers pointing downwards on the right are for speed changes. The upwards-pointing lever to the right is the locking lever for both the drill-head and the arm. The knob on the drum is the stop, start and reverse switch. The small hand-wheel at the bottom is for sensitive drilling. The whole set of controls is in a space of 15 in. × 23 in., and is an excellent example of grouped control, making the operations simple and speedy.

The drilling spindle of a large drilling machine must be extremely rigid, and it requires a well-designed mounting, since it must revolve at high speed without deflection or vibration, even when fully extended. The extension for feed purposes must be fairly long if deep holes are to be drilled; consequently a total feed of 12 in. may be provided. The weight of the spindle is usually balanced by a coil-spring, so that the spindle and drill are easily returned to the top position.

A depth indicator is provided, and movable stops can be set to knock off the power-feed at any desired depth and return the drill to the top position. This speeds up the work and ensures holes of uniform depth.

The radial-arm drilling machine has not the versatility of the lathe or the universal milling machine. It is a machine designed for a particular set of operations, and the design is therefore centred on a sturdy machine which is " fool-proof " and will give the greatest production. Certain precautionary mechanisms should be fitted to these machines, as the class of labour employed is usually " semi-skilled " only. It should not be possible to over-traverse the head on the arm, or the arm on the column, and a definite stop at the maximum extension of the drill spindle is required. It should not be possible to operate the arm-raising mechanism when the drill-head motor is revolving.

In the larger workshops it is usual to employ setters to supervise the setting up of the more intricate jobs, to decide on the sharpness and general suitability of tools, and keep an eye on the standard of work. Drilling is often the last machining operation, and it can be a mortifying experience to see an expensive job scrapped at the end of its course by a careless workman.

A good deal of the work of the setter is concerned with the correct placing and clamping of the work. One serious limitation of the ordinary radial-arm machine is the fact that holes can only be drilled vertically. In consequence, the work often has to be tilted at various angles. In large shops at least one machine is provided with a tilting table to facilitate this class of work, and a machine so equipped is shown in Fig. 312. For smaller jobs two angle plates may be bolted together by one bolt through their vertical faces, as shown in Fig. 313, and the upper plate can then be tilted as required. In heavy engineering special machines are used for drilling angular positioned holes. Fig. 314 shows this type of machine at work on a locomotive boiler. Vee-blocks are also in common use on the drilling-machine table.

Pole-change Motors

The necessary speed changes in some drilling machines are obtained by means of a pole-change motor and a very simple gearbox. The principle of the pole-change motor may be explained briefly as follows. The normal alternating electric current supply is 50 cycles. This means that the current passes through the mains as a series of voltage impulses, the impulse rate being fifty per second, or 3000 per minute. The simplest alternating current induction motor has two poles and a theoretical speed of 3000 r.p.m. Under load, this speed falls to about 2900 r.p.m., and may be considered invariable for normal loads. A motor with four poles has a theoretical speed of 1500 r.p.m. and a normal speed of 1450 r.p.m. The full load speed of all plain A.C. induction motors may be found approximately

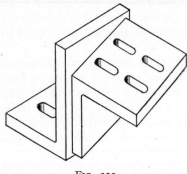

FIG. 313.

[*William Asquith, Ltd.*

FIG. 314.—LARGE PORTABLE DRILLING MACHINE.

by dividing 3000 by half the number of poles and multiplying the result by 0·95.

The motors of many drilling machines have eight or more poles, and some of these may be taken out of the circuit, thus automatically altering the motor speed. A motor might thus be capable of speeds of 2900, 1450 and 720 r.p.m. and if a gearbox with two mechanical changes is built into the drilling machine, then six speeds would be available. The four-spindle machine in Fig. 309 is of this type. The small hand-wheel to the left of each motor controls the pole-change mechanism. Further reference will be made to this question in the next chapter.

Drilling-machine Alignments

The radial-arm machine is dealt with in the following notes. Pillar-type machines are tested in a very similar manner.

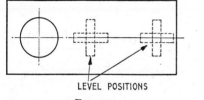

LEVEL POSITIONS

Fig. 315.

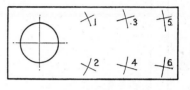

Fig. 316.

The work-table must first be tried for level in both directions (see Fig. 315). The following tests may then be made in turn.

1. Lock the spindle-feed motion in some suitable position and attach an indicator dial-gauge to the lower end so that the plunger makes contact with the table (or, if the table is rough, with a straightedge laid on the table). Swing the arm over the table and take read-

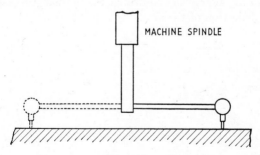

MACHINE SPINDLE

Fig. 317.

ings 1 and 2, as shown in Fig. 316. Move out the drilling-head and take readings 3 and 4, then repeat for positions 5 and 6. For each pair of readings, the drilling-head should be locked on the arm, and the arm should be locked on the column whilst the reading is taken.

2. Insert an accurately ground spindle with a suitably tapered end into the spindle socket, as shown in Fig. 318. Revolve the drill

spindle once with the indicator gauge at *A* and again at *B*. This test will determine whether the socket revolves concentrically with and parallel to the drill-head centre line.

3. Fig. 317 is self-explanatory. The test is to determine whether the spindle is square with the table.

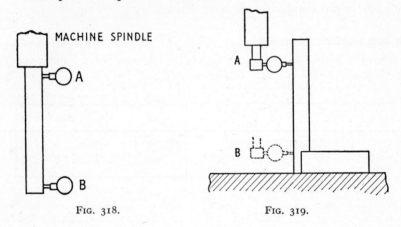

MACHINE SPINDLE

FIG. 318.

FIG. 319.

4. The arrangement shown in Fig. 319 will test the spindle feed for squareness with the table. Positions *A* and *B* are therefore the highest and lowest points of the drill-spindle.

5. Put the drill-head at the outer end of the arm, and arrange an indicator dial-gauge to measure the upward deflection of the arm. Set up a piece of metal under the drill-head and insert the largest suitable drill. Commence to drill at the normal speed and feed, and note the deflection of the arm.

CHAPTER XXVII

SPEED PROGRESSIONS AND GEARBOXES

THE question of cutting speeds and feeds for various materials and different types of cutting tools has already been discussed. In the majority of machine tools various materials have to be machined, and in certain cases either the work or tool diameter may vary. Consider the case of a centre lathe of 12-in. swing. If medium-carbon steel is being machined at 80 ft. per minute and the work diameter is 12 in., then the lathe spindle must revolve at $\frac{80}{\pi} = 25\cdot4$ r.p.m. On the other hand, if the lathe is required to turn 1-in.-diameter brass bar at 200 ft. per minute, then the lathe spindle must revolve at $\frac{200 \times 12}{\pi} = 768$ r.p.m. The two cases are somewhat extreme, since they would not usually both occur on one lathe in a well-arranged workshop; however, they illustrate the problem involved.

The work in large workshops is always " routed " to suitable machines, but nevertheless almost all machine tools require a number of different speeds; the general-purpose lathe in the small workshop or tool-room requires the widest possible speed range. The limiting feature is gearbox design.

Returning to the 12-in.-swing lathe already mentioned, suppose the maximum and minimum speeds are 500 r.p.m. and 20 r.p.m. The minimum cutting speed for 12-in.-diameter work will be $20\pi = 62\cdot8$ ft. per minute. The maximum cutting speed for 1-in.-diameter work will be $\frac{500\pi}{12} = 131$ ft. per minute. There will be a number of intermediate speeds, and the lay-out of these speeds is of great importance.

Suppose there are to be eleven speeds in all, then one method of arranging them would be in **Arithmetic Progression**. With this method the same addition is made between each speed, and the eleven speeds would be as follows.

Speed number	1	2	3	4	5	6	7	8	9	10	11
R.p.m.	20	68	116	164	212	260	308	356	404	452	500

The addition made in each case is therefore 48 r.p.m., and the formula can be deduced as follows :

Let
$$N_1 = \text{first speed}$$
$$N_n = \text{last speed}$$
$$n = \text{number of speeds}$$

Then the speed addition $(a) = \dfrac{N_n - N_1}{n - 1}$

In the case quoted $a = \dfrac{500 - 20}{10} = 48$.

If a graph is plotted with the speed in r.p.m. arranged vertically and the number of speeds arranged horizontally, it will be a straight line (see Fig. 320). However, such a speed range has serious disadvantages. If the cutting speed is assumed to be constant at 60 ft. per minute, then the correct diameter of bar for each spindle speed is as follows :

Speed number .	1	2	3	4	5	6	7	8	9	10	11
R.p.m. of spindle .	20	68	116	164	212	260	308	356	404	452	500
Diam. of bar, ins. .	11·45	3·38	1·98	1·4	1·08	0·88	0·74	0·64	0·57	0·51	0·46

Such a speed range is obviously unsatisfactory—there are too many speeds at the higher end of the range.

The usual method is to arrange machine-tool speeds in **Geometric Progression.** This involves multiplying each speed by a constant to obtain the next higher speed. Using the same symbols as before and letting r = multiplier.

$$N_1 \times r = N_2, \; N_2 \times r = N_3, \text{ and so on.}$$

There will thus be one less multiplication than the number of speeds in the range, and the general formulæ are as follows :

$$(1) \quad N_n = N_1 r^{(n-1)}$$
$$(2) \quad r = \sqrt[(n-1)]{\dfrac{N_n}{N_1}}$$

These may be rewritten :

$$(3) \quad \log N_n = \log N_1 + (n-1)\log r$$
$$(4) \quad \log r = \dfrac{\log N_n - \log N_1}{(n-1)}$$

For the speed range 20 to 500 r.p.m. with eleven speeds, the formulæ may be applied as follows :

$$(1) \quad 500 = 20\, r^{10}$$
$$(2) \quad r = \sqrt[10]{\dfrac{500}{20}}$$
$$= 1·38$$

That is, r is the tenth root of 25.

The speeds and bar sizes for a cutting speed of 60 ft. per minute may now be set down.

Speed number .	1	2	3	4	5	6	7	8	9	10	11
R.p.m. of spindle .	20	27·6	38·2	52·6	72·6	100	138·3	191	264	356	500
Diam. of bar, ins..	11·45	8·3	5·97	4·36	3·15	2·29	1·65	1·2	0·87	0·63	0·46

The distribution of speeds is obviously much better than with the arithmetic progression. If the r.p.m. of the spindle are plotted against speed numbers as before (see Fig. 321), the resulting graph will be a curve. However, if the plot is made on single logarithmic paper, or, alternatively, the logarithms of the spindle r.p.m. are plotted, then a straight line graph will result as will be obvious from equations (3) and (4).

The actual speeds chosen will depend on the particular machine tool and its function. Thus a small pillar drill which takes drills from $\frac{1}{16}$ in. to $\frac{3}{8}$ in. diameter will have a higher set of speeds than a large radial drill with a maximum drill size of 2·5 in. diameter. Again, a shaping machine may have four speeds in all to accommodate different materials and tools used, whilst a general-purpose lathe, with its versatile range of performance, may have twelve or even sixteen speeds.

For simplicity it would be best if all machine-tools had standardised speed ranges, based upon as few multipliers as possible. Considerable progress has been made in this direction. Reference has already been made

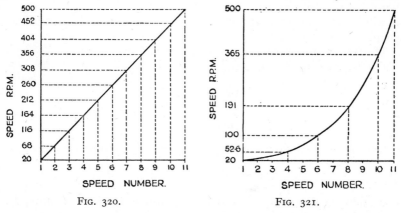

FIG. 320.   FIG. 321.

to the pole-change motors used on drilling and other machines. Consider a motor with interchangeable polar arrangements to give eight, four and two poles. The synchronous speeds will be 750 r.p.m., 1500 r.p.m. and 3000 r.p.m. These three speeds are in geometric progression, the multiplier being two and of course the number of poles is in the same progression.

That is,
$$r = \sqrt{\frac{3000}{750}} = \sqrt{4} = 2$$

Suppose it was desired to increase the number of speeds in the range, then two speeds might be interposed to give five speeds in all.

Again using the formula :
$$r = \sqrt[4]{\frac{3000}{750}} = \sqrt[4]{4} = \sqrt{2} = 1\cdot414$$

The five speeds would be :

750 r.p.m., 1060 r.p.m., 1500 r.p.m., 2120 r.p.m., 3000 r.p.m.

If the motor spindle has a gear-wheel with twenty teeth, and this wheel is arranged to gear alternatively with a twenty- or a twenty-eight-tooth wheel, then the above progression will be closely approached; and in fact a six-speed progression is available thus:

$$8\text{-pole and } 20 \times 28 \text{ gear gives } 535 \text{ r.p.m.}$$
$$8\text{-pole and } 20 \times 20 \text{ gear gives } 750 \text{ r.p.m.}$$
$$4\text{-pole and } 20 \times 28 \text{ gear gives } 1070 \text{ r.p.m.}$$
$$4\text{-pole and } 20 \times 20 \text{ gear gives } 1500 \text{ r.p.m.}$$
$$2\text{-pole and } 20 \times 28 \text{ gear gives } 2140 \text{ r.p.m.}$$
$$2\text{-pole and } 20 \times 20 \text{ gear gives } 3000 \text{ r.p.m.}$$

Such a speed range would be suitable for a drilling machine for $\frac{1}{8}$-in. to $\frac{7}{16}$-in.-diameter drills.

If further subdivision of the range 750—3000 r.p.m. was required, it could be accomplished in a similar manner.

For a seven-speed range $r = \sqrt[6]{4} = \sqrt[3]{2} = 1.26$.

It will be best to consider the question further from the logarithmic view point.

The following multipliers have been used:

$$\text{Antilog of log } 2$$

$$\text{Antilog of } \frac{\log 2}{2}$$

$$\text{Antilog of } \frac{\log 2}{3}$$

Obviously the next extension of the speed range would be a multiplier of

$$\text{Antilog of } \frac{\log 2}{4} = \sqrt[4]{2}.$$

Continuing in this manner, we should eventually reach the multiplier,

$$\text{Antilog of } \frac{\log 2}{10} = \sqrt[10]{2} = 1.072.$$

This would give quite small increments if used in a speed range, but if a still finer ratio was required, we could take $\sqrt[20]{2} = 1.035$.

We have already seen that $N_2 = N_1 \times r$, and that therefore $\log N_2 = \log N_1 + \log r$, and similarly $\log N_3 = \log N_2 + \log r$. Thus the logarithms of a geometric progression are arranged in arithmetic progression, the increment being $\log r$.

Suppose we use $\quad\quad\quad r = \sqrt[40]{10} = \sqrt[12]{2}$

then $\quad\quad\quad\quad\quad\quad \log r = \dfrac{\log 10}{40}$

but $\quad\quad\quad\quad\quad\quad \log 10 = 1$

Therefore $\quad \log r = \frac{1}{40} = 0.025$ and $r = 1.059$.

The speed range may be built up as follows:

$$\log N_2 = \log N_1 + 0.025 \; ; \; \log N_3 = \log N_2 + 0.025 \text{ and so on.}$$

Such a multiplier would give a very fine ratio, but this is coarsened simply by omitting every other term, then $\log N_2 = \log N_1 + 0.05$; and now

$$r = \sqrt[20]{10} = \sqrt[6]{2}$$

$$\log r = \frac{\log 10}{20} = \frac{1}{20} = 0.05 \text{ and } r = 1.122.$$

The ratio can be coarsened again by using

$$r = \sqrt[10]{10} \text{ and } \log r = \frac{\log 10}{10} = 0.1 \text{ and } r = 1.259.$$

and again

$$r = \sqrt[5]{10} \text{ and } \log r = \frac{\log 10}{5} = 0.2 \text{ and } r = 1.585.$$

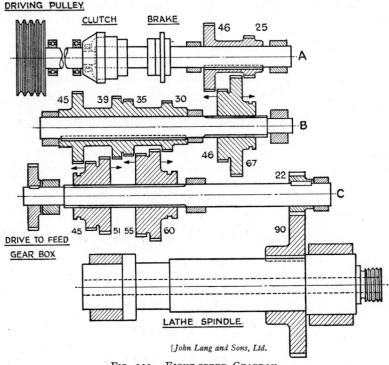

DRIVING PULLEY.

CLUTCH   BRAKE.

[John Lang and Sons, Ltd.

FIG. 322.—EIGHT-SPEED GEARBOX.

The ratios 1.059, 1.22, 1.259 and 1.585 cover most speed ranges quite adequately.   From the 1.059 ratio a series of forty numbers may be built up from which a suitable set of speeds can be obtained, starting and finishing at any desired point, and with any number of steps and using any of the four ratios quoted.   If $r = 1.059$, then consecutive numbers are taken, with $r = 1.122$ alternate numbers are taken, and so on. The numbers obtained can be multiplied or divided by 10, 100, 1000 as required. However, another simple method of obtaining a speed range once the ratio is fixed is by means of an ordinary set of logarithmic tables.

Take $r = 1·259$ and let the first speed be 18 r.p.m.

Log 18 = 1·2553 and log 1·259 = 0·1. Log N_1 will be 1·2553, log N_2 will be 1·3553, log N_3 will be 1·4553, log N_4 will be 1·5553 and so on, and the speed progression is 18, 22·6, 28·6, 35·9, etc.

Fig. 322 illustrates, diagrammatically, the application of a geometric progression in actual practice. This particular gearbox, which is that of a special-purpose lathe with a small number of speeds and a low overall ratio, has been chosen for its simplicity. The driving pulley rotates at 500 r.p.m. The pulley spindle A carries a clutch, a brake and two gears of forty-six teeth and twenty-five teeth which are firmly secured to the spindle. The intermediate spindle B has two sliding gears carried on splines, and four fixed gears. If the sliding gears are moved to the left, then the two 46T gears will mesh, if the sliding gears are moved to the right the 25T and 67T gears will engage. Thus spindle B has two speeds : 500 r.p.m. and 186·8 r.p.m. On spindle C two pairs of sliding gears can be engaged with the four fixed gears on spindle B, thus giving eight speeds to the spindle C.

The lathe spindle is driven through the 22T and 90T gears which are in permanent engagement.

The eight spindle speeds are set out below. The figures in brackets are the true geometric speeds. The slight discrepancies are due to the limitation in the size of the gear used.

$$500 \times \frac{46}{46} \times \frac{45}{45} \times \frac{22}{90} = 122 \ (122·3)$$

$$500 \times \frac{46}{46} \times \frac{39}{51} \times \frac{22}{90} = 93·4 \ (96·15)$$

$$500 \times \frac{46}{46} \times \frac{35}{55} \times \frac{22}{90} = 77·6 \ (75·59)$$

$$500 \times \frac{46}{46} \times \frac{30}{60} \times \frac{22}{90} = 61·1 \ (59·43)$$

$$500 \times \frac{25}{67} \times \frac{45}{45} \times \frac{22}{90} = 45·4 \ (46·72)$$

$$500 \times \frac{25}{67} \times \frac{39}{51} \times \frac{22}{90} = 34·8 \ (36·73)$$

$$500 \times \frac{25}{67} \times \frac{35}{45} \times \frac{22}{90} = 28·8 \ (28·8)$$

$$500 \times \frac{25}{67} \times \frac{30}{60} \times \frac{22}{90} = 22·7 \ (22·7)$$

The geometric ratio may be calculated as follows :

$$r = \sqrt[7]{\frac{122·3}{22·7}} = \sqrt[7]{5·4} = \frac{1·272}{1}$$

The **Norton tumbler gear** shown diagrammatically in Fig. 323 is frequently used to affect the changes necessary for screw cutting and for the various rates of feed of the lathe carriage. The cone of gears is connected to the long, plain gear by means of a tumbler gear which is mounted on the operating lever. To change the speed the lever is used to lift the tumbler gear; the lever and gear may then be moved endways to engage a different gear in the cone. Fig. 324 shows the shift mechanism. In the arrangement shown in Fig. 323 the speed may be varied from 1 : 1 to 1·93 : 1; in modern lathes a small gearbox with about four changes is arranged to provide further ratios, say, from 1 : 1 to 8 : 1. In many lathes the long gear is dispensed with by fitting a sliding gear on splines, this slides along with the tumbler gear. Further ratios may be provided by altering the gear-train which connects the feed-change box to the main spindle gearbox. It will be noted that the speeds produced are not in geometrical

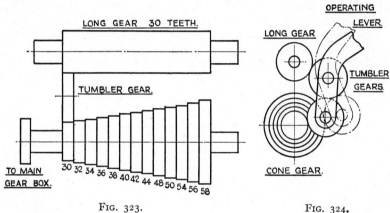

FIG. 323.   FIG. 324.

progression; for screw cutting and rates of feed such a progression would be unsatisfactory. A tumbler gearbox is provided on the lathe shown in Fig. 240. The tumbler lever is seen at the bottom left-hand corner, and by the use of other gears fifty-six feeds in all are provided. A small hole may be noted in each position of the tumbler lever. A small plunger enters this hole when the lever is placed in position, thus providing a positive lock when the gears have been engaged.

In addition to the gearbox, the variations in lathe spindle speeds may be obtained by other methods. Reference has already been made to pole-change motors, and the relationship between the number of poles and the speed of an alternating-current motor has been discussed. The alternating-current **commutator motor** is capable of speed variation, and such motors are sometimes used on machine tools. The gearbox is then simplified, but the motor-control gear becomes more complex.

The **frequency changer** is also used. To understand this, it is necessary to grasp certain elementary points relating to the generation of alternating current. If an alternator with two poles revolves at 3000 r.p.m.—that is, fifty revolutions per second—then an alternating current of fifty cycles per second is generated. This is the frequency used in almost all electrical-power stations in Britain. A two-pole motor on the public supply lines will thus run at 3000 r.p.m. when on light load and about 2900 r.p.m. at full load, a four-pole motor on load runs at 1450 r.p.m., and so on. However, if the frequency is increased, say, to 100 cycles per second, then the two-pole motor will run at 6000 r.p.m. unloaded, and about 5800 r.p.m. on full load : similarly, the speed of the four-pole motor would be doubled. If the frequency can be brought up by stages, then the motor speed will rise correspondingly, and so will the speed of the spindle to which the motor is coupled. The electrical apparatus necessary to produce the changing frequency is complicated, and includes devices for controlling the acceleration of the motor, but the essential principle is simple.

The motors referred to above are for A.C. current. However D.C. motors are also used. The A.C. mains current is altered to D.C. either by a motor generator set or by an *electronic valve rectifier*. The speed of the D.C. motor can be varied over a considerable range.

CHAPTER XXVIII

ESTIMATING MACHINING TIMES

THIS operation is undertaken for three reasons :

    1. In detail, to fix up individual times for piece-work and bonus systems.

    2. In bulk to determine shop loads for progress and planning purposes.

    3. As part of the " make up " in estimating costs for contract work.

Before any times can be decided, it is necessary to analyse the job and set down the proposed machining methods. The details of the machines available must be known—i.e., the speeds and feeds and the maximum permissible work size. Each operation may then be taken in turn, and after deciding on a suitable speed and feed, the actual machining time may be calculated.

A more difficult operation is to decide what length of time will be required to set up the work on the machine, and to remove it after the operation. These times will vary with different workmen, according to individual skill and temperament, and may also be dependent on the availability of lifting appliances, special tools and measuring devices. In practice, an average figure, based on experience, must be taken.

It will be obvious that the rate-fixer is an important person, and in fact the work can be undertaken satisfactorily only by an experienced and well-qualified production engineer. In factories where batch and mass production work is the rule there are a number of aids to the work of the rate-fixer and also that of the workman. Three of these are : *the sequence and process chart, the component sequence drawing,* and *the tool lay-out drawing.*

The sequence and process chart is a list of the operations which must be carried out on the component. Opposite each operation, the type of machine tool and the machine number is given, and also details of any special tools, gauges or fixtures required. From this chart, prepared by a senior man, the actual time required can be estimated. A simple example is shown in Fig. 325.

The purposes of such a chart may be set out as follows :

    1. The rate-fixer can decide what is a reasonable time to allow the workman for the job.

    2. In planning the future work of each shop, the " load " can be estimated for weeks or months ahead on every machine or appliance.

Thus an impending shortage of any type of tool or fixture can be foreseen.

3. In making out an estimate for tendering purposes, charts of similar components that have recently been made can be consulted.

4. The use of such charts in the workshop will ensure that each operation is performed on a suitable machine, and that any special tools, jigs or fixtures will be utilised.

Such charts may be quite simple, or, in the case of the mass production of parts, they may be very elaborate, giving the exact type of cutting tool, the speed, feed and depth of cut to be used, and so on. Such elaboration can be

PROCESS CHART			M.122/007.
NAME OF PART – TRAILER PIN.			MAT–C.H.S.
PART DRG. – P.127/071.	ASSEMBLY – REAR FRAME		
STANDARD QUAN. 300	DATE		
NO.	OPERATION.	SHOP	REMARKS.
1	CUT OFF	BAR.	4'-2" LENGTHS
2	TURN & SCREW	L.M.	WARD No 7 SEE DRG. L 028/411.
3	DRILL PIN HOLE	L,M.	MACHINES 427-30.
4	CASE HARDEN	H.T.	CYANIDE.
5	PASS TO HEAVY VEHICLE STORES		

FIG. 325.

justified only when large numbers of identical components are being made.

Before a set of sequence charts can be made, it is necessary to catalogue certain information : the maximum capacity of each machine tool ; the speeds and feeds available on each machine ; the types of cutting tools available ; all special tools, fixtures and jigs.

The component sequence drawing and tool lay-out drawing are developed from the sequence chart. They are drawings made to instruct the workman how the different operations are to be done. The component sequence drawing is really a series of small drawings showing the component at different stages of manufacture. The older method is to draw the completely machined component, and from this drawing each workman notes the dimensions appertaining to the particular operation being done. The

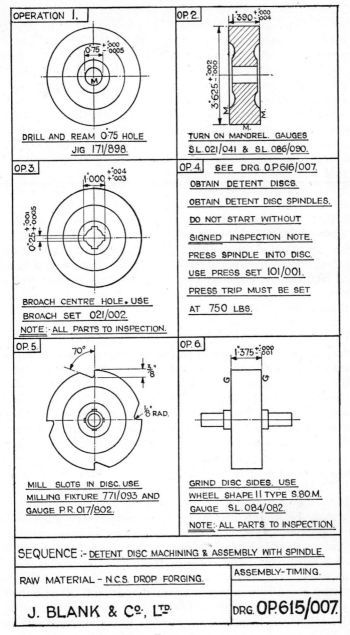

FIG. 326.

drawing has two or more conventional views, and in many cases a great number of dimensions. The method is convenient for the design and drawing offices, since it gives a complete record of the component, but it causes confusion and delay in the workshop. Where only a few parts are to be made this method is still usual, as it is cheap, but for batch or mass production the sequence drawing is more satisfactory. Fig. 326 shows a typical process sequence drawing.

The tool lay-out drawing does not usually apply to the types of machine tool discussed in this book; it is used chiefly in connection with turret, capstan and automatic lathes, presses and other mass-production machines. In this type of drawing the lay-out of tools is shown, the component being indicated as a rule by chain dotted lines. The purpose is to show the workman how the tools are to be arranged to get the most economical production : instead of each workman using his own ideas, good, bad or indifferent; the machining process is carefully considered by a skilled production engineer, and a definite method is settled. The drawings form a permanent record of this method; if improvements are discovered in the shop, these are incorporated in the drawing, and on the next occasion are applied immediately, without recourse to the human memory with all its vagaries.

Perhaps it may be emphasised, in closing, that the main preoccupation of production engineers is with the ratio $\frac{\text{production time}}{\text{total time}}$ for men and machinery. Only when a man is performing some desirable function is he of service; the main purpose of supervision is to see that as much as possible of the available time shall be spent in this way. It is only when a machine is altering the shape, size or texture of a piece of material that it is of use : preparing a machine for the material, or moving the material to and from the machine, is wasted time, and must be eliminated as far as possible. Jigs and fixtures, lifting appliances, transport facilities, a service of ready sharpened tools and accurately set measuring devices are all judged by one standard : do they shorten the time that the machines are idle? The machines and the tools used in them are all judged by the standards : how quickly are components made, and how many components can be made before the machine has to be stopped for adjustment?

These standards were, in the past, applied by foreman and manager, according to their individual temperaments; to-day the standards are applied scientifically. The name of the applied science is **Time and Motion Study.** The foreman and manager of to-day can obtain exact information how a job can best be done; they are still left with the major task, which is that of inducing men to carry out the methods smoothly and quickly. Managers have different ideas as to the most suitable inducements, but it may be noted that many successful managers are convinced that it is best to have frank discussion with the workmen about shop methods and the general policy of the firm.

QUESTIONS

1. (*a*) Define the meaning of the term **base metal** as applied to engineering materials.

(*b*) Give an instance of an expensive alloy and explain why it is expensive, and why the expense is justifiable.

2. Explain why ferrous materials are used to make the majority of engineering components. Name two parts which are almost always made from ferrous materials, and two parts which are rarely made from ferrous materials. Give reasons for your choice.

3. Define the terms **elasticity** and **tenacity**. What is the difference between them and how is a metal tested for these properties?

4. Two materials have the same ultimate tensile strength, but material *A* has a modulus of elasticity of 13,000 tons whilst material *B* has a modulus of elasticity of 6000 tons. Explain what this means and what difference you would expect to find when using $\frac{5}{8}$-in.-diameter bolts of each material.

5. Two material specifications are handed to you, reading as follows:

	A.	B.
Yield point, tons/sq. in.	16	36
Ultimate tensile strength, tons/sq. in.	33	60
Elongation, % on 2 in.	30	14

Draw the approximate load extension diagrams of the two materials on the same graph. Assume that both have the same Modulus of Elasticity.

6. Explain the difference between **elastic extension** and **ductile extension**. Draw, approximately, the load extension curve for mild steel, and indicate the two extensions on it. If the curve drawn was that of material for cold riveting, which would you consider the important points?

7. Explain why steel is heated before being hammered to shape. If grey cast iron is heated to redness and hammered, it flies to pieces: what does this statement tell you about its properties?

8. You are given a piece of brass sheet, 2 in. long, $\frac{1}{2}$ in. wide and $\frac{1}{16}$ in. thick. Suggest a method of testing the ductility of the material.

9. Look up the values and complete the following table:

Material.	U.T.S.	El., %.	Brinell no.
Grey Cast Iron .			
Mild Steel . .			
Wrought Iron . .			

10. Three samples of steel have the properties set out below :

Sample.	U.T.S., tons.	El., %.	Izod impact.	Brinell no.
A	24	34	30	105
B	80	4	10	650
C	50	16	42	280

What are the relative merits of the three steels with respect to the following properties ? Shock resistance ; cutting ability as a knife ; ductility ; wear resistance ; tenacity.

11. (a) What is the difference in action between the power hammer and the hydraulic press ?

(b) Discuss the advantages and disadvantages of drop forging compared with hand forging.

12. (a) Briefly describe the process of drop forging and name two articles produced by this method.

(b) What defect would occur if steel were forged at too low a temperature ?

13. (a) Name two articles which are shaped by cold working.

(b) What properties of a material make it suitable for cold working ?

14. Why is sheet metal annealed before it is cold worked ? If a sheet has to be heated for annealing, why should it not be hot worked to shape ?

15. In the foundry, the hardness of pig iron is usually judged by breaking a pig and examining the fractured surface. Why is this a suitable method ? What elements determine the hardness of cast iron ?

16. In casting small iron wheels for trucks and barrows, an iron bar is used as the centre core. The wheel-bore is then left unmachined. Suggest reasons for this practice.

17. Write brief notes on the following substances in relation to cast iron : (a) iron sulphide ; (b) iron carbide ; (c) silicon.

18. (a) Look up a trade paper and give the current price of pig-iron and the current price of mild-steel plates. Why is the pig-iron cheaper than the plate ?

(b) Why is it customary to keep several grades of pig-iron in a foundry ?

19. Suggest reasons why lathe beds are made in cast iron.

20. (a) Grey cast iron machines readily and no cutting solution is used. Suggest reasons for this.

(b) What is " mottled " cast iron ?

21. What would you expect the carbon content to be of the steel used for each of the following articles : motor-car body ; water piping ; vice body ; spanner ; file ; roller of a roller bearing ? Give brief reasons for your answers.

22. Name two articles which you consider would be more suitable in alloy steel than in plain carbon steel. Give the approximate composition of each alloy and state its outstanding property.

23. Explain what is meant by galvanised sheet-steel, and describe some of its uses.

24. Name four types of sheet-steel, explain briefly how each is prepared and give one use for each type.

25. High-carbon steel bar is a common engineering material, but high-carbon steel tube is most uncommon. Suggest reasons for this.

26. Suggest suitable raw materials for the following parts and give brief reasons for your answers: rivets for a water-tank; body of a small water-valve; body of a very large water-valve; spanner; aircraft under-carriage.

27. Arrange the following materials in order of ductility: pure iron; mild steel; cast iron; 80/20 cupro-nickel; 60/40 brass; malleable cast iron.

28. Explain what is meant by season cracking and describe a treatment for preventing its occurrence. A piece of 70/30 brass sheet cracks on bending; what is the remedy for this defect?

29. With what particular type of engineering component do you associate the following metals? Tungsten; chromium; zinc; molybdenum. Give reasons for your answers.

30. Describe the uses of manganese in engineering materials.

31. What is bright-drawn bar and how is it used? Discuss its advantages and limitations.

32. Give brief definitions of the following terms: billet; terne plate; seam-welded tube; free-cutting steel; rolled section.

33. Distinguish between 70/30 brass and 60/40 brass and state the main physical properties of each. Which is the more suitable for cold working?

34. Make a list of the non-ferrous materials suitable for cold working, and give one example of a cold-worked component in each material.

35. State the approximate composition of a castable alloy of aluminium and of a cold-working alloy of aluminium. In what forms can the cold-working alloy be obtained?

36. State the composition of plumber's solder and explain why it is important to have this particular composition.

37. Write brief notes explaining each of the following terms: critical range; limiting section; austenite; tempering.

38. Describe the method of hardening and tempering a fitter's chisel with a blacksmith's hearth and a bucket of water.

39. A piece of 1·0% carbon-steel bar is 3 in. diameter. It is heated slightly above the upper critical point and plunged into cold water. It is then cut in half with a thin grinding wheel, and the cut surface is tested at various points with the Brinell hardness tester. What results would you expect?

40. A mild-steel pin 2 in. diameter and 1 ft. long is subjected to a heavy rubbing action, and lubrication is difficult. Suggest a treatment for improving the surface wearing properties of the pin and describe this treatment in full.

41. Distinguish between low-temperature and high-temperature tempering, giving the actual temperatures used. Give an illustration of each by naming a part and stating the temperature at which it should be tempered.

42. It has been said that the annealing of steel is a commencing process, but normalising is a finishing process. Discuss this statement.

43. Make sketches of the appearance under the microscope of correctly normalised plain carbon steel with the following carbon contents : 0·1%, 0·4% and 0·7%. Explain why these sketches differ from each other. If the 0·7% steel is heated to 1000° C. and slowly cooled, would any change in appearance be noted under the microscope?

44. Suggest suitable heat treatments for the following parts : a chisel which " snips " at the cutting edge; a spanner which dents easily; a piece of mild-steel sheet which is to be bent up into a bracket. Briefly describe each treatment.

45. Explain what is meant by the term " critical hardening speed ", and discuss its effect on the heat treatment of plain carbon and alloy steels.

46. What are the factors which determine the time required to heat a piece of steel to its upper critical point?

47. Complete the following table, using one of the following terms in each case : good, fair, poor, none. Each material is in its softest state.

Material.	Machining.	Cold working.	Hot working.	Harden by quenching.
Grey cast iron				
Mild steel				
1·0% Carbon steel.				
70/30 brass				
60/40 brass				
Aluminium				

48. Explain why steel " scales " when heated. What are the defects associated with " scaling "?

49. Explain briefly the meaning of each of the following heat-treatment terms : carburising; refractory; secondary air; soaking time.

50. Give the approximate temperatures for each of the following operations : annealing mild steel; heating 1·0% carbon steel for hardening; tempering a carbon steel spring. Briefly outline the method of attaining the correct temperature in each case.

51. Explain what is meant by a continuous furnace. What would be the temperature arrangements in such a furnace (a) when heating steel for quenching, (b) when heating steel for annealing?

52. Describe the process of hardening a high-speed steel tool. Explain why a special furnace is required for this process.

53. Outline the essential properties of a good oil for quenching steel.

54. Why is it important to control the temperature of a furnace very closely? If the temperature of a furnace could not be controlled to closer limits than $\pm 100°$ C., what difficulties would be introduced into the heat treatment of plain carbon steels?

55. Describe the principle of the thermo-couple and explain how it is applied to the observation of high temperatures. How can a thermo-couple be tested for accuracy?

56. Discuss the relative advantages of fusible cones, thermo-electric pyrometers and optical pyrometers.

57. Write brief notes on the following moulding-shop operations : withdrawing the pattern ; feeding ; venting.

58. Describe the process of making the complete mould for a large cast-iron elbow pipe, the lower half of the mould being in the shop floor.

59. Describe the process of making a loam mould for a large rectangular pipe.

60. Describe : (a) odd-side moulding ; (b) the use of chaplets. What is a core print? Describe an application of a " loose piece " on a pattern.

61. Discuss the advantages and limitations of plate moulding.

62. Describe the following defects in a casting, and briefly explain how they are prevented : scabs ; drawing ; cold shuts.

63. What are the essential properties of a good moulding sand? Describe the tests which may be applied to moulding sand to determine : (a) its green strength ; (b) the grain size.

64. Distinguish between fixed and portable sand slingers, and discuss the types of work for which each is suitable.

65. Discuss the relative merits of " squeeze " and " jolt " moulding machines.

66. What is the difference between plain jolt moulding machines and roll-over machines? Suggest a typical job for each type.

67. Describe : (a) double-squeeze machine moulding, and (b) the under-sand-frame principle.

68. Describe the uses of the various types of moulding-shop conveyors.

69. What are the advantages of shot blasting over hand fettling of castings? Describe the main points of a small shot-blasting cabinet.

70. Reducing the dimensional tolerances on a die-casting almost invariably increases the cost. Suggest reasons for this.

71. By means of suitable examples, discuss the relative merits of die castings and drop forgings.

72. You are required to check a number of try-squares. A true surface plate and a micrometer are available, but not a true square. Describe a suitable method.

73. An end standard 12 in. long is obtained, and it is desired to make a

few end-gauges to each of the following lengths : 1·24 in. ; 0·3975 in. ; 0·875 in. Assume that grinding and lapping machines are available and explain step by step, with figures, how the end-gauges could be made.

74. What is " secular change "? How does it affect fine measurement and how can it be minimised in a gauge?

75. Give the minimum number of slip-gauges required to build up the following dimensions : 3·04 in. ; 1·10 in. ; 1·375 in. ; 4·1997 in. A standard eighty-one-piece set is available.

76. Given a set of slip-gauges, a short straight-edge and a toolmaker's flat ; suggest a suitable method of testing each of the following parts. A flat gauge 0·045 in. thick ; a plug-gauge 1·0 in. diameter ; a 1·501-in. snap-gauge.

77. Draw out to a large scale, a portion of a rule marked in $\frac{1}{16}$-in. divisions. Make a short vernier scale to give readings to 0·01 in., and fix it to your main rule at the dimension : 1·67 in.

78. Discuss the relative advantages of a 12-in. vernier caliper, and a set of micrometers to cover the range 0—12 in.

79. Make sketches of the following micrometer readings : 0·493 in. ; 0·717 in.

80. Make sketches of the following vernier readings : 0·271 in. ; 0·488 in.

81. What accuracy would you expect to obtain when measuring a round bar approximately 3 in. diameter (a) with a rule and calipers, (b) with a 3·0625-in. snap-gauge and a set of feelers? Give reasons for your answers.

82. Explain carefully how you would measure a 1½-in.-diameter hole using inside calipers and an outside micrometer. State what degree of accuracy you would expect and what precautions must be taken to ensure this accuracy.

83. It is decided to make a micrometer with thimble divisions 0·125 in. apart. If the micrometer has a spindle with the usual number of threads per inch, what will be the diameter of the thimble?

84. Illustrate with sketches, three uses of the vernier height gauge.

85. State the limit of accuracy of each of the following measuring devices and explain briefly how you would make a check if the accuracy was in doubt : a set of feelers ; a steel rule ; a vernier height gauge.

86. (a) Some micrometers have twenty divisions on the thimble. What will be the number of threads per inch of the spindle?

(b) What difference is to be noted between the anvils of an outside micrometer and an inside micrometer? Why is this difference necessary?

87. A taper gauge 1 in. maximum diameter and 4 in. long has an included angle of 10°. Make a sketch showing a sine bar set up for checking the gauge, and state the size of slip-gauges you would place under each roller.

88. Make a sketch of an angular vernier reading of 3° 40'.

89. A spirit level is 10 in. long. The bubble moves 0·1 in. when a

feeler 0·001 in. thick is placed under one end of the level. What is the radius of the tube?

90. Two flat-gauges are placed on a toolmaker's flat. Two rollers of equal diameter are obtained, and one is placed on each gauge. The centre distance of the two rollers is 1·0 in. A level with a tube radius of 120 ft. is placed on the rollers, and the bubble moves ⅛ in. from the level position. The smaller gauge is known to be 0·75 in. high. What is the height of the larger gauge?

91. Two shafts each running in two bearings are to be co-axial, and are to have their adjoining ends ¼ in. apart. Explain carefully how they could be set in this position.

92. A small eccentric is mounted on a shaft. The eccentric is supposed to be circular and to have a " throw " of 0·0200 in. Describe the fixtures and instruments required and outline a method of checking the eccentric.

93 A shaft 3 in. diameter has six splines equally spaced. The splines are each 0·375 in. wide with parallel sides, and the diameter across the top of the splines is 3·5 in. Explain how you would check the following points : (a) the diameter across the splines, (b) the diameter of the shaft, (c) the width of the splines, (d) the spacing out of the splines, (e) the parallelism of the splines to the axis of the shaft.

94. You are given a rectangular block of metal 1 in. × ½ in. × ⅜ in. thick. Outline three methods of determining the thickness of the block to fine limits. With each method, state the degree of accuracy and explain what determines this accuracy.

95. A shaft is to be 4·0 in. diameter, with a total tolerance of 0·001 in. Give the shaft dimension (a) with unilateral limits, (b) with bilateral limits. If a bush $4·003 \, {}^{+·001}_{-·001}$ in. is placed on the shaft, what will be the maximum and minimum clearances for the sizes (a) and (b) of the shaft?

96. Give a suitable size, with limits, for the bore of a cast-iron bush which is to be a light interference fit on a shaft $3·0 \, {}^{+·0005}_{-·000}$ in. diameter. State the maximum and minimum interference.

97. A hole $1·5 \, {}^{+·000}_{-·001}$ in. diameter is bored in a plate and a plug is to be fitted into it. The plug must be a close clearance fit. The maximum clearance is to be 0·002 in. Give the plug size with suitable limits.

98. A spindle is to be $2·0 \, {}^{+·002}_{-·000}$ in. long, and is to have two diameters. The smaller diameter must have a length of $1·0 \, {}^{+·001}_{-·000}$ in. Sketch the spindle and dimension your sketch. State the maximum and minimum lengths of the larger diameter.

99. A bar is to be machined $1·765 \, {}^{+·003}_{-·000}$ in. diameter, and then ground

$1.750 {}^{+ \cdot 0005}_{- \cdot 000}$ in. diameter. Calculate the maximum and minimum amounts to be removed by grinding.

100. A certain component which is mass produced in a machine-shop is to be $1.0 {}^{+ \cdot 0003}_{- \cdot 000}$ in. diameter. Large quantities are constantly rejected by the inspection department, but the shop foreman always disputes the matter. If you were asked to investigate the difficulty, how would you proceed?

101. A hole is $1.25 {}^{+ \cdot 001}_{- \cdot 001}$ in. diameter, and a shaft which fits it is $1.25 {}^{- \cdot 0005}_{- \cdot 0015}$ in. diameter. Answer the following questions:

    (*a*) Is this a transition fit?
    (*b*) Are the limits unilateral?
    (*c*) What is the total tolerance on the shaft?
    (*d*) What is the nominal size?

You should add brief explanations where you consider these are necessary.

102. The pin shown in Fig. 327 is to have the 1·5-in. dimension checked. Sketch a simple receiver gauge for this operation, and explain which parts of the gauge must be accurately made and how the gauge is set before the pin is inserted.

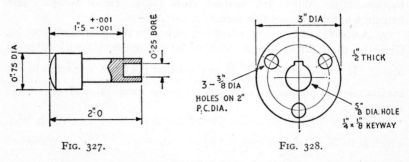

FIG. 327.   FIG. 328.

103. In the small wheel shown in Fig. 328 it is important that the keyway is on the same centre line as one of the holes. Sketch a suitable receiver gauge to check this point.

104. A 5-in. bore tee-pipe 16 in. long and 8 in. from the centre to each face has been machined on the flanges. It is to be checked to ensure that the three faces are square to each other, and is then to be marked out to British Standard Table " D " on each flange. Describe these operations in detail.

105. A round bar 4 in. diameter is to have octagonal flats machined on one end. The distance across each pair of flats is to be $2\frac{3}{4}$ in. Describe a method of marking out the bar for machining and a method of checking the finished bar.

106. Twenty-four holes each $\frac{7}{8}$ in. diameter are to be marked out in the smallest possible circle. The edges of the holes and the circumscribing circle must not be less than $\frac{3}{8}$ in. apart at the nearest points. Make a drawing of this work.

107. Twelve holes are spaced out equally on a 12-in.-diameter pitch circle. Draw two centre lines at right angles to each other and passing through the centres of four of the holes. Considering these as datum lines, state the positions of the remaining holes on rectangular co-ordinates.

108. If the three 0·625-in.-diameter holes shown in Fig. 205 have been drilled, and parallel plugs fitted, calculate the overall size of slip-gauges to check the straight-line distances between the plugs, and suggest a " build up " from the eighty-one-piece set.

109. Discuss the considerations which determine the most economic life for the cutting edge of various tools.

110. A boring tool with a depth of section of 1 in. is boring a 5-in.-diameter hole. Calculate the minimum front clearance. Suggest a means whereby this front clearance angle may be reduced.

111. A planer tool is cutting with a depth of $\frac{1}{4}$ in. and a feed per stroke of 0·010 in. The chip of metal presses on the tool with an intensity of 180,000 lb. per sq. in. What is the load on the tool?

112. Briefly describe two methods of generating a flat surface. Would you consider the lathe parting-off tool to be a form tool? Give reasons for your answer.

113. A lathe tool is cutting a bar 4 in. diameter revolving at a speed of 110 r.p.m. The depth of cut is $\frac{3}{16}$ in., and the feed is 0·016 in. per revolution. Calculate (a) the cutting speed in feet per minute, (b) the volume of metal removed in cub. in. per minute.

114. Explain the function of the leadscrew of a centre lathe. Could a lathe leadscrew be used to graduate a rule? Outline the principle involved and state the conditions which must be maintained to ensure accurate graduation.

115. It is not usual to have power-feed to the top slide of a lathe. Why is this so? What is the purpose of arranging the top slide with a swivelling motion? Can the top slide be used to turn cylindrical work?

116. A mandrel 16 in. long is to be turned in a lathe to a taper of 0·012 in. per foot on the diameter. Calculate a suitable set-over for the tailstock. If several mandrels were required, what precautions would be required to ensure that all had the same taper?

117. Sketch a simple component suitable for manufacture between centres in a lathe and describe its manufacture.

118. Cast-iron rings 6 in. diameter, 1 in. wide and 5·25 in. bore have been turned in a centre lathe. It is desired to reduce the width slightly. With the aid of sketches, show how this could be done.

119. A right-angled plate with faces 1 ft. square is to have a 4-in.-

diameter hole bored in the centre of one face. Explain, with sketches, how this operation could be done on a centre lathe.

120. A bar $1·5 {}^{+·002}_{-·000}$ in. diameter and 18 in. long is to be turned from $1\frac{3}{4}$-in.-diameter black bar and a hole $\frac{1}{2}$ in. diameter, 2 in. deep, is to be drilled up one end of it. Describe these processes as performed on a centre lathe.

121. Calculate suitable change-wheels for cutting the following threads : 17 T.P.I.; $5\frac{1}{4}$ T.P.I. The lathe used has a 2 T.P.I. leadscrew. .

122. Discuss the factors which influence the depth of cut used in various lathe operations.

123. What parts of a lathe take the thrust of cutting : (a) in turning bars with a knife-tool, (b) in surfacing the end of a cylinder ?

124. A lathe is turning all work to a slight but irregular taper at one end. Suggest possible causes for this defect, and explain how it may be rectified.

125. A casting gripped in a lathe chuck is bored out 3 in. diameter to a depth of 2 in. It is found that the hole is 0·002 in. bigger in diameter at the bottom than at the top. What is wrong with the lathe and how can it be corrected?

126. An annular groove in a shaft is 0·4 in. deep, 0·7 in. wide at the top and 0·5 in. wide at the bottom. It is turned in a lathe with a form-tool which has no top-rake and 6° front clearance angle. Calculate the dimensions of the tool nose measured at right angles to the clearance face, and sketch the tool.

127. Contrast the following operations as performed on an ordinary lathe and on a vertical boring mill : (a) facing up the flanges of a short pipe of large diameter; (b) boring a hole approximately 2 ft. diameter with a taper of 10° included angle in a casting 2 ft. 6 in. diameter and 4 ft. long.

128. What defects would you expect to find in work machined on a planer : (a) with a worn cross slide ; (b) with worn table guideways?

129. Two mild-steel bars each 1 ft. long and 1 in. square section are fastened to a planer table. One is lightly machined with a single-point tool in the usual way ; the other is lightly machined with a flat-nose tool $1\frac{1}{4}$ in. wide, no cross-feed being used. What differences might be found in the two surfaces and why would this difference occur?

130. A small rectangular block machined on three faces on a shaping machine at one setting has two vertical faces slightly inclined to each other. What defect in the shaping machine would produce this defect?

131. A casting has two machined faces which are known to be parallel to each other. It is placed on a shaping machine with one face clamped down to the machine-table, and the other face is then machined up again. It is discovered that the two surfaces are no longer parallel to each other. How would this defect arise, and how can its re-occurrence be prevented?

132. The stroke-wheel of a shaping machine revolves at 40 r.p.m. The shaper stroke is 14 in., and the ratio $\dfrac{\text{cutting time}}{\text{total time}}$ is $\dfrac{7}{12}$. What is the average cutting speed in feet per minute?

133. The rectangular face of a forging is 12 in. × 8 in., and is to be machined on a shaping machine. The over-run at each end of the stroke is to be $1\frac{1}{2}$ in. and the average cutting speed is 60 ft. per minute. The ratio $\dfrac{\text{cutting time}}{\text{return time}}$ is $\dfrac{9}{7}$. Calculate the minimum cutting time at $\frac{1}{64}$-in. feed per stroke.

134. Explain carefully how you would drill and spot-face the holes in the tee-pipe described in Q. 89.

135. Calculate a suitable speed in r.p.m. for a 1-in.-diameter H.S.S. drill working in mild steel. If such a drill when working on a steel block is dulled at the cutting edge after a few minutes drilling, what are the most probable causes?

136. A radial-arm drilling machine has a loose table. The table is put in position with swarf underneath one edge. What will be the effect on the following operations : (a) drilling and counterboring a hole in a casting which is resting on a machined face on the table ; (b) reaming a hole which has already been drilled squarely to a machined face ; (c) drilling a hole through a shaft held in vee-blocks, the hole being intended to pass through the axis of the shaft?

137. In spot-facing a surface with a loose cutter fixed in a cutter bar, upon what does the flatness of the surface depend? Suggest suitable speeds in r.p.m. for the following operations : (a) spot-facing grey cast iron to a diameter of 3 in. with a high-carbon steel cutter ; (b) drilling $\frac{1}{2}$-in.-diameter holes to a depth of 6 in. in mild steel with a H.S.S. drill. Give reasons for your answers and mention any special precautions that should be taken.

138. Complete the following table for not less than five machine tools. The centre lathe is given as an example :

Machine tool.	Operation.	Cutting motion.	Feed motion.	Motion to adjust cutting depth.
Centre lathe.	Generating cylinder.	Work revolves.	Tool moves in straight line.	Tool moves in straight line.

139. The following are all centre lathe operations : generating a cylinder ; generating a cone ; generating two parallel flat surfaces ; producing a round hole ; producing an internal thread ; forming annular grooves on a cylinder. Take each operation in turn and suggest another machine tool and briefly describe how the operation would be performed on this machine tool.

140. Calculate a suitable speed range for a drilling machine for H.S.S. twist drills from $\frac{3}{8}$ in. to 1 in. diameter.

141. Lay out a speed range with twelve speeds for a centre lathe, starting at 14 r.p.m. The highest speed is to give a cutting speed of 120 ft. per minute on a bar 1 in. diameter.

142. A geometric progression is to have eight speeds beginning with 18 r.p.m. and extending to 90·2 r.p.m. Calculate the common ratio and the remaining six speeds.

143. Show whether the following speeds are in a geometric progression : 10·5, 11·27, 12·11, 13, 13·96, 15, 16·22, 17·42, 18·71. If necessary, correct the speeds to give a true geometric progression.

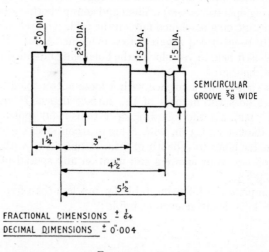

FRACTIONAL DIMENSIONS $\pm \frac{1}{64}$
DECIMAL DIMENSIONS $\pm 0''\!\cdot\!004$

Fig. 329.

144. Estimate a machining time for making ten pins in the centre lathe to the particulars given in Fig. 329.

145. Four rings, each 8 in. diameter, 6 in. bore and 2 in. wide, are to be made from the grey iron casting shown in Fig. 330. Calculate a suitable machining time. The finished rings are to have a tolerance of 0·004 in. on all dimensions.

146. Give a suitable machining time for shaping the surfaces marked M and drilling the two holes in the mild-steel component shown in Fig. 331.

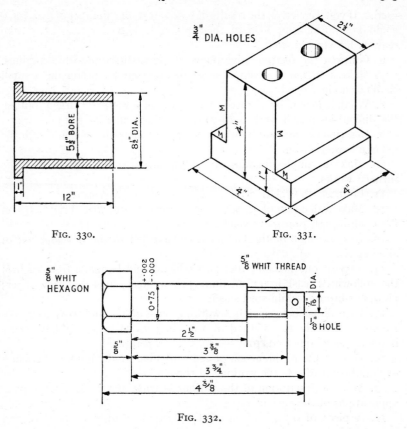

FIG. 330.

FIG. 331.

FIG. 332.

147. Estimate a total machining time, including drilling the hole for sixteen bolts to the particulars given in Fig. 332. The bolts are to be made from bright-drawn hexagon bar in a centre lathe.

SECTION B

1. Explain why the extensometer used in the tensile test requires to register very accurately. An extensometer is mounted on gauge points 2·0 in. apart on a mild-steel specimen. A tensile stress of 4 tons/sq. in. is induced. Calculate the extension recorded. $E = 13,000$ tons.

2. (a) Make a sketch of a well-known type of extensometer.

(b) Explain why the length between gauge point and diameter of a tensile test specimen must always be measured accurately.

3. Describe the Brinell hardness test and discuss its limitations.

4. Briefly outline the various tests which indicate the ductility of a material.

5. Make a sketch of the Izod impact testing machine and the specimen

used. If you were given the results of tensile tests of a number of materials, could you form some idea of their probable impact strengths? Give reasons for your answer.

6. Contrast the relative advantages of die castings and drop forgings.

7. Make a sketch of a simple press tool lay-out for producing a small shallow cup in 70/30 brass.

8. What is meant by the work hardening of a metal? Briefly outline the difficulties which work hardening introduces into press-tool work.

9. Describe the method by which a simple iron casting is made with the aid of a loose pattern.

10. Make a simple diagram of a blast furnace and explain how the furnace works.

11. Contrast the relative merits of iron and steel castings.

12. Make a diagram of an open-hearth furnace and write brief notes on the open-hearth process of steel-making.

13. Discuss some of the factors that have led to the development of alloy steels.

14. Suggest one machine-tool part which could be made from each of the following : cast iron ; medium-carbon steel ; nickel-chrome steel ; phosphor-bronze ; mild-steel sheet.

15. Distinguish between a hot-working brass and a cold-working brass. Describe carefully the method of annealing 70/30 brass. What occurs if this brass is annealed from too high a temperature?

16. Discuss the phenomenon of age hardening in aluminium alloys and explain how it affects the working of these alloys.

17. Write a description of the various bearing metals and give typical applications of the various types.

18. A piece of 0·7% carbon steel is heated steadily to 800° C. and quenched in water. It is then reheated to 800° C. and cooled very slowly. Describe the various structural changes which occur during these processes.

19. Describe carefully, with the aid of sketches, how martensite breaks down in the tempering of a high-carbon steel.

20. Describe the process of case hardening mild steel, and explain the necessity for the various operations.

21. Discuss the problem of distortion in the heat treatment of steel and explain how it is minimised.

22. How and why is bright annealing performed?

23. Outline the process of hardening and tempering a nickel-chrome molybdenum steel. Give approximately the variation in physical properties obtained by alteration to the tempering temperature of this steel.

24. Make a sketch of a salt-bath furnace, explain its function and give the composition of the salt used.

25. Make a sketch of an industrial thermo-couple. What are the relative merits of the different materials used for thermo-couples?

26. Write a brief description of the manufacture of slip gauges.

27. Describe with the aid of sketches, the principle of any comparator with which you are familiar.

28. Sketch and describe a bench micrometer fitted with a fiducial indicator.

29. Briefly describe the use of slip-gauge accessories and give three typical applications.

30. (a) Make a sketch showing how an outside micrometer is adjusted for wear.

(b) Give the number of threads per unit of length on the spindle and the number of thimble divisions of a micrometer reading to 0·01 m/m.

31. Make a sketch and explain the principle of a clinometer.

32. Describe an optical projector and explain how it is used.

33. What is an auto-collimator and how is it used?

34. Make sketches of a limit-gauge for a taper hole and a limit depth-gauge.

35. Describe a limit system with which you are familiar and explain how the part drawings, the gauges and the inspection procedure are linked up.

36. Describe with the aid of sketches, the use of fixed bushes and slip-bushes in jig work.

37. Discuss the various methods used in the machine-shop to produce flat surfaces; divide the methods into generating processes and forming processes.

38. Write an account of the methods of manufacture of metallic carbide tips for cutting tools.

39. Discuss the influence of top rake on lathe form-tools, and explain how the Whitworth thread form-tool is modified if top rake is used.

40. Make a sketch showing the bearings and mounting of a lathe spindle.

41. It is desired to cut a thread of 3 m/m pitch, single start, on a lathe with a $\frac{1}{2}$-in.-pitch leadscrew. Calculate suitable change-wheel sizes.

42. Discuss the various causes of " chattered " work in the centre lathe and suggest suitable remedies.

43. Describe a suitable method of determining: (a) that a lathe bed 40 ft. long is level throughout its length; (b) that the headstock and tailstock centres are co-axial.

44. Discuss the advantages of fitting automatic " sizing " devices to machine tools. Sketch and describe one such device.

45. A large factory with a wide variety of machinery is setting up a machine-shop for maintenance purposes. Choose about ten machine tools to equip this shop and explain the reasons for your choice.

46. Make a sketch of a boring tool for use on long bores such as gun-barrels, and explain the working principle.

47. Describe a method of producing a rough vee-thread in a hole with

U

a single-point tool mounted on a drilling-machine spindle. On what factors would the accuracy of the thread depend? What features would limit the number of thread pitches that could be produced?

48. Describe an inspection system with which you are familiar and state what occurs : (*a*) when a part is rejected by inspection ; (*b*) when a part is outside the drawing limits but can be rectified ; (*c*) when a part is wrong and cannot be made to coincide with the drawing, but is considered usable if slight modifications are made. If you consider that the system is faulty, suggest improvements.

A SELECTION OF BRITISH STANDARD SPECIFICATIONS

British Standard Specifications are issued by the British Standards Institution. This Institution was formed to ensure that the minimum number of different components should be made to perform any given function; that all components should be made from the most suitable material; that sound designs should be used; to form a basis of agreement between manufacturers and users. Manufacturers can thus be protected against unreasonable demands and customers can be protected against badly designed and unsuitable parts.

The various branches of industry nominate experts from their staffs and various committees consisting of industrial representatives, government representatives and representatives of the professional institutions meet to deliberate on each specification before it is issued. From time to time, each specification is reviewed to see if it can be improved in the light of experience. The following specifications are of particular importance to production engineers. In each case the specification number and the year of issue are stated.

4—1932. Channels and beams for structural purposes.

10—1928–32. Tables of pipe flanges for land use.

18—1938. Tensile testing of metals.

21—1938. Pipe threads.

29—1941. Carbon steel forgings for ship and marine engine purposes.

32—1935. Steel bars for the production of machined parts for general engineering purposes.

51—1939. Wrought iron for general engineering purposes.

84—1940. Screw threads of Whitworth form.

122—1938. Milling cutters and reamers.

131—1933. Notched bar test-pieces.

224—1938. Steel for die blocks for drop-forging.

240—1937. Brinell hardness testing, methods and tables for.

249—1940. Brass bars (high-speed screwing and turning).

250—1940. High-tensile brass bars and sections.

251—1940. Naval brass (Admiralty mixture) bars and sections (suitable for machining and forging) and forgings.

252—1940. Naval brass (special mixture) bars and sections (suitable for machining and forging) and forgings.

265, 266, 267—1936. Cold-rolled brass sheets, strip and foil.

308—1943. Engineering drawing-office practice.

321—1938. General grey iron castings.

328—1928. Twist and straight flute-drills.

361, 362, 363—1929. Aluminium alloy castings.

369—1940. Phosphor-bronze bars and rods for general engineering purposes.

382, 383—1940. Bronze (gun-metal) ingots and castings for general engineering purposes.

395, 396—1930. Wrought light aluminium alloy (duralumin) sheets, strips and tubes for general engineering purposes.

414—1931. Wrought light aluminium alloy (Y Alloy) sheets and strip (heat treated) for general engineering purposes.

426—1931. Lathe centres.

427—1931. Diamond pyramid hardness numbers, tables of.

436—1940. Machine-cut gears. A. Helical and straight spur.

477—1933. Wrought light aluminium alloy (duralumin), bars for general engineering purposes.

478—1933. Wrought Y-alloy bars for general engineering purposes.

485—1934. Tests on thin metal sheet and strip.

498—1933. Engineer's files and rasps.

499—1939. Welding and cutting, nomenclature, definitions and symbols for.

532—1934. Light aluminium alloy (duralumin) forgings for general engineering purposes.

533—1934. Y-alloy forgings for general engineering purposes.

592—1940. Carbon steel castings for ships, and for marine engines and general engineering purposes.

600R—1942. Quality control charts.

620—1935. Dimensions of grinding wheels and methods of attachment.

711–713—1936. Cold-rolled brass sheets, strips and foil.

739—1937. Machine-tool elements, dimensions for.

754—1937. System for the direction of rotation of machine-tool hand-wheels and levers relative to movement produced.

786—1938. High-duty iron castings.

817—1938. Cast-iron surface plates and tables for inspection and marking purposes.

818—1938. Cast-iron straight edges.

847—1939. Cold-rolled mild-steel strip for general engineering purposes.

852—1939. Tool-maker's straight edges.

863—1939. Steel straight edges of rectangular section.

869—1939. Tool-maker's flats and high-precision surface plates.

870—1939. Micrometers (external).

887—1940. Vernier callipers.

888—1940. Slip (or block) gauges and their accessories.

891—1940. Method for direct-reading hardness testing (Rockwell principle).

906—1940. Engineer's parallels (steel).

907—1940. Dial-gauges for linear measurements.

919—1940.   Screw-thread-gauge tolerances.

939—1941.   Engineer's squares.

949—1941.   Screwing taps, dimensions, limits and tolerances for.

957—1941.   Feeler-gauges.

958—1941.   Precision levels for engineering workshops.

959—1941.   Internal micrometers.

969—1941.   Tolerances for plain limit-gauges.

970—1947.   Wrought steels.

971—1944.   Wrought steels (companion document to BSS 970).

979—1941.   Test code for open-hearth melting furnaces for the refining of steel.

985—1941.   Combined drills and countersinks, dimensions of.

991—1941.   Data on cast-iron.

1001-2—1941.   High-tensile brass bars and sections.

1003-4—1942.   High-purity zinc and zinc alloys.

1021-8 and 1158-9—1944.   Copper-alloy ingots and castings.

1041—1943.   British Standard code for temperature measurement.

1044—1942.   Recommended designs for plug-ring and gap-gauges.

1052—1942.   Mild steel wire for general engineering purposes.

1054—1942.   Engineer's comparators for external measurements.

1958-61—1942.   Phosphor-bronze and leaded-bronze ingots and castings.

1089—1942.   Workhead spindles for internal and universal grinding machines, including plain grinding machines with live spindles.

1098—1943.   Dimensions of drilling jig-bushes.

1100—1943-6.   Office aid to the factory.

1111—1943.   Summary of British and American standard specifications for iron and steel.

1119—1943.   High-speed steel butt-welded blanks for shanked type cutting tools.

1120—1943.   Diamond-tipped boring tools.

1131—1943.   Bronze oil-retaining bearings.

1148—1943.   Diamond-tipped turning tools.

1157—1944.   Tapping-drill sizes.

1161—1944.   Aluminium-alloy sections.

1272-1280—1945.   Magnesium-alloy ingots and castings.

1296—1946.   Shapes of butt-welded lathe and planer tools.

1916—1953.   Limits and fits for engineering.

Handbook No. 2.   British Standards for workshop practice.

BIBLIOGRAPHY

" Practical Microscopical Metallography," Greaves and Wrighton. (Chapman and Hall.)

" Metallurgy for Engineers," E. C. Rollason. (Edward Arnold.)

" Engineering Materials " (2 vols.), A. W. Judge. (Pitman.)

" Modern Metallurgy for Engineers," F. T. Sisco. (Pitman, N.Y.)

" The Structure of Steel," E. N. Simons and E. Gregory. (Blackie.)

" Steel Manufacture," E. Gregory and E. N. Simons. (Pitman.)

" Steels for the User," R. T. Rolfe. (Chapman and Hall.)

" The Mechanical Working of Steel," E. Gregory and E. N. Simons. (Pitman.)

" The Alloys of Iron and Carbon " (2 vols.), S. Epstein and F. T. Sisco. (McGraw-Hill.)

" Introduction to Ferrous Metallurgy," E. C. Teichert. (McGraw-Hill.)

" The Manufacture and Fabrication of Steel," E. C. Teichert. (McGraw-Hill.)

" Metallography and Heat Treatment of Steel," E. C. Teichert. (McGraw-Hill.)

" Metallography and Heat Treatment of Iron and Steel," A. Sauveur. (McGraw-Hill.)

" Steel and its Practical Applications," Barr and Honeyman. (Blackie.)

" What is Steel ? " Leopold Scheer. (Macdonald and Evans.)

" The Physical Structure of Alloys," C. E. Beynon. (Edward Arnold.)

" Principles of Powder Metallurgy," W. D. Jones. (Edward Arnold.)

" High-speed Steel," Grossman and Bain. (John Wiley, N.Y.)

" The Alloys of Iron and Silicon," Greiner, Marsh and Stoughton. (McGraw-Hill.)

" Chromium Steels," R. H. Greaves. (H.M.S.O.)

" The Alloys of Iron and Molybdenum," J. L. Gregg. (McGraw-Hill.)

" The Alloys of Iron and Chromium," Kinzel and Crafts. (McGraw-Hill.)

" The Alloys of Iron and Tungsten," J. L. Gregg. (McGraw-Hill.)

" The Strength of Materials," A. Morley. (Longmans, Green.)

" The Hardness of Metals," F. C. Lea. (Griffin.)

" Creep of Metals," H. J. Tapell. (Oxford Univ. Press.)

" Mechanical Testing," Batson and Hyde. (Chapman and Hall.)

" Testing and Inspection of Engineering Materials," Davis, Troxell and Wiskocil. (McGraw-Hill.)

" The Hardness of Metals and its Measurement," H. O'Neill. (McGraw-Hill.)

" The Heat Treatment of Steel," E. Gregory and E. N. Simons. (Pitman.)

" Applied Chemistry for Engineers," E. S. Gyngell. (Edward Arnold.)

" Modern Furnace Technology," H. Etherington. (Griffin.)

" Principles of Heat Treatment," M. A. Grossman. (Am. Society of Metals, Cleveland.)

" Metal Spraying and Sprayed Metal," W. E. Ballard. (Griffin.)

" Duralumin and its Heat Treatment," P. L. Seed. (Griffin.)

" Temperature Control," A. J. Ansley. (Chapman and Hall.)

" Heat Treatment of Iron and Steel" (2 vols.), D. K. Bullens. (John Wiley, N.Y.)

" General Foundry Practice," McWilliam and Longmuir. (Griffin.)

" Modern Foundry Practice," E. P. Arnold. (Odhams Press.)

" A Manual of Foundry Practice," J. Laing and R. T. Rolfe. (Chapman and Hall.)

" Press-tool Practice " (3 vols.), P. S. Houghton. (Chapman and Hall.)

" Engineering Precision Measurements," A. W. Judge. (Chapman and Hall.)

" Toolroom Practice " (5 vols.). (Yellow Back Series.) (Machinery Pub. Co.)

" Precision Workshop Methods," H. J. Davies. (Edward Arnold.)

" Gauging and Fine Measurements " (3 vols.), F. H. Rolt. (Macmillan.)

" Gauge Design and Gauge-making." (Industrial Press.)

" Dictionary of Applied Physics," R. T. Glazebrook.   (Macmillan.)
" Optical Measuring Instruments."   (Paul Elek.)
" Gauge-making."   (H.M.S.O.)
" Screw Gauges."   (H.M.S.O.)
" Precision Measurement in the Metal-working Industry " (2 vols.).   (Syracuse University Press, N.Y.)
" Production Engineering Jig and Tool Design," E. J. H. Jones.   (Newnes.)
" Principles of Interchangeable Manufacture."   (Industrial Press.)
" Jigs, Tools and Fixtures," P. Gates.   (Technical Press.)
" Jigs and Fixtures," F. H. Colvin and L. L. Haas.   (McGraw-Hill.)
" Engineering Inspection Practice," A. T. King.   (Newnes.)
" Cutting Tools for Metal Machining," M. Kurrein and F. C. Lea.   (Griffin.)
" Modern Machine Tools," H. C. Town.   (Pitman.)
" Magnetic Tools and Appliances in Engineering Production," E. Malloy.   (Newnes.)
" Cutting-tool Practice," Town and Potter.   (Paul Elek.)
" Turning and Boring Practice," F. H. Colvin and F. A. Stanley.   (McGraw-Hill.)
" Drilling and Surfacing Practice," F. H. Colvin and F. A. Stanley.   (McGraw-Hill.)
" Grinding Practice," F. H. Colvin and F. A. Stanley.   (McGraw-Hill.)
" Gear-cutting Practice," F. H. Colvin and F. A. Stanley.   (McGraw-Hill.)
" Machine-tools and their Operation," F. H. Colvin and F. A. Stanley.   (McGraw-Hill.)
" Running a Machine-shop," F. H. Colvin and F. A. Stanley.   (McGraw-Hill.)
" Running an Engine Lathe," F. H. Colvin and F. A. Stanley.   (McGraw-Hill.)
" Running a Milling Machine," F. H. Colvin.   (McGraw-Hill.)
" Machine-tools at Work," C. O. Herb.   (Industrial Press.)
" Engineering Machine-shop Practice," B. R. Hilton.   (Pitman.)
" Testing Machine-tools," G. Schlesinger.   (Machinery Pub. Co.)
" Design and Shop Practice," R. T. Kent.   (John Wiley, N.Y.)
" Workshop Practice " (8 vols.), W. H. Atherton.   (Pitman.)
" Workshop Practice," E. Pull and F. J. Taylor.   (Technical Press.)
" Engineering Tools and Processes," H. Hesse.   (D. Van Nostrand, N.Y.)
" Workshop Technology " (2 vols.), W. A. J. Chapman.   (Edward Arnold.)
" Engineering Materials, Machine Tools and Processes," W. Steeds.   (Longmans, Green.)
" General Engineering Workshop Practice."   (Odhams Press.)
" Senior Workshop Calculations," W. A. J. Chapman.   (Edward Arnold.)
" Works Organisation and Management," E. J. Larkin.   (Pitman.)
" Modern Works Management," G. S. Mason.   (Pitman.)
" Planning, Estimating and Rate-fixing," A. C. Whitehead.   (Pitman.)
" Engineering Economics " (2 vols.), T. H. Burnham.   (Pitman.)
" Machine-shop Year Book and Production Engineers' Manual " (2 vols.).   (Paul Elek.)
" American Machinist Handbook," F. H. Colvin and F. A. Stanley.   (McGraw-Hill.)
" Machinery Handbook."   (Machinery Pub. Co.)
" Procedure Handbook of Arc Welding Design and Practice."   (Lincoln Co.)
" Arc Welding Foundation."   (Machinery Pub. Co.)
" Electric Welding in Shipbuilding."   Admiralty (H.M.S.O.)
" The Practice of Arc Welding," W. Heigh.   (Pitman.)
" Electric Arc and Oxy-acetylene Welding," E. A. Atkins and A. G. Walker.   (Pitman.)
" The Welding of Cast Iron," L. Tibbenham.   (Pitman.)
" Welding Handbook."   (American Welding Society, N.Y.)
" Gas Welding and Cutting," C. G. Brainbridge.   (Louis Cassier.)
" Design for Welding in Mechanical Engineering," F. Koenigsberger.   (Longmans, Green.)

INDEX